Fundamental Concepts of Bioinformatics

Dan E. Krane
Wright State University, Department of Biological Sciences

Michael L. Raymer
Wright State University, Department of Computer Science

Pearson Education International
San Francisco ▪ Boston ▪ New York
Cape Town ▪ Hong Kong ▪ London ▪ Madrid ▪ Mexico City
Montreal ▪ Munich ▪ Paris ▪ Singapore ▪ Sydney ▪ Tokyo ▪ Toronto

Senior Project Manager: Peggy Williams
Editorial Assistant: Michael McArdle
Production Editors: Larry Lazopoulos, Jamie Sue Brooks
Production Service: Matrix Productions, Inc.
Composition: Omegatype Typography, Inc.
Text Design: Carolyn Deacy
Cover Design: Jennifer Dunn
Copyeditor: Loretta Palagi
Proofreader: Sally Scott
Manufacturing Supervisor: Vivian McDougal
Marketing Manager: Josh Frost
Cover and Text Printer: Phoenix Color

ISBN 0-321-10922-X

www.aw.com/bc

1 2 3 4 5 6 7 8 9 10 – PBT – 08 07 06 05 04 03

Contents

1 Molecular Biology and Biological Chemistry 1

The Genetic Material 2
Nucleotides 2
Orientation 3
Base pairing 5
The central dogma of molecular biology 6

Gene Structure and Information Content 7
Promoter sequences 7
The genetic code 9
Open reading frames 9
Introns and exons 12

Protein Structure and Function 13
Primary structure 13
Secondary, tertiary, and quaternary structure 14

The Nature of Chemical Bonds 15
Anatomy of an atom 17
Valence 17
Electronegativity 18
Hydrophilicity and hydrophobicity 19

Molecular Biology Tools 19
Restriction enzyme digests 20
Gel electrophoresis 21
Blotting and hybridization 21
Cloning 23
Polymerase chain reaction 24
DNA sequencing 25

Genomic Information Content 27
C-value paradox 27
Reassociation kinetics 28

Chapter Summary 30

Readings for Greater Depth 31

Questions and Problems 31

2 Data Searches and Pairwise Alignments 33

Dot Plots 34

Simple Alignments 35

Gaps 36
Simple gap penalties 37
Origination and length penalties 37

Scoring Matrices 38

Dynamic Programming: The Needleman and Wunsch Algorithm 41

Global and Local Alignments 45
Semiglobal alignments 45
The Smith-Waterman Algorithm 46

Database Searches 48
BLAST and its relatives 48
FASTA and related algorithms 50
Alignment scores and statistical significance of database searches 51

Multiple Sequence Alignments 52

Chapter Summary 53

Readings for Greater Depth 53

Questions and Problems 54

3 Substitution Patterns 57

Patterns of Substitutions within Genes 58
Mutation rates 58
Functional constraint 59
Synonymous vs. nonsynonymous substitutions 61

Indels and pseudogenes 62
Substitutions vs. mutations 62
Fixation 63

Estimating Substitution Numbers 65
Jukes-Cantor model 65
Transitions and transversions 67
Kimura's two-parameter model 67
Models with even more parameters 68
Substitutions between protein sequences 69

Variations in Evolutionary Rates between Genes 70

Molecular Clocks 71
Relative rate test 71
Causes of rate variation in lineages 73

Evolution in Organelles 74

Chapter Summary 74

Readings for Greater Depth 74

Questions and Problems 75

4 Distance-Based Methods of Phylogenetics 77

History of Molecular Phylogenetics 78

Advantages to Molecular Phylogenies 79

Phylogenetic Trees 80
Terminology of tree reconstruction 80
Rooted and unrooted trees 81
Gene vs. species trees 83
Character and distance data 84

Distance Matrix Methods 85
UPGMA 86
Estimation of branch lengths 88
Transformed distance method 90
Neighbor's relation method 91
Neighbor-joining methods 92

Maximum Likelihood Approaches 93

Multiple Sequence Alignments 93

Chapter Summary 94

Readings for Greater Depth 95

Questions and Problems 95

5 Character-Based Methods of Phylogenetics 97

Parsimony 98
Informative and uninformative sites 98
Unweighted parsimony 99
Weighted parsimony 104

Inferred Ancestral Sequences 104

Strategies for Faster Searches 105
Branch and bound 105
Heuristic searches 107

Consensus Trees 108

Tree Confidence 109
Bootstrapping 109
Parametric tests 111

Comparison of Phylogenetic Methods 112

Molecular Phylogenies 112
The tree of life 112
Human origins 114

Chapter Summary 114

Readings for Greater Depth 115

Questions and Problems 115

6 Genomics and Gene Recognition 117

Prokaryotic Genomes 118

Prokaryotic Gene Structure 120
Promoter elements 121
Open reading frames 124
Conceptual translation 125
Termination sequences 125

GC Content in Prokaryotic Genomes 126

Prokaryotic Gene Density 127

Eukaryotic Genomes 127

Eukaryotic Gene Structure 129
  Promoter elements 130
  Regulatory protein binding sites 131

Open Reading Frames 133
  Introns and exons 134
  Alternative splicing 135

GC Content in Eukaryotic Genomes 137
  CpG islands 137
  Isochores 141
  Codon usage bias 142

Gene Expression 143
  cDNAs and ESTs 143
  Serial analysis of gene expression 145
  Microarrays 145

Transposition 148

Repetitive Elements 148

Eukaryotic Gene Density 150

Chapter Summary 151

Readings for Greater Depth 151

Questions and Problems 152

7 Protein and RNA Structure Prediction 155

Amino Acids 156

Polypeptide Composition 159

Secondary Structure 160
  Backbone flexibility, Φ and Ψ 160
  Accuracy of predictions 161
  The Chou-Fasman and GOR methods 162

Tertiary and Quaternary Structure 164
  Hydrophobicity 165
  Disulfide bonds 166
  Active structures vs. most stable structures 167

Algorithms for Modeling Protein Folding 167
  Lattice models 168

Off-lattice models 170
Energy functions and optimization 171

Structure Prediction 172
Comparative modeling 173
Threading: Reverse protein folding 174

Predicting RNA Secondary Structures 175

Chapter Summary 176

Readings for Greater Depth 177

Questions and Problems 178

8 Proteomics 179

From Genomes to Proteomes 180

Protein Classification 181
Enzyme nomenclature 181
Families and superfamilies 182
Folds 183

Experimental Techniques 184
2D electrophoresis 184
Mass spectrometry 185
Protein microarrays 187

Inhibitors and Drug Design 187

Ligand Screening 188
Ligand docking 189
Database screening 190

X-Ray Crystal Structures 191

NMR Structures 197

Empirical Methods and Prediction Techniques 197

Post-Translational Modification Prediction 198
Protein sorting 199
Proteolytic cleavage 202
Glycosylation 202
Phosphorylation 203

Chapter Summary 203

Readings for Greater Depth 204

Questions and Problems 205

Appendix 1: A Gentle Introduction to Computer Programming and Data Structures 207

Creating and Executing Computer Programs 208

Variables and Values 209
Data typing 210
Basic operations 211

Program Control 211
Statements and blocks 212
Conditional execution 212
Loops 216

Readability 217
Structured programming 217
Comments 218
Descriptive variable names 219

Data Structures 219
Arrays 220
Hashes 221
Working with strings 222

Subroutines and Functions 224

Input and Output 229

Regular Expressions 231

Where to Go from Here 232

Readings for Greater Depth 233

Questions and Problems 234

Appendix 2: Enzyme Kinetics 235

Enzymes as Biological Catalysts 236

The Henri–Michaelis–Menten Equation 238
V_{max} and K_m 239
Direct plot 240
Lineweaver–Burk reciprocal plot 240
Eadie–Hofstee plot 241

Simple Inhibition Systems 241
Competitive inhibition 242
Noncompetitive inhibition 244

Irreversible inhibition 246
Effects of pH and temperature 246

Readings for Greater Depth 246

Questions and Problems 246

Appendix 3: Sample Programs in Perl 249

Example 1: Conceptual Translation 250

Example 2: Dot Plot 252

Example 3: Relative Rate Test 255

Example 4: UPGMA 256

Example 5: Common Ancestor 259

Example 6: Splice Junction Recognition 263

Example 7: Hydrophobicity Calculator—The 2D-HP Model 266

Example 8: Atomic Density Calculation 270

Example 9: Enzyme Kinetics—Linear Regression 273

Glossary 277

Solutions to Selected Problems 289

Index 303

Preface

This book arose primarily from our own need for a text that we would be happy to recommend to our own undergraduate students interested in bioinformatics. We believe strongly that the best work in this new field arises from the interaction of individuals who are well versed in two disciplines, biology and computer science, that often have little in common in terms of language, approaches to problem solving, and even physical location within universities and colleges.

There is no particular shortage of books that catalog (and occasionally explain) websites with useful bioinformatics tools for biologists interested in analyzing their own data. There are also a few written for computer scientists that describe strategies for making algorithms more computationally efficient. Yet, a fundamental problem exists in the way that texts prepare students for work in bioinformatics. Most aim to train life sciences students to use existing web-based programs without fostering an understanding of the relative importance of different variables or how those programs might be customized for specific applications. The smaller number of books that are designed to teach computer scientists to write programs using established algorithms typically fail to convey an understanding of what constitutes biological significance or the limitations of molecular data gathering. While the very nature of bioinformatics requires an understanding of the objectives and limitations of both disciplines, students are rarely exposed to both.

The demand for bioinformaticians is very high, and the trend in bioinformatics education (as well as much of higher education in general) has been to move away from islands of information. Many graduate programs in bioinformatics are responding to the demands of the marketplace and their students by providing extensive remedial training in either biology or computer science for those who have graduated with degrees in the other area. These graduate programs in bioinformatics tend to be at least one, and usually two years longer than traditional graduate experiences. Our goal with this book is to reach students while it is still easy for them to become comfortable thinking about problems and arriving at solutions both as biologists and as computer scientists. By focusing on the actual algorithms at the heart of bioinformatics, our aim is to train computer scientists and biologists to have a common language and basis of understanding. After a general introduction to molecular biology and chemistry (primarily for the benefit of computer scientists and biology majors who have not yet encountered this material), the text revolves around algorithms that students could use to solve problems with pencil and paper. With that level of appreciation in place, it is not hard to illustrate how computers can provide invaluable assistance for larger and more complex data sets. Along the way, students are also introduced to existing databases and encouraged to use real data to test their skills. While mathematical and statistical calculations are included, all are fairly simple and understandable without a mastery of calculus. Sample programs, as well as examples of state-of-the-art web-based software based upon those same algorithms are also provided.

While new algorithms and methods are constantly being brought to bear on the problems of molecular biology, there remains a fundamental set of techniques and concepts that computer scientists and biologists use to address data-driven problems. A firm understanding of these fundamentals will allow students from both backgrounds to advance in their studies of computational molecular biology and bioinformatics. Several features of this text are specifically designed to provide students from varying backgrounds with their first taste of bioinformatics:

- A language-independent, pen-and-paper approach to problem solving allows students to understand the algorithms underlying various bioinformatics techniques, without becoming mired down in the syntactic details of implementing programs in a specific language or operating system.

- A hands-on, problem-solving approach is used to present the material, and the end-of-chapter questions are closely related to example problems presented in the text. Solutions for odd-numbered questions are provided in the text, while solutions for the remaining questions are available at the instructor's web site.

- Each chapter addresses the issues involved in biological data collection and bench experimentation, as well as the algorithmic issues involved in designing analysis techniques. Thus, students from any background will develop an appreciation for the parameters and complexities involved in both of these key aspects of bioinformatics.

- Appendix 1 provides non-programmers with their first programming experience using Perl. General concepts that are applicable to all structured programming languages are emphasized, so that students will be well equipped to learn new languages and programming methods after this brief introduction.

- Appendix 3 provides example algorithms in Perl that illustrate key concepts from each chapter of the text. These examples avoid Perl-specific constructs, instead focusing on general problem-solving approaches and algorithmic techniques that can be applied to a wide range of bioinformatics problems.

The work of assembling this book has been a greater challenge than either of us appreciated at its start. We never intended for it to be an encyclopedic review of the published literature in bioinformatics, but still found ourselves wanting to cite many excellent papers that we could not for reasons of time and space. We have also benefited from a great deal of support and help. The authors express their heartfelt thanks to David Paoletti for his excellent work in designing the algorithms for Appendix 3, as well as the various students who provided critical feedback on the initial versions of the text, figures, and example problems as we have used them for our own undergraduate bioinformatics courses here at Wright State University. We are likewise grateful to Michele Sordi, whose encouragement and guidance helped this text to germinate from an idea into reality, and to Peggy Williams for her creative suggestions, support and ubiquitous wit. Much of the credit for the finished product is due our production editor, Larry Lazopoulos, and to the first rate production staff at Matrix Productions, including Merrill Peterson and Michele Ostovar. Lastly, we are deeply appreciative to our wives, Carissa M. Krane and Delia F. N. Raymer, for their patience and understanding during those frequent times when the demands of writing took precedence over the matters of our families.

CHAPTER

1

Molecular Biology and Biological Chemistry

Biology has at least 50 more interesting years.

James D. Watson,
December 31, 1984

The Genetic Material
Nucleotides
Orientation
Base pairing
The central dogma of molecular biology

Gene Structure and Information Content
Promoter sequences
The genetic code
Open reading frames
Introns and exons

Protein Structure and Function
Primary structure
Secondary, tertiary, and quaternary structure

The Nature of Chemical Bonds
Anatomy of an atom
Valence
Electronegativity
Hydrophilicity and hydrophobicity

Molecular Biology Tools
Restriction enzyme digests
Gel electrophoresis
Blotting and hybridization
Cloning
Polymerase chain reaction
DNA sequencing

Genomic Information Content
C-value paradox
Reassociation kinetics

The most distinguishing characteristic of living things is their ability to store, utilize, and pass on information. Bioinformatics strives to determine what information is biologically important and to decipher how it is used to precisely control the chemical environment within living organisms. Since that information is stored at a molecular level, the relatively small number of tools available to molecular biologists provides our most direct insights into that information content. This chapter provides a brief introduction or review of the format in which genetic information is maintained and used by living organisms as well as the experimental techniques that are routinely used to study it in molecular biology laboratories. Since that information is most relevant in terms of the effects that it has on the chemistry of life, that too is briefly reviewed.

The Genetic Material

DNA (deoxyribonucleic acid) is the genetic material. This is a profoundly powerful statement to molecular biologists. To a large extent, it represents the answer to questions that have been pondered by philosophers and scientists for thousands of years: "What is the basis of inheritance?" and "What allows living things to be different from nonliving things?" Quite simply, it is the information stored in DNA that allows the organization of inanimate molecules into functioning, living cells and organisms that are able to regulate their internal chemical composition, growth, and reproduction. As a direct result, it is also what allows us to inherit our mother's curly hair, our father's blue eyes, and even our uncle's too-large nose. The various units that govern those characteristics at the genetic level, be it chemical composition or nose size, are called **genes.** Prior to our understanding of the chemical structure of DNA in the 1950s, what and how information was passed on from one generation to the next was largely a matter of often wild conjecture.

Nucleotides

Genes themselves contain their information as a specific **sequence** of nucleotides that are found in DNA molecules. Only four different bases are used in DNA molecules: guanine, adenine, thymine, and cytosine (**G, A, T,** and **C**). Each base is attached to a phosphate group and a deoxyribose sugar to form a nucleotide. The only thing that makes one nucleotide different from another is which nitrogenous base it contains (Figure 1.1). Differences between each of the four nitrogenous bases is fairly obvious even in representations of their structures such as those in Figure 1.1, and the enzymatic machinery of living cells routinely and reliably distinguishes between them. And, very much like binary uses strings of zeros and ones and the English alphabet uses combinations of 26 different letters to convey information, all of the information within each gene comes simply from the order in which those four nucleotides are found along lengthy DNA molecules. Complicated genes can be many thousands of nucleotides long, and

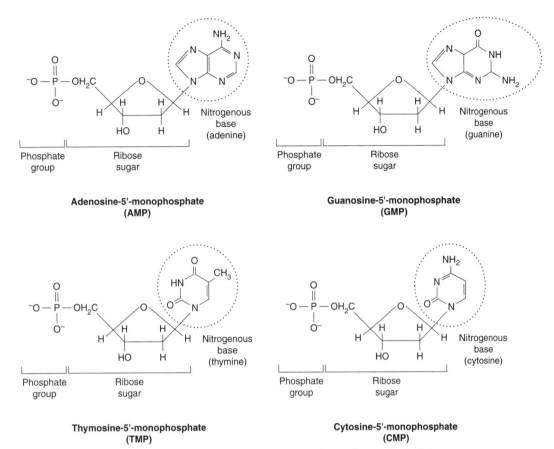

FIGURE 1.1 *Chemical structure of the four nucleotides used to make DNA. Each nucleotide can be considered to be made of three component parts: (1) a phosphate group, (2) a central deoxyribose sugar, and (3) one of four different nitrogenous bases.*

all of an organism's genetic instructions, its **genome,** can be maintained in millions or even billions of nucleotides.

Orientation

Strings of nucleotides can be attached to each other to make long **polynucleotide** chains or, when considered on a very large scale, **chromosomes.** The attachment between any two nucleotides is always made by way of a **phosphodiester bond** that connects the phosphate group of one nucleotide to the deoxyribose sugar of another (Figure 1.2). (Ester bonds are those that involve links made by oxygen atoms—phosphodiester bonds have a total of two ester bonds, one on each side of a phosphorous atom.)

All living things make these phosphodiester bonds in precisely the same way. Notice in Figure 1.2 that each of the five carbon atoms in a deoxyribose sugar has

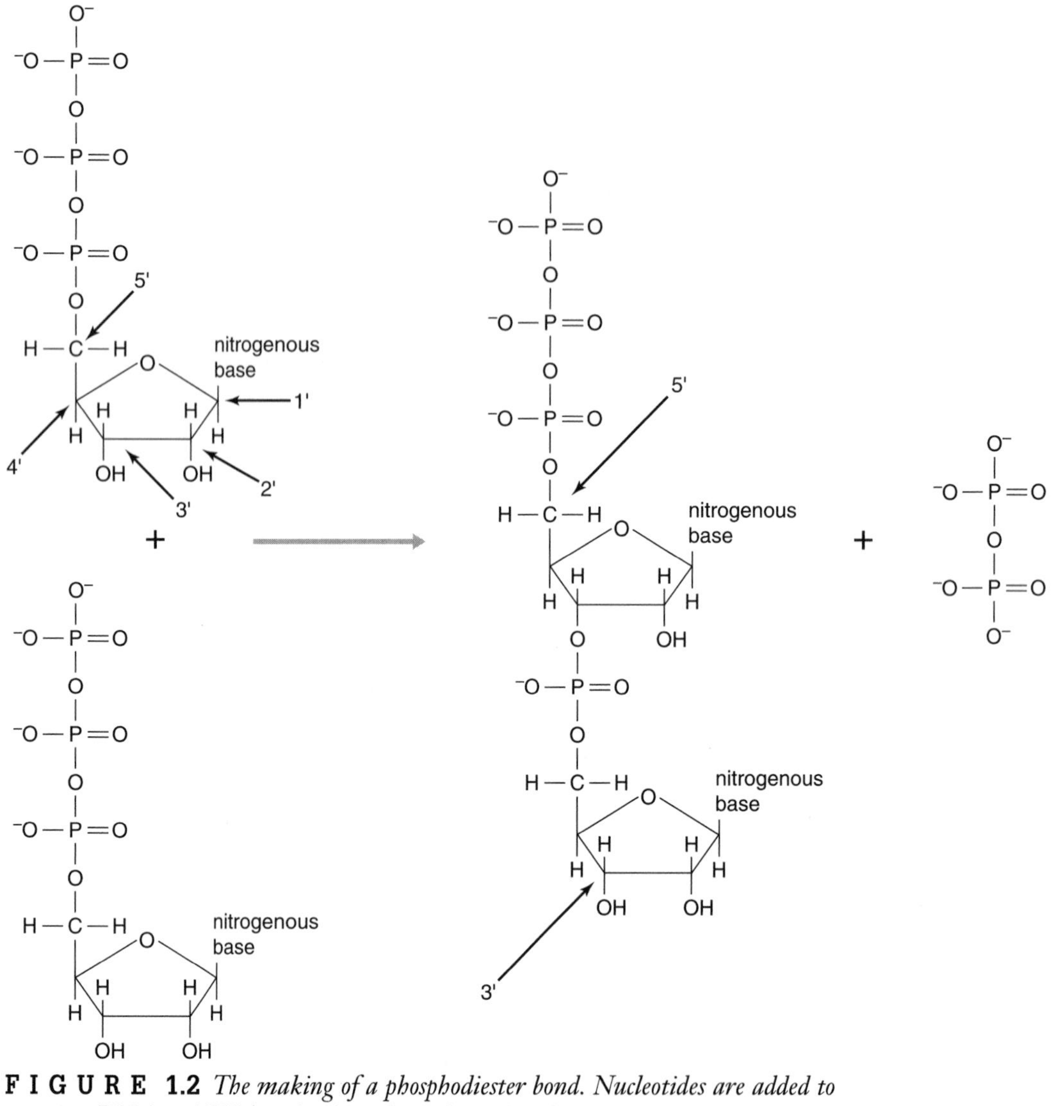

FIGURE 1.2 *The making of a phosphodiester bond. Nucleotides are added to growing DNA and RNA molecules only at their 3' ends.*

been assigned a specific numeric designation (1' through 5') by organic chemists. The phosphate group(s) of any single, unattached nucleotide are always found on its 5' carbon. Those phosphate groups are used to bridge the gap between the 5' carbon of an incoming deoxyribose sugar and the 3' carbon of a deoxyribose sugar at the end of a preexisting polynucleotide chain. As a result, one end of a string of nucleotides always has a 5' carbon that is not attached to another nucleotide, and the other end of the molecule always has an unattached 3' carbon. The difference between the 5' and 3' ends of a polynucleotide chain may seem subtle.

However, the orientation it confers to DNA molecules is every bit as important to cells as is our knowing that in written English we read from left to right and from top to bottom to understand the information content.

Base Pairing

A common theme throughout all biological systems and at all levels is the idea that structure and function are intimately related. Watson and Crick's appreciation that the DNA molecules within cells typically exist as double-stranded molecules was an invaluable clue as to how DNA might act as the genetic material. What they reported in their classic 1953 paper describing the structure of DNA is that the information content on one of those strands was essentially redundant with the information on the other. DNA could be replicated and faithfully passed on from one generation to another simply by separating the two strands and using each as a template for the synthesis of a new strand.

As we have already discussed, the information content in a DNA molecule comes from the specific sequence of its nucleotides. While the information content on each strand of a double-stranded DNA molecule is redundant it is not exactly the same—it is **complementary.** For every G on one strand, a C is found on its complementary strand and vice versa. For every A on one strand, a T is found on its complementary strand and vice versa. The interaction between G's and C's and between A's and T's is both specific and stable. The nitrogenous base guanine with its two-ringed structure is simply too large to pair with a two-ringed adenine or another guanine in the space that usually exists between two DNA strands. By the same token, the nitrogenous base thymine with its single-ringed structure is too small to interact with another single-ringed cytosine or thymine. Space is not a barrier to interaction between G's and T's or A's and C's but their chemical natures are incompatible, as will be described later in this chapter. Only the pairing between the nitrogenous bases G and C (Figure 1.3a) and the pairing between the nitrogenous bases A and T (Figure 1.3b) have both the right spacing and interaction between their chemical groups to form stable **base pairs.** In fact, the chemical interaction (specifically, three hydrogen bonds that form between G's and C's and two hydrogen bonds that form between A's and T's) between the two different kinds of base pairs is actually so stable and energetically favorable that it alone is responsible for holding the two complementary strands together.

Although the two strands of a DNA molecule are complementary they are not in the same 5'/3' orientation. Instead, the two strands are said to be **antiparallel** to each other, with the 5' end of one strand corresponding to the 3' end of its complementary strand and vice versa. Consequently, if one strand's nucleotide sequence is 5'-GTATCC-3', the other strand's sequence will be 3'-CATAGG-5'. By convention, and since most cellular processes involving DNA occur in the 5' to 3' direction, the other strand's sequence would typically be presented as: 5'-GGATAC-3'. Strictly speaking, the two strands of a double-stranded DNA molecule are *reverse* complements of each other. Sequence features that are 5' to a particular reference point are commonly described as being "upstream" while those that are 3' are described as being "downstream."

(a) Guanine∷∷∷∷∷∷Cytosine
(three hydrogen bonds)

(b) Adenine ∷∷∷∷∷∷ Thymine
(two hydrogen bonds)

F I G U R E 1.3 *Base pairing between the nitrogenous bases in DNA molecules. (a) Guanine and cytosine are capable of specifically interacting by way of three hydrogen bonds, while (b) adenine and thymine interact by way of two hydrogen bonds.*

The Central Dogma of Molecular Biology

While the specific sequence of nucleotides in a DNA molecule can have important information content for a cell, it is actually proteins that do the work of altering a cell's chemistry by acting as biological catalysts called **enzymes.** In chemistry catalysts are molecules that allow specific chemical reactions to proceed more quickly than they would have otherwise occurred. Catalysts are neither consumed nor altered in the course of such a chemical process and can be used to catalyze the same reaction many times. The term *gene* is used in many different ways, but one of its narrowest and simplest definitions is that genes spell out the instructions needed to make the enzyme catalysts produced by cells. The

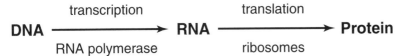

F I G U R E 1.4 *The central dogma of molecular biology. Information in cells passes from DNA to RNA to proteins. RNA is made from DNA molecules during transcription by RNA polymerases. Proteins are made from the information content of RNA molecules as they are translated by ribosomes. DNA polymerases also make copies of DNA molecules during the replication process of cell division.*

process by which information is extracted from the nucleotide sequence of a gene and then used to make a protein is essentially the same for all living things on Earth and is described by the grandly named **central dogma** of molecular biology. Quite simply, information stored in DNA is used to make a more transient, single-stranded polynucleotide called RNA (ribonucleic acid) that is in turn used to make proteins (Figure 1.4). The process of making an RNA copy of a gene is called **transcription** and is accomplished through the enzymatic activity of an **RNA polymerase.** There is a one-to-one correspondence between the nucleotides used to make RNA (G, A, U, and C where "U" is an abbreviation for uracil) and the nucleotide sequences in DNA (G, A, T, and C, respectively). The process of converting that information from nucleotide sequences in RNA to the amino acid sequences that make a protein is called **translation** and is performed by a complex of proteins and RNA called **ribosomes.** Protein synthesis and structure are discussed at the end of this chapter.

Gene Structure and Information Content

Formatting and its interpretation are important considerations for any information storage system, be it a written text or a cell's DNA molecule. All cells go about interpreting their genetic instructions in the same way and rely on specific signals to "punctuate" their genes. Much of the "language" of DNA and the rules of its interpretation were worked out very early in the history of life on earth and, because of their central importance, have changed very little over the course of billions of years. As a result, both prokaryotic (bacteria) and eukaryotic (more complicated organisms like yeast, plants, pets, and people) organisms all use not only the same "alphabet" of nucleotides but also use essentially the same format and approach for storing and utilizing their genetic information.

Promoter Sequences

Gene expression, the process of using the information stored in DNA to make an RNA molecule and then a corresponding protein, can have significant energetic and opportunity costs for a cell. Organisms that express unneeded proteins are less likely to survive and reproduce relative to competitors that regulate their gene expression more appropriately. As a result, all cells place particular emphasis on controlling gene expression at its very start by making two crucial distinctions. First, they must reliably distinguish between those parts of an organism's genome that correspond to the beginnings of genes and those that do not. Second, they must be able to determine which genes code for proteins that are needed at any particular time.

Since RNA polymerases are responsible for the initiation of gene expression through their synthesis of RNA copies of genes, it is reasonable that the burden of making those two distinctions falls on them. Certainly not every nucleotide in a genome can correspond to the start of a gene any more than every letter on a printed page can correspond to the beginning of a sentence with useful information content. By the same token, RNA polymerases cannot simply look for any *one* particular nucleotide, like A, when looking for the start of a gene because each nucleotide occurs by chance so frequently throughout a cell's DNA. However, particular combinations of nucleotides are not as likely to occur by chance, and the greater the number of nucleotides involved, the smaller a chance occurrence becomes. The probability (P) that a string of nucleotides will occur by chance alone can be determined by the relatively simple formula $P = (1/4)^n$ if all nucleotides are present at the same frequency and where n is the string's length. Prokaryotic RNA polymerases actually scan along DNA looking for a specific set of approximately 13 nucleotides (1 nucleotide that serves as a transcriptional start site, 6 that are 10 nucleotides 5' to the start site, and 6 more that are 35 nucleotides 5' to it) that mark the beginning of genes. Those nucleotides, taken as a whole and in the proper positions relative to each other, are called **promoter sequences.** Given that most prokaryotic genomes are only a few million nucleotides long, these promoter sequences, which should occur only by chance about once in every 70 million nucleotides, allow RNA polymerases to uniquely identify the beginnings of genes with great statistical confidence. Eukaryotic genomes tend to be several orders of magnitude larger than those of prokaryotes and, as a result, eukaryotic RNA polymerases tend to recognize larger and more complex promoter sequences so that they too can reliably recognize the beginning of genes.

Two French biochemists, F. Jacob and J. Monod, were the first to obtain direct molecular insights into how cells distinguish between genes that should be transcribed and those that should not. Their work on prokaryotic gene regulation earned them a Nobel Prize in 1965 and revealed that the expression of structural genes (those that code for proteins involved in cell structure or metabolism) was controlled by specific regulatory genes. The proteins encoded by these regulatory genes are typically capable of binding to a cell's DNA near the promoter of the genes whose expression they control in some circumstances but not in others. It is the ability of these regulatory proteins to bind or not bind to specific nucleotide sequences in a fashion that is dependent on their ability to sense a cell's chemical environment that allows living things to respond appropriately to their environment. When the binding of these proteins makes it easier for an RNA polymerase to initiate transcription, **positive regulation** is said to have occurred. **Negative regulation** describes those situations where binding of the regulatory protein prevents transcription from occurring. Eventually, most prokaryotic structural genes were found to be turned on or off by just one or two regulatory proteins. Eukaryotes, with their substantially more complicated genomes and transcriptional needs, use larger numbers (usually seven or more) and combinations of regulatory proteins to control the expression of their structural genes.

The Genetic Code

While nucleotides are the building blocks that cells use to make their information storage and transfer molecules (DNA and RNA, respectively), amino acids are the units that are strung together to make the proteins that actually do most of the work of altering a cell's chemical environment. The function of a protein is intimately dependent on the order in which its amino acids are linked by ribosomes during translation and, as has already been discussed, that order is determined by the instructions transcribed into RNA molecules by RNA polymerases. However, although only four different nucleotides (nt) are used to make DNA and RNA molecules, 20 different amino acids (each with its own distinctive chemistry) are used in protein synthesis (Figure 1.5a) (1 nt ≠ 1 aa; $4^1 < 20$). There cannot be a simple one-to-one correspondence between the nucleotides of genes and the amino acids of the proteins they encode. The 16 different possible pairs of nucleotides also fall short of the task (2 nt ≠ 1 aa; $4^2 < 20$). However, the four nucleotides can be arranged in a total of 64 different combinations of three ($4^3 = 64$). As a result, it is necessary for ribosomes to use a **triplet code** to translate the information in DNA and RNA into the amino acid sequence of proteins. With only three exceptions, each group of three nucleotides (a **codon**) in an RNA copy of the coding portion of a gene corresponds to a specific amino acid (Table 1.1). The three codons that do not instruct ribosomes to insert a specific amino acid are called **stop codons** (functionally equivalent to a period at the end of a sentence) because they cause translation to be terminated. This same genetic code seems to have been in place since the earliest history of life on earth and, with only a few exceptions, is universally used by all living things today.

Notice in Table 1.1 that 18 of the 20 different amino acids are coded for by more than one codon. This feature of the genetic code is called **degeneracy.** It is therefore possible for mistakes to occur during DNA replication or transcription that have no effect on the amino acid sequence of a protein. This is especially true of mutations (heritable changes in the genetic material) that occur in the third (last) position of a codon. Each amino acid can be assigned to one of essentially four different categories: nonpolar, polar, positively charged, and negatively charged (Figure 1.5b). A single change within a triplet codon is usually not sufficient to cause a codon to code for an amino acid in a different group. In short, the genetic code is remarkably robust and minimizes the extent to which mistakes in the nucleotide sequences of genes can change the functions of the proteins they encode.

Open Reading Frames

Translation by ribosomes starts at translation-initiation sites on RNA copies of genes and proceeds until a stop codon is encountered. Just as three codons of the

(a) Side chain

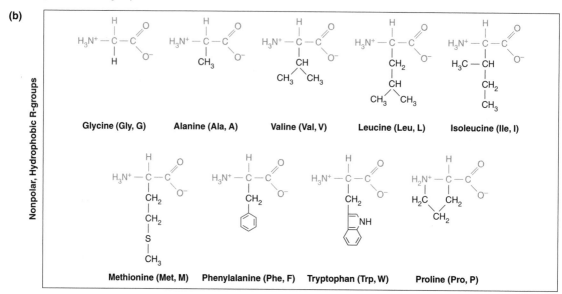

FIGURE 1.5 (a) Chemical structure of a generic amino acid. The amino group, alpha carbon, and carboxyl groups are identical for all 20 amino acids while each has its own distinctive R group. (b) Chemical structure of the 20 different amino acids complete with their distinctive R groups. Amino acids are grouped according to the properties of their side chains, shown in black. Standard three-letter and one-letter abbreviations for each of the amino acids are shown in parentheses.

(b)

Nonpolar, Hydrophobic R-groups

Glycine (Gly, G)   Alanine (Ala, A)   Valine (Val, V)   Leucine (Leu, L)   Isoleucine (Ile, I)

Methionine (Met, M)   Phenylalanine (Phe, F)   Tryptophan (Trp, W)   Proline (Pro, P)

Polar, Hydrophilic R-groups

Serine (Ser, S)   Threonine (Thr, T)   Cysteine (Cys, C)   Tyrosine (Tyr, Y)   Asparagine (Asn, N)   Glutamine (Gln, Q)

Electrically charged

Acidic

Aspartic acid (Asp, D)   Glutamic acid (Glu, E)

Basic

Lysine (Lys, K)   Arginine (Arg, R)   Histidine (His, H)

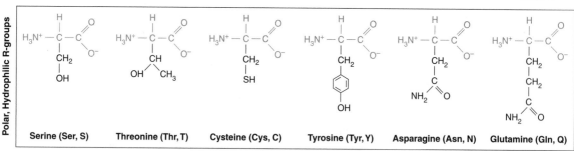

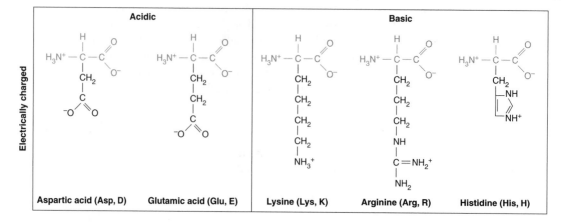

T A B L E 1.1 A summary of the coding assignments of the 64 triplet codons. *Standard three-letter abbreviations for each of the most commonly used 20 amino acids are shown. The universality of the genetic code encompasses animals (including humans), plants, fungi, archaea, bacteria, and viruses. Small variations in the code exist in mitochondria and certain microbes. For instance, in a limited number of bacterial genes, a special UGA codon, normally a termination codon, is used as a codon for an unusual, 21st naturally occurring, amino acid selenocysteine. A 22nd naturally occurring amino acid, pyrrolysine, is coded for by UAG (a stop codon for most organisms) in some bacterial and eukaryotic species.*

Base at 5' End of Codon ↓	(5') . . . pNpNpN . . . (3') in mRNA				Base at 3' End of Codon ↓
	Middle Base of Codon →				
	U	C	A	G	
U	phe (UUU)	ser	tyr	cys	U
	phe	ser	tyr	cys	C
	leu	ser	termination	termination	A
	leu	ser	termination	trp	G
C	leu	pro	his	arg	U
	leu	pro	his	arg	C
	leu	pro	gln	arg	A
	leu	pro	gln	arg	G
A	ile	thr	asn	ser	U
	ile	thr	asn	ser	C
	ile	thr	lys	arg	A
	met (and initiation)	thr	lys	arg	G
G	val	ala	asp	gly	U
	val	ala	asp	gly	C
	val	ala	glu	gly	A
	val	ala	glu	gly	G

genetic code are reserved as stop codons, one triplet codon is always used as a **start codon.** Specifically, the codon AUG is used both to code for the amino acid methionine as well as to mark the precise spot along an RNA molecule where translation begins in both prokaryotes and eukaryotes. Accurate translation can only occur when ribosomes examine codons in the phase or **reading frame** that is established by a gene's start codon. Unless a mistake involving some multiple of three nucleotides occurs, alterations of a gene's reading frame change every amino acid coded downstream of the alteration, and such alterations typically result in the production of a truncated version of the protein due to ribosomes encountering a premature stop codon.

Most genes code for proteins that are hundreds of amino acids long. Since stop codons occur in a randomly generated sequence at about every 20th triplet codon (3 codons out of 64), one of the reading frames of the RNA copies of most genes has unusually long runs of codons in which no stop codons occur. These strings of codons uninterrupted by stop codons are known as **open reading frames** (ORFs) and are a distinguishing feature of many prokaryotic and eukaryotic genes.

Introns and Exons

The messenger RNA (mRNA) copies of prokaryotic genes correspond perfectly to the DNA sequences present in the organism's genome with the exception that the nucleotide uracil (U) is used in place of thymine (T). In fact, translation by ribosomes almost always begins while RNA polymerases are still actively transcribing a prokaryotic gene.

Eukaryotic RNA polymerases also use uracil in place of thymine, but much more striking differences are commonly found between the mRNA molecules seen by ribosomes and the nucleotide sequences of the eukaryotic genes that code for them. In eukaryotes the two steps of gene expression are physically separated by the nuclear membrane, with transcription occurring exclusively within the nucleus and translation occurring only after mRNAs have been exported to the cytoplasm. As a result, the RNA molecules transcribed by eukaryotic RNA polymerases can be modified before ribosomes ever encounter them. The most dramatic modification that is made to the primary RNA transcripts of most eukaryotic genes is called **splicing** and involves the precise excision of internal sequences known as **introns** and the rejoining of the **exons** that flank them (Figure 1.6). Splicing is far from a trivial process and most eukaryotic genes have a large number of sometimes very large introns. An extreme example is the gene associated with the disease cystic fibrosis in humans, which has 24 introns and is over 1 million nucleotides (1 mega base pair or 1 Mb) long even though the mRNA seen by ribosomes is only about 1,000 nucleotides (1 kilo base pair or 1 kb) long. Failure to appropriately splice the introns out of a primary eukaryotic RNA transcript typically introduces frame shifts or premature stop codons that render useless any protein translated by a ribosome. Regardless of the tissue or even the organism being considered, the vast majority of eukaryotic introns conform to what is known as the "GT–AG rule," meaning that the first two nucleotides in the DNA sequence of all introns begin with the dinucleotide GT and end with the dinucleotide AG. Pairs of nucleotides occur too often just by chance to be a sufficient signal for the enzyme complexes responsible for splicing in eukaryotes, **spliceosomes,** and approximately six additional nucleotides at the 5' and 3' ends of introns are also scrutinized—sometimes differently in some cell types relative to others. This **alternative splicing** allows a huge increase in the diversity of proteins that eukaryotic organisms can use and is accomplished by often subtle modifications of spliceosomes and accessory proteins that are responsible for recognizing intron/exon boundaries.

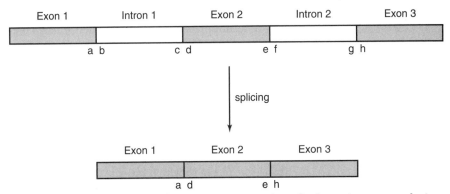

F I G U R E 1.6 *Splicing of the primary transcripts of eukaryotic genes results in the removal of introns and the precise joining of exons. Intron sequences are quickly degraded once they are removed while the spliced mRNA is exported out of the nucleus for translation by ribosomes.*

Protein Structure and Function

Proteins are the molecular machinery responsible for performing most of the work of both prokaryotic and eukaryotic cells. The tasks undertaken by proteins are incredibly diverse. **Structural proteins,** such as collagen, provide rigidity and support in bones and connective tissues. Other proteins called **enzymes** act as biological catalysts, like the digestive enzyme pepsin that helps to break down and metabolize food. Proteins are also responsible for transportation of atoms and small molecules throughout an organism (e.g., hemoglobin), signaling and intercellular communication (e.g., insulin), absorbing photons to enable vision (e.g., rhodopsin), and myriad other functions.

Primary Structure

Following the genetic instructions contained in messenger RNA, proteins are translated by ribosomes as linear polymers (chains) of amino acids. The 20 amino acids have similar chemical structures (Figure 1.5a), varying only in the chemical group attached in the R position. The constant region of each amino acid is called the *backbone*, while the varying R group is called the *side chain*. The order in which the various amino acids are assembled into a protein is the sequence, or **primary structure,** of the protein. As with DNA, the protein chain has directionality. One end of the protein chain has a free amino (NH) group, while the other end of the chain terminates in a carboxylic acid (COOH) group. The individual amino acids in the protein are usually numbered starting at the **amino terminus** and proceeding toward the **carboxy terminus.**

After translation, a protein does not remain in the form of a simple linear chain. Rather, the protein collapses, folds, and is shaped into a complex globular structure. The order in which the various amino acids are assembled into a protein

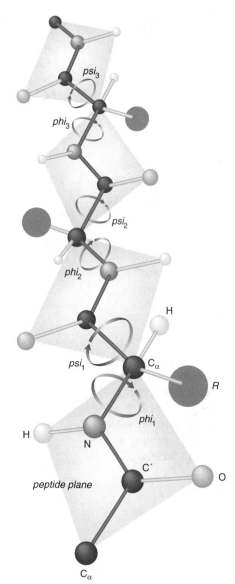

FIGURE 1.7 *Rigid and mobile regions of the protein backbone. Most of the backbone is rigid. The chemical bonds to the alpha carbons are rotatable. The angles of rotation for each alpha carbon's bonds are called phi (ϕ) and psi (ψ).*

largely determines the structure into which it will fold. The unique structure into which a particular protein will fold is called the **native structure** of the protein. The native structures of proteins give them unique properties that allow them to perform their particular roles in the context of a living organism.

The chemistry of a protein backbone forces most of the backbone to remain planar (Figure 1.7). The only "movable" segments of the protein backbone are the bonds from the nitrogen to the alpha carbon (the carbon atom to which the side chain is attached) and the bond between the alpha carbon and the carbonyl carbon (the carbon with a double bond to an oxygen atom). These two chemical bonds allow for circular (or "dihedral") rotation, and are often called phi (ϕ) and psi (ψ), respectively. Thus, a protein consisting of 300 amino acids will have 300 phi and psi angles, often numbered ϕ_1, ψ_1 through ϕ_{300}, ψ_{300}. All of the various conformations attainable by the protein come from rotations about these 300 pairs of bonds.

Secondary, Tertiary, and Quaternary Structure

Careful examination of proteins whose structures are known reveals that a very small number of patterns in local structures are quite common. These structures, formed by regular intramolecular hydrogen bonding (described below) patterns, are found in nearly every known protein. The location and direction of these regular structures make up the **secondary structure** of the protein. The two most common structures are the α-helix and the β-sheet (Figure 1.8). Often, the secondary structures are the first portions of the protein to fold after translation. Alpha (α) helices are characterized by phi and psi angles of roughly $-60°$, and exhibit a spring-like helical shape with 3.6 amino acids per complete 360° turn. Beta (β) strands are characterized by regions of extended (nearly linear) backbone conformation with $\phi \approx -135°$ and $\psi \approx 135°$. Beta strands assemble into one of two types of beta sheets, as illustrated in Figure 1.9 on page 16. In anti-parallel sheets, adjacent strands run in opposite directions as you move along the protein backbone from amino to carboxy terminus. In parallel sheets, the strands run in the same direc-

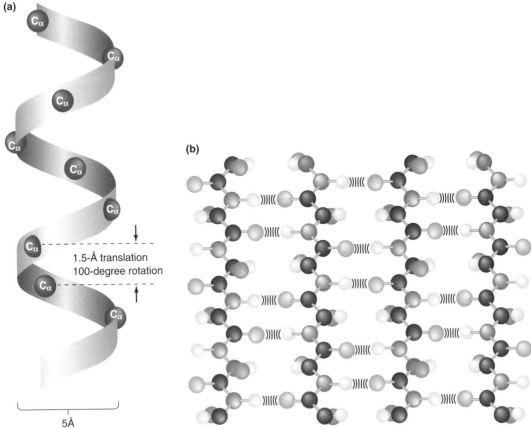

FIGURE 1.8 *Elements of secondary structure: (a) the alpha (α) helix and (b) the beta (β) sheet.*

tions. To make this possible, the strands of parallel beta sheets are often composed of amino acids that are nonlocal in the primary structure of the protein (Figure 1.9).

The regions of secondary structure in a protein pack together and combine with other less structured regions of the protein backbone to form an overall three-dimensional shape, which is called the **tertiary structure** of the protein. Often an active enzyme is composed of two or more protein chains that come together into a single large complex. When this occurs, the overall structure formed by the interacting proteins is commonly referred to as the **quaternary structure** of the enzyme.

The Nature of Chemical Bonds

As seen already, descriptions of nucleotides and proteins require at least a familiarity with the idea of chemical and hydrogen bonds. Much, if not all, of what we

FIGURE 1.9
Parallel and anti-parallel beta sheets. Note that the hydrogen bonds (dotted lines) give greater energetic stability in anti-parallel sheets.

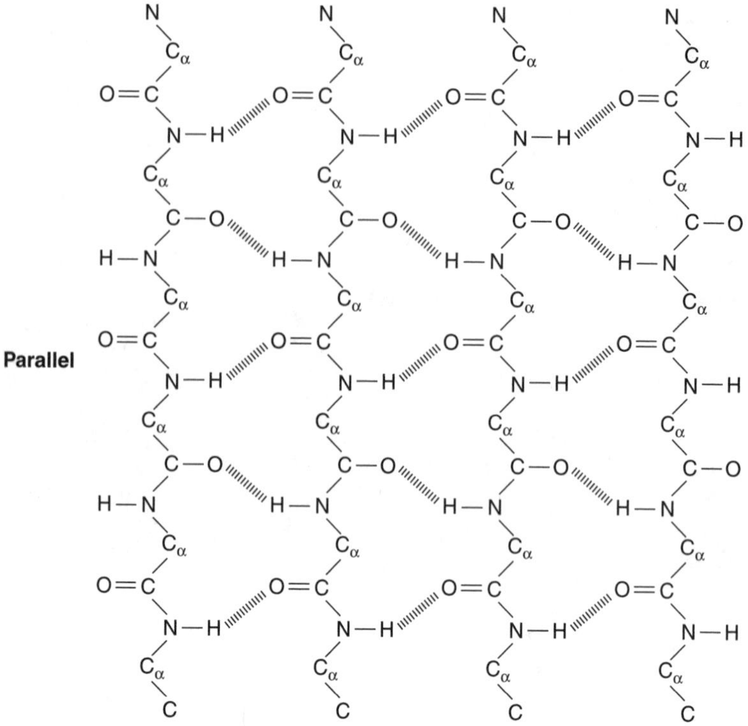

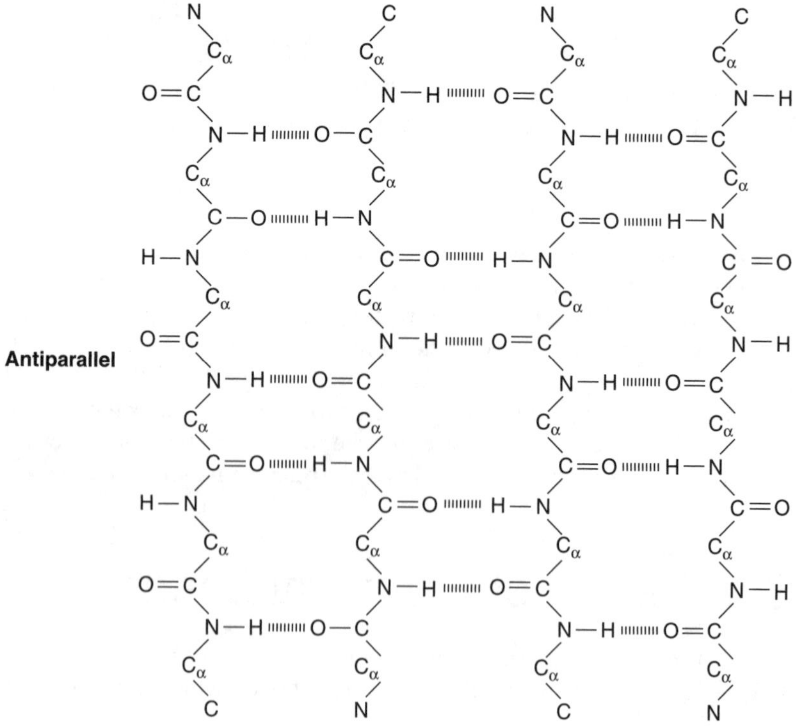

consider to be essential to life can be reduced to a set of chemical reactions and the characteristics of the enzymes that control the rate at which they occur. Even a passing understanding of basic chemistry gives deep insights into the way in which enzymes function and how molecules like proteins and DNA interact. Local differences in hydrophobicity and hydrophilicity, for instance, are fundamentally important to the functioning of most enzymes. L. Pauling won a Nobel Prize in 1962 for a book he wrote that made sense of such differences at a subatomic level. The following section describes the essence of his approach.

Anatomy of an Atom

By definition, **elements** are things that cannot be further reduced by chemical reactions. Elements themselves are made of individual atoms, which, in turn, are also made of smaller, subatomic particles. These smaller component parts of elements and atoms can only be separated by physical reactions, not chemical ones. Nuclear physicists have discovered hundreds of subatomic particles. Only three, however, are stable and particularly important to the discussion of the chemistry of living things. Those three subatomic particles are neutrons (weighing 1.7×10^{-24} gram and having no charge), protons (also weighing 1.7×10^{-24} gram and possessing one positive charge), and electrons (having only 1/2000th the mass of a proton or neutron and possessing a single negative charge). The number of protons in the nucleus of an atom determines what element it is. Generally, for every proton in an atomic nucleus there is an electron in orbit around it to balance the electrical charges. Electrons move in orbits at the speed of light and a relatively long way off from the nucleus. As a result, atoms are mostly empty space.

It also takes more and more energy for an electron to be moved away from the positive charges of atomic nuclei. Similarly, it takes more energy to carry a rock to the 20th floor of a building than it does to carry it to the 19th. The further an electron is from the nucleus of its atom, the more potential energy it must have. Packets of energy can be parceled out in a number of ways at the level of atoms, and one of the more common is through light (photons). Light plus an electron often results in an electron that is residing at an orbital with a higher energy level. Electrons often release light (a packet of energy) when they go from high to low orbitals. The amount of energy required for such a transition is narrowly defined and is known as a quantum (hence the term *quantum leap*). Electrons do not have predictable orbits in the same way that planets do. In fact, the best estimates that can be made about the position of an atom's electrons are based on confidence about where the electron is most likely to be at a given time. *Orbitals* are the three-dimensional space in which an electron spends 90% of its time.

Valence

Because the negative charges of electrons are repulsive to each other, only two can share an orbital at any given time. Electrons with the lowest amounts of energy are found in an orbital closest to the nuclei of atoms known as **1s.** It is a spherical orbital and, again, it holds only two electrons. The second highest energy level for electrons has a total of four orbitals (**2s,** and **2p;** the 2s orbital is also spherical and the three 2p orbitals are dumbbell shaped).

The chemical properties of an atom depend on its outermost shell of electrons. Since atoms are mostly empty space, nuclei never meet in normal chemical reactions—only electrons way out at the edge of the atoms ever have an opportunity to interact. Although the number of protons in an atom never changes during a chemical reaction, the relative positions (and sometimes even the number) of electrons do.

Although maintaining a balance of charges (i.e., one electron for every proton in an atom) is Nature's highest priority, there is also a strong tendency to keep an atom's outermost shell of orbitals completely full or completely empty. These potentially conflicting tendencies can be resolved by allowing the electron orbitals of atoms to overlap. The sharing of electrons that results from the overlapping of those orbitals is typically part of a long-term association between the two atoms and is the basis of **covalent bonding.** Since the atoms of some elements such as helium, $_2$He (the subscript number before an atomic symbol such as He states the number of protons in an atom's nucleus), have no unpaired electrons in their outermost orbital they are not chemically reactive and are never covalently bound to other atoms. In the same way, $_{10}$Ne (in which both the 1s orbital and all four of the level-2 orbitals are filled with a total of 10 electrons) and $_{18}$Ar are also unreactive. Atoms with similar valences have similar chemical properties: Carbon, $_6$C (in which each of the four level-2 orbitals has a single electron), and silicon, $_{14}$Si (in which each of the four level-3 orbitals has a single electron), react very similarly and are both capable of making four covalent bonds. As a result, the number of unpaired electrons in an atom's outermost orbital, its **valence,** takes on a special significance and represents its bonding capacity: $_1$H = 1, $_8$O = 2, $_7$N = 3, $_6$C = 4. The shape and size of compounds (a complex of two or more covalently bound atoms) are largely governed by the valences of the atoms that comprise them.

Electronegativity

The chemistry of living things is complicated by the fact that different nuclei have different affinities for electrons. The higher an atom's affinity for electrons, the higher its **electronegativity.** The relative electronegativity of an atom is a function of how many electrons it needs to acquire or to donate in order to completely fill or empty its outermost shell of orbitals. For instance, $_1$H and $_6$C both have outermost shells of electrons that are half full. Since their electronegativities are essentially the same, atoms are shared evenly in the covalent bonds between hydrogen and carbon atoms. This is substantially different from what occurs in the covalent bonds between hydrogen and carbon with oxygen. Since $_8$O must either gain just two electrons or lose six, it is much more electronegative than hydrogen or carbon. Electrons involved in the covalent bonds of water (H_2O), for instance, tend to spend more time in the vicinity of the oxygen atom than the hydrogen atom. **Polar bonds** such as these result in a slight separation of charge that makes the oxygens of water molecules slightly negative and the hydrogens slightly positive. The slight separation of charges that result from polar covalent bonds allows for an important type of interaction between molecules called **hydrogen bonding.** Every water molecule is typically loosely associated with a network of other water molecules because the slight positive charges of their hydrogen atoms give them an affinity for the slight negative charges of the oxygens in their neighbors. Much less energy is required to break the association caused by hydrogen bonding than by covalent bonding because no electrons are shared between atoms in hydrogen bonds.

Hydrophilicity and Hydrophobicity

Chemists have found that most chemicals can be easily placed in one of just two categories: those that interact with water and those that do not. Molecules with polar bonds, like water itself, have some regions of positive and negative charge on their surfaces that are capable of forming hydrogen bonds with water. This makes them **hydrophilic** (literally, "water friendly") and allows them to be easily dissolved in watery solutions like the interior of a living cell. Other molecules that have atoms joined by only nonpolar covalent bonds are **hydrophobic** (literally, "afraid of water") and have much less basis of interaction with water molecules. In fact, their physical presence actually gets in the way of water molecules interacting with each other and prevents them from offsetting their partial charges. As a result, molecules such as fats that are composed primarily of carbon–carbon and carbon–hydrogen bonds are actually excluded from watery solutions and forced into associations with each other such as those observed in a cell's lipid bilayer membrane.

Molecular Biology Tools

Recognizing the information content in the DNA sequences of prokaryotic genomes is invariably easier than the equivalent task in more complicated eukaryotic genomes. For example, while the mRNA copies of both prokaryotic and eukaryotic genes have long ORFs, the DNA sequences of eukaryotic genes themselves often do not due to the presence of introns (see Chapter 6). The problem of identifying protein coding information within eukaryotic DNA sequences is further compounded by the fact that what may be an intron in one kind of eukaryotic cell may be an exon in another (described in greater detail in Chapter 6). These problems and others associated with deciphering the information content of genomes are far from insurmountable once the rules used by cells are known. In a quickly growing number of cases, it is bioinformaticians who recognize these rules from patterns they observe in large amounts of sequence data. It is the surprisingly small number of tools commonly used by molecular biologists, however, that both generates the raw data needed for such analyses and tests the biological significance of possible underlying rules. A set of roughly six different laboratory techniques, taken together, defines the entire discipline of molecular biology. These techniques are briefly described in this section.

Restriction Enzyme Digests

The Nobel Prize–winning work of Wilkins, Watson, and Crick in 1953 told the story of how DNA could act as the genetic material. Subsequent experiments confirmed this hypothesis, but it was not until nearly 20 years later that H. Smith and others made a serendipitous discovery that allowed researchers to manipulate DNA molecules in a specific fashion and to begin to decipher DNA's actual information content. In the course of studying what causes some bacterial cells to better defend themselves against viral infections, Smith and his colleagues found that bacteria produced enzymes that introduce breaks in double-stranded DNA molecules whenever they encounter a specific string of nucleotides. These proteins, **restriction enzymes,** can be isolated from bacterial cells and used in research laboratories as precise "scissors" that let biologists cut (and later "paste" together) DNA molecules. The very first of these proteins to be characterized was given the name *Eco*RI (*Eco* because it was isolated from *Escherichia coli*; R because it restricted DNA; I because it was the first such enzyme found in *E. coli*). *Eco*RI was found to cleave DNA molecules between G and A nucleotides whenever it encountered them in the sequence 5'-GAATTC-3' (Figure 1.10). Since then over 300 types of restriction enzymes have been found in other bacterial species that recognize and cut DNA molecules at a wide variety of specific sequences. Notice that *Eco*RI, like many restriction enzymes, cleaves (or digests) double-stranded DNA molecules in a way that leaves a bit of single-stranded DNA at the end of each fragment. The nucleotide sequences of those single-stranded regions (5'-AATT-3' in the case of *Eco*RI) are naturally complementary to each other. The resulting potential for base pairing makes these **sticky ends** capable of holding two DNA fragments together until another special enzyme called **ligase** can permanently link (or ligate) them together again by rebuilding the phosphodiester bonds that were broken by the restriction enzyme. Restriction enzymes that do not give rise to sticky ends create **blunt ends** that can be ligated to other blunt-ended DNA molecules.

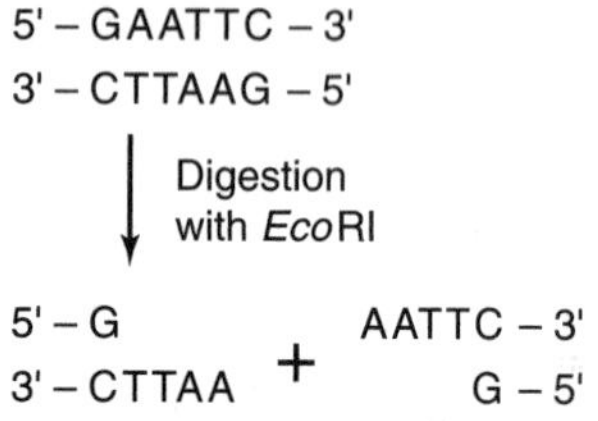

The string of nucleotides recognized by *Eco*RI, its **restriction site**, should occur randomly in DNA sequences only once every $(1/4)^n$ base pairs where n equals 6 or, on average, once every 4,096 base pairs. Some restriction enzymes have smaller restriction sites (such as *Hinf*I, which finds and restricts at 5'-GATC-3' on average once every 256 base pairs) while others have larger sites (such as *Not*I, which finds and restricts at 5'-GCGGCCGC-3' on average once every 65,536 base pairs). Simply cutting a DNA molecule and determining how many fragments are made and the order in which the breaks occur when multiple restriction enzymes are used provide some limited insight into the specific organization and sequence of that DNA molecule. Such experiments are termed **restriction mapping.** Restriction enzymes also allowed the isolation and experimental manipulation of individual genes for the very first time.

5' – GAATTC – 3'
3' – CTTAAG – 5'

↓ Digestion
  with *Eco*RI

5' – G   AATTC – 3'
3' – CTTAA **+**   G – 5'

FIGURE 1.10

Digestion with the restriction enzyme EcoRI. EcoRI introduces staggered breaks in DNA molecules whenever it encounters its recognition site (5'-GAATTC-3'). The single-stranded overhanging regions that result are capable of base pairing with each other and are referred to as sticky ends.

Gel Electrophoresis

When dealing with a genome that is millions of base pairs long (such as *E. coli*'s) or even billions of base pairs long (such as the human genome), complete digestion with even a very specific restriction enzyme such as *Not*I can yield hundreds of thousands of DNA fragments. Separating all of those different fragments from each other is commonly accomplished by **gel electrophoresis,** another of the tools of molecular biology. In gel electrophoresis, DNA (or RNA or protein) fragments are loaded into indentations called wells at one end of a porous gel-like matrix typically made either from agarose or acrylamide. When an electric field is applied across these gels, the charged molecules naturally migrate toward one of the two electrodes generating the field. DNA (and RNA) with its negatively charged phosphate backbone is drawn toward the positively charged electrode. Very simply, small molecules have an easier time working their way through the gel's matrix than larger ones, and separation of the molecules on the basis of their size occurs (Figure 1.11). Larger molecules remain closer to the wells than smaller molecules, which migrate more quickly.

Blotting and Hybridization

Finding the single piece of DNA that contains a specific gene among hundreds or thousands is very much akin to the idea of finding a needle in a haystack even when the DNA fragments are size fractionated. Molecular biologists routinely

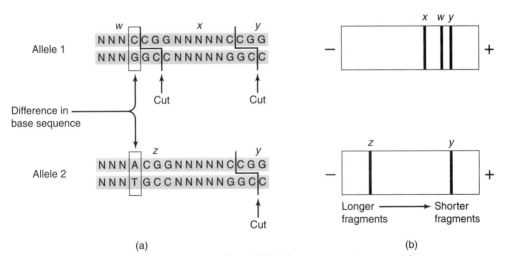

F I G U R E 1.11 *Gel electrophoresis allows DNA fragments to be separated on the basis of their size. (a) Differences in DNA sequences can cause differences in the places where restriction enzymes break double-stranded DNA molecules. (b) The differences in the sizes of the restriction fragments that result can be easily detected by gel electrophoresis. Allele 1 has three bands (corresponding to regions w, x, and y, while allele 2 gives rise to two bands corresponding to regions z and y.*

employ another technique, **blotting and hybridization,** to draw attention to the one fragment they wish to study. In blotting, polynucleotides are transferred from the fragile gel that was used to separate them onto a more solid support such as a piece of nitrocellulose paper or a nylon membrane. This blotting process is mechanically simple and entails placing the membrane in contact with the gel and then using capillary action to pull the DNA up from the gel and onto the membrane. While water molecules can pass through the membrane (and be drawn into absorbent paper towels or a weak vacuum above it), DNA molecules are too large and remain associated with the membrane in the same relative positions that they had moved to during gel electrophoresis. Ultraviolet light or even simple baking can then be used to permanently attach the DNA fragments to the membrane.

A membrane prepared in this way is then ready for the second step in this detection process. Hybridization occurs when a labeled fragment of single-stranded DNA called a **probe** is allowed to base pair with the nucleic acids that have been transferred to a membrane. Typically 20 or more nucleotides in length, probes can be chosen on the basis of their being likely to find only one fragment of DNA on the membrane to which they can base pair. Probes can be chemically synthesized from scratch or can be fragments of DNA that have already been isolated in other experiments and even from related genes in different organisms. Any of a number of means can be used to label or tag a probe ranging from radioactivity to fluorescent dyes and even attaching enzymes that catalyze unusual reactions. These probes are allowed to wash over a membrane (often for several hours or even overnight) as part of a watery mix that also contains salt, pH buffers, and detergent. The stringency of the hybridization, particularly salt concentration and temperature, can be manipulated to allow probes to bind to sequences with less than perfect matches. At the end of the hybridization procedure, unbound probe is washed off and the membrane is examined to see where base pairing between the probe and its target sequence has occurred.

A variant of these membrane-based hybridization systems is the powerful **microarray** or DNA chip technology. Here, thousands and even tens of thousands of nucleotide sequences are each affixed to individual positions on the surface of a small silica (glass) chip. Fluorescently labeled copies of the RNA transcripts (cDNAs, described further in Chapter 6) from an organism being studied can then be washed over that surface and allowed to hybridize to complementary nucleotides. After washing, a laser is used to excite the fluorescent tags and then photodetectors quantify the amount of signal associated with each spot of known sequence. A popular application of this methodology results in the determination of relative RNA levels associated with huge numbers of known and predicted genes in a single experiment for a variety of organisms using commercially available microarrays. Quite literally, accurate measurements of *every* single gene (and even every processing variant of every gene) can be precisely assessed. The sensitivity of DNA chip technology is truly remarkable in that it can confirm the presence of as little as one transcript being present in every tenth cell of an experiment. Significant computational efforts are associated with the generation of such chips (ensuring the distinctiveness of each of the thousands of bound probes alone is challenging) as well as the interpretation of their results. (Variation among replicate experiments, evaluation of differences between test and control conditions, and determination of expression associations are all complicated by an abundance of data.)

Cloning

While cells manipulate and extract information from single DNA molecules on a routine basis, molecular biologists typically require quantities of material that are almost visible to the naked eye (many millions of molecules) for most of their analyses. DNA sequencing reactions (described below) in particular require higher purity and larger amounts of DNA than can be practically obtained through restriction enzyme digestion of genomic DNA and gel electrophoresis. A fairly simple solution to this problem has been to invoke the assistance of cells in the generation of sufficient quantities and qualities of specific DNA molecules for such purposes. In essence, **cloning** involves the insertion of specific DNA fragments into chromosome-like carriers called **vectors** that allow their replication in (and isolation from) living cells. Since all the copies of the fragment are identical, they are known as **molecular clones** and they can be purified for immediate study or stored in collections known as libraries for future analyses.

Once a restriction fragment that contains a sequence of particular interest has been generated as described above, its sticky ends can be used to help ligate it into a vector that has been cut with a restriction enzyme that has complementary sticky ends. The first vectors to be used were derived from bacterial viruses and from small extra-chromosomal pieces of DNA in prokaryotic cells called plasmids. These vectors are easy to manipulate in the laboratory and are especially useful for cloning relatively small pieces of DNA (ranging in size from dozens to 25,000 nucleotides in length). Newer alternatives derived from bacterial and yeast chromosomes are better suited for very large fragments of DNA (ranging from 100,000 to 1,000,000 base pairs long), but are not as amenable to handling and characterization. All vectors must have several features in common to be useful to molecular biologists. Those features include sequences that allow them to be replicated inside of living cells, sequences that confer a novel ability to their host cell so their presence can be detected, and distinguishing physical traits (such as size or shape) that allow them to be separated from the host cell's DNA.

A collection of genes, each of which is cloned into a vector, is known as a **genetic library.** An ideal genomic library would contain one copy of every segment of an organism's DNA. For example, if a 4,600,000-nucleotide-long genome (such as *E. coli*'s) were completely digested with a restriction enzyme such as *Eco*RI, then a total of more than 1,000 DNA fragments with an average length of 4,096 base pairs would each need to be cloned to make a complete genomic library. The number of clones (genome size divided by average fragment length) in such a perfect genomic library defines a **genomic equivalent.** Unfortunately, making a genomic library cannot be accomplished by simply digesting the genomic DNA of a single cell and making clones of each fragment. The cloning process is not efficient and it is usually necessary to harvest DNA from hundreds or thousands of cells to clone a single fragment. Further, the random nature of the cloning process ensures that some fragments will be cloned multiple times while others are not represented at all in one genomic equivalent. Increasing the number of clones in a genomic library increases the likelihood that it will contain at least one copy of any given segment of DNA. A genomic library with four to five genomic equivalents has, on average, four to five copies of every DNA segment and a 95% chance of containing at least one copy of any particular portion of the organism's genome. Details of this calculation are provided in Chapter 6. These realities have two practical implications: (1) Vectors that allow the cloning of larger fragments are better for making genomic libraries because fewer clones are needed to make a genomic equivalent, and (2) cloning the last 5% of a genome is often as difficult as cloning the first 95%.

In many cases a useful alternative to a genomic library is a **cDNA library.** The portions of a genome that are typically of greatest interest are those that correspond to the regions that code for proteins. One thing that all protein coding regions have in common is the fact that they are all converted into mRNAs before they are translated by ribosomes. Those mRNAs can be separated from all the other polynucleotides within a cell by means of a special enzyme called **reverse transcriptase,** which converts them back into complementary DNA (cDNA) sequences and then clones those cDNAs as part of a library. Simply showing up in a cDNA library is often enough to attach significance to a portion of a genome since cells usually only make mRNA copies of genes that are functionally important. Further, the relative abundance of cDNAs within a library from any given organism or cell type gives an indication as to how much a particular gene is expressed. A disadvantage to cDNA sequences, though, is that they typically contain only the information that is used by ribosomes in making proteins and not the important regulatory sequences and introns usually associated with genes. As a result, complete understanding of a gene's structure and function usually comes only after characterization of both its genomic and cDNA clone. The creation of screening libraries to determine which clones contain sequences of interest is accomplished by similar kinds of blotting and hybridization strategies used to distinguish between one DNA fragment and another.

Polymerase Chain Reaction

Molecular cloning provides a means of organizing and indefinitely maintaining specific portions of a genome in a way that also allows large quantities of that region to be isolated and used in more detailed analyses. When little information about the sequence of the region is known and large quantities of a region are needed, a powerful alternative to cloning is the use of the **polymerase chain reaction (PCR)** method. Developed by K. Mullis in 1985, PCR relies on an understanding of two idiosyncrasies associated with DNA polymerases (the enzymes responsible for replicating DNA during cell division). First, like RNA polymerases, all DNA polymerases add new nucleotides onto just the 3' (and never the 5') end of a DNA strand during synthesis; hence, there is a definite directionality to DNA synthesis. Second, while it is the job of a DNA polymerase to make double-stranded DNA molecules by using the information inherent to a single-stranded DNA molecule, DNA polymerases can only begin DNA synthesis by adding nucleotides onto the end of an existing DNA strand (Figure 1.12). PCR takes advantage of those two quirks of DNA polymerases to drive the replication of very specific regions of a genome that are of interest to a molecular biologist. One double-stranded copy of such a region can be replicated into two double-stranded copies after one round of amplification. Those two copies can each be duplicated to give rise to four copies during a second round of amplification. In just a couple of hours and after 20 to 30 such rounds of exponential amplification, a specific region of DNA is usually present in enormously higher quantities (theoretically, 2^{20} to 2^{30} or 1,048,576 to 1,073,741,824 copies, assuming that only one copy was present at the start of the process) than other DNA sequences present at the start of the process (Figure 1.12). These amplified DNA molecules are produced much more quickly and efficiently than those obtained from clones yet they can be used in many of the same ways. The amplifying nature of PCR gives it the additional advantage of being able to start with much smaller quantities of material (such as those typically associated with museum or even fossil and forensic specimens) than are usually amenable to cloning experiments.

DNA synthesis occurs only at specific segments of a genome during PCR amplification because of the specific primers that are added to the reaction mixture at the very start of the amplification process. Like the probes used in hybridization experiments, PCR primers are typically 20 or more nucleotides in length to ensure that each can bind specifically to only one target sequence within an organism's genome. The specific sequences used to make primers in the first place typically come from DNA sequence analyses of similar regions in closely related organisms and at some point usually require the more laborious process of cloning and screening described earlier.

DNA Sequencing

The ultimate molecular characterization of any piece of DNA comes from determining the order or sequence of its component nucleotides. All DNA sequencing strategies involve the same three steps: (1) the generation of a complete set of subfragments for the region being studied whose lengths differ from each other by a single nucleotide, (2) labeling of each fragment with one of four different tags that are dependent on the fragment's terminal nucleotide, and (3) separating those fragments by size in a way (usually some form of acrylamide gel electrophoresis) that allows the sequence to be read by detecting the order in which the different tags are seen.

A. M. Maxam and W. Gilbert developed the first successful DNA sequencing strategy in the late 1970s. However, the **Maxam-Gilbert method** relied on chemical degradation to generate the DNA subfragments needed for sequencing, so it quickly fell out of favor when a safer and more efficient DNA polymerase-based method was developed by F. Sanger a few years later. The Sanger approach is sometimes referred to as a **chain-termination method** because the subset of

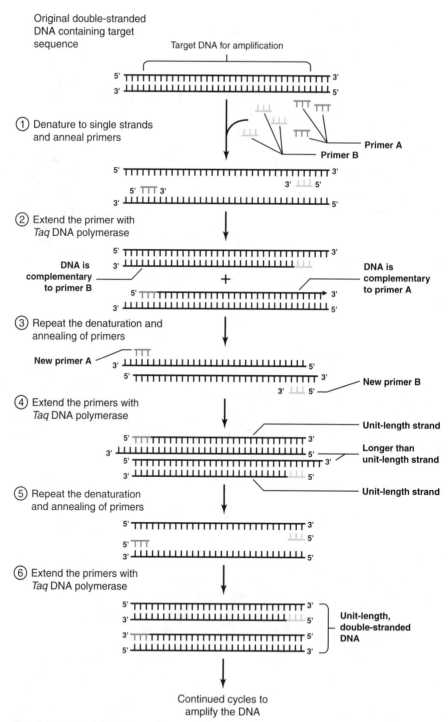

FIGURE 1.12 *The polymerase chain reaction.*

fragments needed for sequencing is generated by the incorporation of modified nucleotides that prevent a DNA polymerase from adding any additional bases to the chain (Figure 1.13). Those chain-terminating nucleotides differ from their normal counterparts in that they are missing their 3' hydroxyl group (see Figure 1.2) onto which the next nucleotide in a growing DNA strand is usually attached. They usually also have a tag such as a fluorescent dye that allows for their detection when they are size fractionated.

In an ideal sequencing reaction the modified and normal nucleotides are mixed in a ratio that allows DNA polymerases to randomly incorporate a chain terminator only once in every 500 or so nucleotides so that a complete set of sub-fragments from a region up to 1,000 base pairs long can be sequenced at one time. Improvements in the methodology and particularly in the automation of DNA sequencing now make it possible for a single analyst to generate tens and even hundreds of thousands of base pairs of DNA sequence data in a single day— quite a contrast to the 50 base pairs of sequence data for which Gilbert (along with Sanger) shared a Nobel Prize in 1980. Still, the short size (roughly 1,000 base pairs) of each piece of sequence information relative to the overall size of a genome (billions of base pairs in many eukaryotes) and even to genes (sometimes hundreds of thousands of nucleotides long) can make assembling sequences of useful size a computationally challenging task.

Genomic Information Content

As mentioned earlier, an organism's genome can be millions or billions of base pairs long. It was possible to obtain interesting insights into how complex a genome was and how much useful information it contained long before it was possible to determine the order in which its nucleotides were arranged. Even now that automated sequencing has made the sequencing of complete genomes feasible, those earliest approaches used to characterize genomes as a whole still provide useful insights into the quantity and complexity of their genetic information.

C-Value Paradox

In 1948 the discovery was made that the amount of DNA in every cell of a given organism is the same. These measures of a cell's total DNA content are referred to as **C values** (Figure 1.14). Interestingly, while genome size within a species is constant, large variations across species lines have been observed but not in a way that correlated well with organismal complexity. The absence of a perfect correlation between complexity and genome size is often called the **C-value paradox** (Figure 1.14). Total DNA amounts often differ by 100-fold or more even between very similar species. The clear (but difficult to prove) implication is that a large portion of the DNA in some organisms is expendable and does not contribute significantly to an organism's complexity.

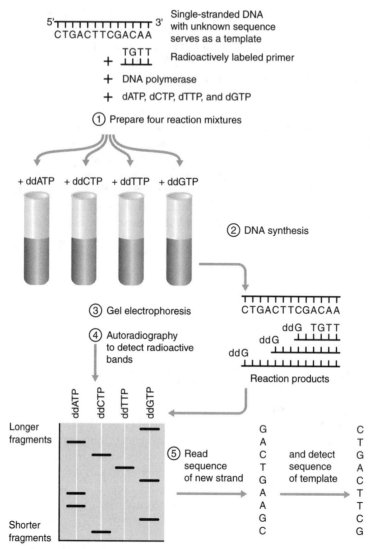

F I G U R E 1.13 *The Sanger dideoxy method of DNA sequencing.*

Reassociation Kinetics

When the complementary strands of double-stranded DNA are separated (denatured) by heat or alkali treatment, they can readily reform (renature) a conventional double-stranded structure when conditions are returned to those typically encountered inside a cell. Quite a bit can be learned about the structure of genomes simply by examining the way in which their denatured DNA renatures. In the simplest terms, the more unique a sequence in a genome, the more time it will take for each strand to find and hybridize to its complement. Studies

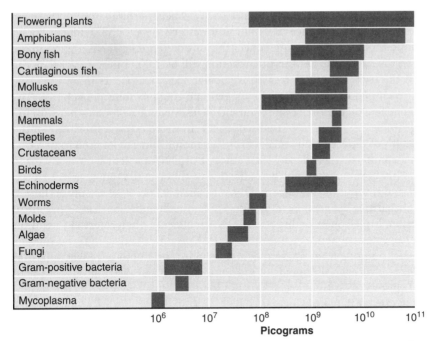

F I G U R E 1.14 *The DNA contents of the haploid genomes of a variety of different organisms. C values are generally correlated to morphological complexity in simpler eukaryotes but vary significantly among more complex eukaryotes. The range of DNA content within a phylum is indicated by the shaded areas.*

by R. Britten and others in the 1960s revealed that the time course of DNA renaturation could be conveniently described by a **cot equation.** The cot equation relates the fraction of single-stranded DNA remaining (c/c_0) after t seconds of renaturing multiplied by the amount of denatured genomic DNA at the start of the experiment (c_0). A specific value, $c_0t_{1/2}$, derived from such experiments can be obtained for any organism and is directly proportional to the number of nucleotides of nonrepeated sequence within the organism's DNA. Measuring the time ($t_{1/2}$) required for one-half of the single-stranded DNA to renature ($c/c_0 = 0.5$) allows an experimental determination of the total amount of unique genetic information encoded in a genome. Since the $c_0t_{1/2}$ is the product of the concentration and time required to proceed halfway, a greater $c_0t_{1/2}$ implies a slower reaction and reflects a situation in which there are fewer copies of any particular sequence within a given mass of DNA.

For example, if the c_0 of DNA is 10 picograms (pg), it will contain 2,000 copies of each sequence in a bacterial genome whose size is 0.005 pg, but will contain only 2 copies of each sequence present in a eukaryotic genome of size 5 pg. So, the same absolute amount of DNA (c_0) will provide a concentration of each eukaryotic sequence that is 2,000/2 = 1,000 times lower than that of each bacterial sequence. Since the rate of renaturation depends on the concentration of complementary sequences, for the eukaryotic sequences to renature at the same rate as the bacterial sequences it would be necessary to have 1,000 times as much eukaryotic DNA. If the starting concentrations of genomic DNA are the same, however, the $c_0t_{1/2}$ of the eukaryotic reaction will be 1,000 times longer than the $c_0t_{1/2}$ of the bacterial reaction if no particular sequence occurs more than one time in each genome. If an organism's genome contains multiple copies of the same sequence, then its $c_0t_{1/2}$ values should be less than those for another with the same genome size but no repeated sequences. In short, $c_0t_{1/2}$ is a measure of the total length of different sequences within a genome and can be used to describe genomic complexity. While the total amount of DNA present within any given genome (its C value) may not be indicative of the overall complexity of an organism, the amount of single-copy DNA it contains (its $c_0t_{1/2}$) usually is (Figure 1.14). Disparities between C values and $c_0t_{1/2}$ usually indicate that an organism contains multiple copies of disposable DNA sequences often referred to as **junk DNA.** Repeated sequences within this junk DNA differ widely in terms of their complexity (ranging from single and dinucleotide repeat units to repeat units that are hundreds or even thousands of nucleotides long) and distribution (arranged in local clusters or scattered relatively randomly) within a genome, as will be discussed in greater detail in Chapter 6.

Chapter Summary

DNA is an information storage molecule for cells. The specific order of its four different nucleotides is transcribed by RNA polymerases into mRNAs that are then translated by ribosomes into proteins. Twenty different amino acids are used to make proteins, and the specific order and composition of those building blocks play an important role in establishing and maintaining the structure and function of enzymes. Molecular biologists have a fairly limited set of tools to study DNA and its information content. Restriction enzymes cut DNA molecules when they encounter specific strings of nucleotides. Electrophoresis allows such DNA fragments to be separated on the basis of their size and charge. Blotting and hybridization techniques allow specific DNA fragments to be found within a mixture of other DNA fragments, while cloning allows specific molecules to be propagated and used over and over again. PCR is a popular and versatile alternative to cloning that allows specific DNA fragments to be amplified and characterized. Ultimate characterization of a DNA molecule comes from determining the order of its nucleotides and can be accomplished by DNA sequencing techniques. Reassociation kinetics have revealed that a cell's DNA content (its C value) does not always correspond directly to an organism's information content due to the large amounts of "junk DNA" found in complex organisms.

Readings for Greater Depth

Numerous textbooks give excellent overviews of molecular biology. For a concise description of genes and our understanding of them, try P. Portin, 1993, The concept of the gene: Short history and present status, *Q. Rev. Biol.* **68:** 173–223.

Discovery of the structure of DNA won Watson and Crick a Nobel Prize. Their classic single-page paper describing their insight is J. D. Watson and F. H. C. Crick, 1953, Genetical implications of the structure of deoxyribonucleic acid, *Nature* **171:** 964–967.

Watson himself relates the dramatic and often unscientific race to discover the structure of DNA in a very informative and often humorous book that has also been made into a major motion picture: J. D. Watson, 1968, *The Double Helix: A Personal Account of the Discovery of the Structure of DNA.* Atheneum, New York.

Reassociation experiments and "junk DNA" are both described in R. J. Britten, D. E. Graham, and B. R. Neufeld, 1974, Analysis of repeating DNA sequences by reassociation. *Methods Enzymol.* **29:** 363–418.

A general text that describes the structure of genes and the experimental techniques used to study them is B. Lewin, 2000, *Genes VII*, Oxford University Press, New York.

Questions and Problems

* **1.1** Deoxyribonucleic acid (DNA) differs from ribonucleic acid (RNA) in two ways: (1) RNA uses the nitrogenous base uracil in place of DNA's thymine, and (2) the hydroxyl (OH) group attached to the 2' carbon of the deoxyribose sugar of RNA is replaced with just a hydrogen (H) in DNA. Sketch the chemical structures of the deoxyribose sugar used by DNA and the ribose sugar used by RNA.

1.2 What is the complementary sequence to the following string of nucleotides? Be sure to label the 5' and 3' ends of the sequence that you write. 5'-GGATCGTAGCCTA-3'.

* **1.3** Diagram the "central dogma" of molecular biology complete with labels that indicate the portions that correspond to transcription and translation and indicate what enzymes are responsible for those important steps.

1.4 Organic molecules that contain hydroxyl groups (—OH) are called alcohols. Would you expect such molecules to be hydrophobic or hydrophilic? Why?

* **1.5** Examine the chemical structures of the amino acid R groups shown in Figure 1.5b. What atom(s) is found in the R groups that are in the hydrophilic amino acids that generally is absent in the nonpolar group?

1.6 How frequently would you expect to find the sequence of nucleotides provided in Question 1.2 in a DNA molecule simply as a result of random chance? Assume that each of the four nucleotides occurs with the same frequency.

* **1.7** How many nucleotides long would a DNA sequence need to be in order for it to not be found by chance more than once in a genome whose size is 3 billion base pairs long?

1.8 Distinguish between positive and negative regulation of gene expression.

* **1.9** What sequence of amino acids would the following RNA sequence code for if it were to be translated by a ribosome?: 5'-AUG GGA UGU CGC CGA AAC-3'. What sequence of amino acids would it code for if the first nucleotide were deleted and another "A" were added to the 3' end of the RNA sequence?

1.10 A circular piece of DNA known to be 4,000 bp long is cut into two pieces when treated with the restriction enzyme *Eco*RI: One piece is 3,000 bp long and the other is 1,000 bp long. Another restriction enzyme, *Bam*HI, cuts the same DNA molecule into three pieces of the following lengths: 2,500, 1,200, and 300 bp. When both *Eco*RI and *Bam*HI are used to cut the DNA molecule together, fragments of the following sizes are generated: 1,600, 1,200, 900, 200, and 100 bp. Use this information to make a restriction enzyme map of this circular DNA molecule.

* **1.11** How does a cDNA library differ from a genomic library?

Data Searches and Pairwise Alignments

It is a capital mistake
to theorize before
one has data.

Sir Arthur Conan Doyle
(1859–1930)

Dot Plots

Simple Alignments

Gaps

Simple gap penalties

Origination and length penalties

Dynamic Programming: The Needleman and Wunsch Algorithm

Global and Local Alignments

Semiglobal alignments

The Smith-Waterman algorithm

Database Searches

BLAST and its relatives

FASTA and related algorithms

Alignment scores and statistical significance
of database searches

Multiple Sequence Alignments

In a very real sense, any alignment between two or more nucleotide or amino acid sequences represents an explicit hypothesis regarding the evolutionary history of those sequences. As a direct result, comparisons of related protein and nucleotide sequences have facilitated many recent advances in understanding the information content and function of genetic sequences. For this reason, techniques for aligning and comparing sequences, and for searching sequence databases for similar sequences, have become cornerstones of bioinformatics.

This chapter describes the methods by which alignments between two or more related nucleotide or polypeptide sequences can be found, evaluated, and used to search through databases of sequence information for genes or proteins relevant to a particular research problem. Closely related sequences are typically easy to align and, in fact, alignment can provide a strong indicator of how closely related the sequences are. Sequence alignments provide important information for solving many of the key problems in bioinformatics including determining the function of a newly discovered genetic sequence; determining the evolutionary relationships among genes, proteins, and entire species; and predicting the structure and function of proteins.

Dot Plots

One of the simplest methods for evaluating similarity between two sequences is to visualize regions of similarity using **dot plots.** To construct a simple dot plot, the first sequence to be compared is assigned to the horizontal axis of a plot space and the second is then assigned to the vertical axis. Dots are then placed in the plot space at each position where both of the sequence elements are identical. Adjacent regions of identity between the two sequences give rise to diagonal lines of dots in the plot (Figure 2.1a).

Such plots quickly become overly complex and crowded when large, similar sequences are compared, as seen in Figure 2.1b. Sliding windows that consider more than just one position at a time are an effective way to deal with this problem. Figure 2.1c illustrates this method for a window size of 10 and also invokes a similarity cutoff of 8. First, nucleotides 1–10 of the X-axis sequence are compared with nucleotides 1–10 of the sequence along the Y axis. If 8 or more of the 10 nucleotides (nt) in the first comparison are identical, a dot is placed in position (1,1) of the plot space. Next the window is advanced one nucleotide on the X axis, so that nucleotides 2–11 of the X-axis sequence are now compared with 1–10 of the sequence along the Y axis. This procedure is repeated until each 10 nt subsequence of the X axis has been compared to nts 1–10 of the Y axis. Then the Y-axis window is advanced by one nucleotide, and the process repeats until all 10 nt subsequences of both sequences have been compared.

As illustrated in Figure 2.1c, the sliding window can significantly reduce the noise in the dot plot, and make readily apparent the regions of significant similarity between the two sequences. Window sizes and cutoff scores can both be varied easily depending on the similarity of the two sequences being compared. The ultimate objective is typically to choose criteria that draw attention to regions of significant similarity without allowing noise levels to be distracting. A trial and error approach is often best when first analyzing new data sets.

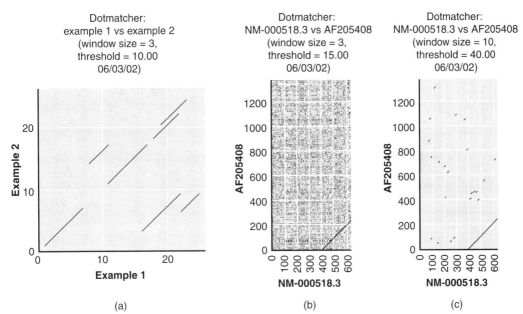

F I G U R E 2.1 *(a) A simple dot plot for two DNA sequences that share extensive regions of similarity. (b) A complete dot plot comparing nucleotide sequences from the beta (β) globin genes of human* (Homo sapiens) *and orangutan* (Pongo pygmaeus). *(c) The same two beta (β) globin gene sequences using a window of 10 nucleotides and a similarity cutoff of 8.*

Simple Alignments

An **alignment** between two sequences is simply a pairwise match between the characters of each sequence. A true alignment of nucleotide or amino acid sequences is one that reflects the evolutionary relationship between two or more **homologs** (sequences that share a common ancestor). Homology is not a matter of degree—at any given position in an alignment, sequences (and individual positions) either share a common ancestor or they do not. In contrast, the overall similarity between two sequences can be described as a fractional value. As described in greater detail in Chapter 3, three kinds of changes can occur at any given position within a sequence: (1) a mutation that replaces one character with another, (2) an insertion that adds one or more positions, or (3) a deletion that deletes one or more positions. Insertions and deletions have been found to occur in nature at a significantly lower frequency than mutations. Since there are no homologs of inserted or deleted nucleotides in compared sequences, **gaps** in alignments are commonly added to reflect the occurrence of this type of change.

In the simplest case, where no internal gaps are allowed, aligning two sequences is simply a matter of choosing the starting point for the shorter sequence. Consider the following two short sequences of nucleotides: AATCTATA and AAGATA. These two sequences can be aligned in only three different ways when no gaps are allowed, as shown in Figure 2.2. To determine which of the three

AATCTATA	AATCTATA	AATCTATA
AAGATA	AAGATA	AAGATA

F I G U R E 2.2 *Three possible simple alignments between two short sequences.*

alignments shown in Figure 2.2 is optimal (e.g., is most likely to represent the true relationship between the sequences assuming that they are homologous), we must decide how to evaluate, or score, each alignment.

While dot plots are useful for visual inspection of the regions of similarity between two sequences, a numeric scoring system for evaluating sequence similarity has obvious advantages for objective determination of optimal alignments. In the simple, gap-free alignments shown in Figure 2.2, the scoring function is determined by the amount of credit an alignment receives for each aligned pair of identical residues (the **match score**) and the penalty for aligned pairs of nonidentical residues (the **mismatch score**). The score for a given alignment is:

$$\sum_{i=1}^{n} \begin{cases} \text{match score; if } seq1_i = seq2_i \\ \text{mismatch score; if } seq1_i \neq seq2_i \end{cases}$$

where n is the length of the longer sequence. For example, assuming a match score of 1 and a mismatch score of 0, the scores for the three alignments shown in Figure 2.2 would be 4, 1, and 3, from left to right.

Gaps

Consideration of the possibility of insertion and deletion events significantly complicates sequence alignments by vastly increasing the number of possible alignments between two or more sequences. For example, the two sequences in Figure 2.2, which can be aligned in only three different ways without gaps, can be aligned in 28 different ways when two internal gaps are allowed in the shorter sequence. Figure 2.3 shows just three of those possible alignments.

AATCTATA	AATCTATA	AATCTATA
AAG—AT-A	AA—G—ATA	AA——GATA

F I G U R E 2.3 *Three possible gapped alignments between two short sequences.*

Simple Gap Penalties

In scoring an alignment that includes gaps, an additional term, the **gap penalty,** must be included in the scoring function. A simple alignment score for a gapped alignment can be computed as follows:

$$\sum_{i=1}^{n} \begin{cases} \text{gap penalty; if } seq1_i = \text{'--' or } seq2_i = \text{'--'} \\ \text{match score; if no gaps and } seq1_i = seq2_i \\ \text{mismatch score; if no gaps and } seq1_i \neq seq2_i \end{cases}$$

For example, assuming a match score of 1, a mismatch score of 0, and a gap penalty of –1, the scores for the three gapped alignments shown in Figure 2.3 would be 1, 3, and 3, from left to right. The first alignment in Figure 2.3 with its score of 1 is still the one that is least likely to represent the true evolutionary relationship between these sequences if these criteria are the ones on which we rely.

Origination and Length Penalties

Using simple gap penalties, it is not uncommon to find a number of equally optimal alignments between two sequences. One method to further distinguish between alignments is to differentiate between those that contain many isolated gaps and those that contain fewer, but longer, sequences of gaps. As mentioned earlier, mutations are rare events but insertions and deletions appear to be even less common. In a very real sense, any given pairwise alignment represents a hypothesis about the evolutionary path two sequences have taken since they last shared a common ancestor. When competing hypotheses are being considered, the one that invokes the fewest number of unlikely events is, by definition, the one that is most likely to be correct. Consider two arbitrary sequences of lengths 12 and 9. Any alignment between these two sequences will necessarily have three gaps in the shorter sequence. Assuming the two sequences are truly homologous from beginning to end, the difference in length can be accounted for by nucleotide insertions in the longer sequence, nucleotide deletions in the shorter sequence, or a combination of the two. Since there is no way to determine, without knowing the original precursor sequence, whether a gap was caused by an insertion in one sequence or a deletion in the other, such events are commonly referred to as insertion/deletion, or **indel,** events.

Since multiple nucleotide insertions and deletions are not uncommon relative to single-nucleotide indels, it is statistically more likely that the difference in length between the two sequences is the result of a single 3-nt indel than by multiple insertions or deletions. Thus we can bias our alignment scoring function to reward alignments that are more likely from an evolutionary perspective by assigning a smaller gap penalty for alignments that extend an existing sequence of gaps than for originating a new gap sequence by inserting a gap between two nongap positions. The gap penalty is thus broken into two parts: an **origination penalty** for starting a new series of gaps in one of the sequences being aligned, and a **length penalty** that depends on the number of sequential missing characters. By assigning a length penalty that is smaller than the origination penalty, the scoring function rewards alignments that place gaps together in sequential positions. Consider the three alignments in Figure 2.3. Using an origination penalty of –2, a length penalty of –1, a match score of +1 and a mismatch score of 0, the scores for the three alignments shown are –3, –1, and +1, from left to right. Note that the last two alignments, both of which were scored +3 using a uniform gap penalty, now receive differing scores. The rightmost alignment, which unites the two gap positions into a single indel that is two characters long, is preferred over the middle alignment, which contains two indels that are each one character long.

Scoring Matrices

Just as the gap penalty can be broken down to reward the most evolutionarily likely alignments, the mismatch penalty can be used to provide further discrimination between similar alignments. In our previous examples, each nongap position in which the aligned nucleotides (or amino acids) did not match resulted in the same penalty to the alignment score. Again relying on the assumption that two sequences being aligned are truly homologous, we can immediately observe that some substitutions are more common than others. For example, consider two protein sequences, one of which has an alanine in a given position. A substitution to another small, hydrophobic amino acid, such as valine, would be less likely to have an impact on the function of the resulting protein than a substitution to a large, charged residue such as lysine. Intuitively, it seems that the more conservative substitution would be more likely to maintain a functional protein and less likely to be selected against than a more dramatic substitution. Thus, in scoring an alignment, we might want to score positions in which an alanine is aligned with a valine more favorably than positions in which an alanine is aligned with a bulky or charged amino acid like lysine.

Once the alignment score for each possible pair of nucleotides or residues has been determined, the resulting **scoring matrix** is used to score each nongap position in the alignment. For nucleotide sequence alignments, scoring matrices are generally quite simple. For example, BLAST—a commonly used tool for aligning and searching nucleotide sequences that is described in greater detail later in this chapter—defaults to a very simple matrix that assigns a score of +5 if the two aligned nucleotides are identical, and –4 otherwise. Figure 2.4 illustrates several alternative scoring matrices for nucleotide alignments. The rightmost matrix provides a mild reward for matching nucleotides, a mild penalty for **transitions**—substitutions in which a purine (A or G) is replaced with another purine or a pyrimadine (C or T) replaces another pyrimadine—and a more severe penalty for **transversions,** in which a purine is replaced with a pyrimidine (C or T) or vice versa.

Several criteria can be considered when devising a scoring matrix for amino acid sequence alignments. Two of the most common are based on observed chemical/physical similarity and observed substitution frequencies. For example, in similarity-based matrices, pairing two different amino acids that both have aromatic functional groups might receive a significant positive score, while pairing

Identity Matrix

	A	T	C	G
A	1	0	0	0
T	0	1	0	0
C	0	0	1	0
G	0	0	0	1

BLAST Matrix

	A	T	C	G
A	5	-4	-4	-4
T	-4	5	-4	-4
C	-4	-4	5	-4
G	-4	-4	-4	5

Transition Transversion Matrix

	A	T	C	G
A	1	-5	-5	-1
T	-5	1	-1	-5
C	-5	-1	1	-5
G	-1	-5	-5	1

F I G U R E 2.4 *Scoring matrices for aligning DNA sequences.*

an amino acid that has a nonpolar functional group with one that has a charged functional group might result in a scoring penalty. Scoring matrices have been derived based on residue hydrophobicity, charge, electronegativity, and size. Another similarity-based matrix for amino acids is based on the genetic code: A pair of residues is scored according to the minimum number of nucleotide substitutions necessary to convert a codon from one residue to the other (see Table 1.1 in Chapter 1). One problem with similarity-based matrices results from the difficulty of combining these various physical, chemical, and genetic scores into a single meaningful matrix.

A more common method for deriving scoring matrices is to observe the actual substitution rates among the various amino acid residues in nature. If a substitution between two particular amino acids is observed frequently, then positions in which these two residues are aligned are scored favorably. Likewise alignments between residues that are not observed to interchange frequently in natural evolution are penalized. One commonly used scoring matrix based on observed substitution rates is the **point accepted mutation (PAM)** matrix. The scores in a PAM matrix are computed by observing the substitutions that occur in alignments between similar sequences (see Box 2.1). First, an alignment is constructed between sequences with very high (usually >85%) identity. Next, the **relative mutability,** m_j, for each amino acid, j, is computed. The relative mutability is simply the number of times the amino acid was substituted by any other amino acid. For example, the relative mutability of alanine, m_a, is computed by counting the number of times alanine is aligned with non-alanine residues. Next, A_{ij}, the number of times amino acid j was replaced by amino acid i, is tallied for each amino acid pair i and j. For example, A_{cm} is the number of times methionine residues were replaced with cysteine in any pair of aligned sequences. Finally, the substitution tallies (the A_{ij} values) are divided by the relative mutability values, normalized by the frequency of occurrence of each amino acid, and the log of each resulting value is used to compute the entries, R_{ij}, in the PAM-1 matrix. The resulting matrix is sometimes referred to as a **log odds matrix,** since the entries are based on the log of the substitution probability for each amino acid.

The normalization of each matrix entry is done such that the PAM matrix represents substitution probabilities over a fixed unit of evolutionary change. For

BOX 2.1 Construction of a PAM Matrix

1. Construct a multiple sequence alignment. Multiple alignments are discussed further later in this chapter. Below is an example of a simplified multiple alignment:

    ACGCTAFKI   GCGCTLFKI
    GCGCTAFKI   ASGCTAFKL
    ACGCTAFKL   ACACTAFKL
    GCGCTGFKI

2. From the alignment, a phylogenetic tree is created, indicating the order in which the various substitutions shown by the alignment might have taken place. Phylogenetic trees are discussed in detail in Chapters 4 and 5. For now, however, simply note that the tree suggests which substitutions occurred in the sequences involved in the multiple alignment. Consider the following phylogenetic tree, which shows various substitutions among the amino acids in the previous multiple alignment:

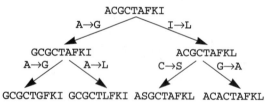

3. For each amino acid type, the frequency with which it is substituted by every other amino acid is calculated. It is assumed that substitutions are equally likely in each direction, so a substitution such as A→G would also count as a G→A substitution. For example, to determine the frequency, $F_{G,A}$, of A to G substitutions, we count all A→G and G→A branches in the tree. For the tree above, $F_{G,A}$ = 3.

4. Compute the relative mutability, m_i, of each amino acid. The relative mutability is the number of times the amino acid is substituted by any other amino acid in the phylogenetic tree. This number is then divided by the total number of mutations that *could* have affected the residue. This denomina-

tor is calculated as the total number of substitutions across the entire tree times two, multiplied by the frequency of the amino acid, times a scaling factor of 100. The value 100 is used so that the PAM-1 matrix will represent 1 substitution per 100 residues. For example, consider the A residues in the phylogenetic tree above. There are a total of 4 mutations involving A. We divide this value by the number of mutations in the entire tree times two (6 × 2 = 12), times the relative frequency of A residues (10 A's out of 63 total residues in the alignment = 0.159), times 100. Thus m_A = 4/12 × 0.159 × 100 = 0.0209.

5. Compute the mutation probability, M_{ij}, for each pair of amino acids.

$$M_{ij} = \frac{m_j F_{ij}}{\sum_i F_{ij}}.$$ For our example,

$$M_{G,A} = \frac{0.0209 \times 3}{4} = 0.0156.$$

The denominator, $\sum F_{ij}$, is simply the total number of substitutions involving A in the phylogenetic tree.

6. Finally, each M_{ij} is divided by the frequency of occurrence, f_i, of residue i, and the log of the resulting value becomes the entry R_{ij} in the PAM matrix. The frequency of occurrence is simply the number of occurrences of the residue in the multiple alignment, divided by the total number of residues. For G, the frequency of occurrence from our multiple alignment is f_G = 0.1587 (10 G residues divided by 63 total residues). So the entry in our PAM matrix for $R_{G,A}$ would be log(0.0156/0.1587) = log(0.0982) ≈ –1.01.

7. By repeating for each pair of amino acids, we obtain the off-diagonal entries, R_{ij}, of the PAM matrix for our alignment data and phylogenetic tree. The diagonal entries are computed by taking M_{jj} = 1 – m_j, and then following step 6 to obtain R_{jj}.

PAM-1, this unit is 1 substitution (or accepted point mutation) per 100 residues, or one **PAM unit.** In other words, the probabilities in the PAM-1 matrix answer the following question: "Suppose I start with a given polypeptide sequence M at time t, and observe the evolutionary changes in the sequence until 1% of all amino acid residues have undergone substitutions at time $t + n$. Let the new sequence at time $t + n$ be called M'. What is the probability that a residue of type j in M will be replaced by i in M'?" The answer to this question can be obtained from entry R_{ij} of the PAM-1 matrix. By multiplying the PAM-1 matrix by itself, we can approximate the substitution rates over multiple PAM units. The particular PAM matrix that is most appropriate for a given sequence alignment depends on the length of the sequences and on how closely the sequences are believed to be related. It is more appropriate to use the PAM-1 matrix to compare sequences that are closely related, whereas the PAM-1000 matrix might be used to compare sequences with very distant relationships. In practice, the PAM-250 matrix is a commonly used compromise.

Another popular scoring matrix, the BLOSUM matrix, is also derived by observing substitution rates among similar protein sequences. For BLOSUM, ungapped alignments of related proteins are grouped using statistical clustering techniques (described in Chapter 4), and substitution rates between the clusters are calculated. This clustering approach helps to avoid some statistical problems that can occur when the observed substitution rate is very low for a particular pair of amino acids. Like the PAM matrices, various BLOSUM matrices can be constructed to compare sequences with different degrees of relatedness. The significance of the numbering for BLOSUM matrices, however, can be thought of as the inverse of the PAM numbers. In other words, lower numbered PAM matrices are appropriate for comparing more closely related sequences, while lower numbered BLOSUM matrices are used for more distantly related sequences. As a rule of thumb, a BLOSUM-62 matrix is appropriate for comparing sequences of approximately 62% sequence similarity, while a BLOSUM-80 matrix is more appropriate for sequences of about 80% similarity.

Dynamic Programming: The Needleman and Wunsch Algorithm

Once a method for scoring alignments is selected, an algorithm to find the best alignment or alignments between two sequences can be developed. The most obvious method, exhaustive search of all possible alignments, is generally not feasible. For example, consider two modest-sized sequences of 100 and 95 nucleotides. If we were to devise an algorithm that computed and scored all possible alignments, our program would have to test ~55 million possible alignments, just to consider the case where exactly five gaps are inserted into the shorter sequence. As the lengths of the sequences grow, the number of possible alignments to search quickly becomes **intractable,** or impossible to compute in a reasonable amount of time. We can overcome this problem by using **dynamic programming**, a method of breaking a problem apart into reasonably sized subproblems, and using these partial results to compute the final answer. S. Needleman and C. Wunsch were the first to apply a dynamic programming approach to the problem of sequence alignment. Their algorithm, which is similar to the one presented below, is one of the cornerstones of bioinformatics.

The key to understanding the dynamic programming approach to sequence alignment lies in observing how the alignment problem is broken down into subproblems. Suppose we have the following two sequences to align: CACGA and CGA. Assume for now that we are using uniform gap and mismatch penalties. There are three possibilities for the first position in our alignment: (1) We can place a gap in the first sequence (not likely in this case since the first sequence is longer), (2) place a gap in the second sequence, or (3) place a gap in neither sequence. For the first two cases the alignment score for the first position will equal the gap penalty, while the rest of the score will depend on how we align the remaining parts of each sequence. For the last case the alignment score for the first position will equal the match bonus, since we are aligning two C's. Again, the rest of the score will depend on how we align the remaining sequences. This breakdown of the problem is illustrated in Figure 2.5.

If we knew the score for the best alignment we could achieve between ACGA and GA, we could immediately compute the score for the first row in the table. Likewise, if we knew the score for the best alignment we could achieve between the remaining sequences for the second and third rows of the table, then we could compute the best score obtainable for each of the three choices for the initial position of our alignment. With all three scores computed, choosing one of the three possibilities would be a simple matter of selecting the one that leads to the best alignment score.

Suppose we begin our alignment by choosing the first row in Figure 2.5, and aligning the initial C in each sequence. We would go on to compute the score for aligning the sequence ACGA and GA. As we continue our search, progressing through all possible sequence alignments, we are likely to encounter the same

First Position	Score	Sequences Remaining to be Aligned
C C	+1	ACGA CGA
– C	–1	CACGA GA
C –	–1	ACGA CGA

F I G U R E 2.5 *Three possibilities for aligning the first position in the sequences CACGA and CCGA. The match bonus is +1, the mismatch score is 0, and the gap penalty is –1.*

question many times: What is the best possible score for aligning ACGA and GA? The dynamic programming method uses a table to store partial alignment scores, so that we can avoid re-computing them on the fly.

The dynamic programming algorithm computes optimal sequence alignments by filling in a table of partial sequence alignment scores until the score for the entire sequence alignment has been calculated. The algorithm utilizes a table in which the horizontal and vertical axes are labeled with the two sequences to be aligned. Figure 2.6 illustrates the partial alignment score table for the two sequences ACAGTAG and ACTCG, where the gap penalty is –1, the match bonus is +1, and the mismatch score is 0. An alignment of the two sequences is equivalent to a path from the upper left corner of the table to the lower right. A horizontal move in the table represents a gap in the sequence along the left axis. A vertical move represents a gap in the sequence along the top axis, and a diagonal move represents an alignment of the nucleotides from each sequence.

At the outset of the algorithm, the first row and column of the table are initialized with multiples of the gap penalty, as shown in Figure 2.6. We begin filling in the table with position (2,2), the second entry in the second row. This position represents the first column of our alignment. Recall that we have three possibilities for this first position: a gap in the first sequence, a gap in the second sequence, or an alignment of the nucleotides from each sequence (no gap). Likewise, we can fill the first position in the table with one of three possible values:

1. We can take the value from the left (2,1) and add the gap penalty, representing a gap in the sequence along the left axis;

2. We can take the value from above (1,2) and add the gap penalty, representing a gap in the sequence along the top axis; or

3. We can take the value from the diagonal element above and to the left (1,1) and add the match bonus or mismatch penalty for the two nucleotides along the axes, representing an alignment of the two nucleotides.

To fill in the table, we take the maximum value of these three choices. For the example in Figure 2.6, we obtain the values –2, –2, and 1, respectively, for the three options, and so we select the maximal value, 1. This is equivalent to an alignment between the initial A in each of the two sequences. Once we have position (2,2) filled, we can fill in the rest of row 2 in a similar manner, followed by row 3, and likewise for the rest of the table. Figure 2.7 illustrates the completed table. By way of example, consider position (2,3) in the table. The three choices for filling in this position are:

		A	C	T	C	G
	0	–1	–2	–3	–4	–5
A	–1	1				
C	–2					
A	–3					
G	–4					
T	–5					
A	–6					
G	–7					

F I G U R E 2.6 *A partial scores table for aligning sequences ACTCG and ACAGTAG. The gap penalty is –1, the match score is +1, and the mismatch score is 0. The first entry to be filled in is position (2,2) (score shown in gray).*

		A	C	T	C	G
	0	–1	–2	–3	–4	–5
A	–1	1	0	–1	–2	–3
C	–2	0	2	1	0	–1
A	–3	–1	1	2	1	0
G	–4	–2	0	1	2	2
T	–5	–3	–1	1	1	2
A	–6	–4	–2	0	1	1
G	–7	–5	–3	–1	0	2

F I G U R E 2.7 *The completion of the partial scores table from Figure 2.6.*

1. We can take the value from the left (1) and add the gap penalty (–1), resulting in the value 0;

2. We can take the value from above (–2) and add the gap penalty, resulting in the value –3; or

3. We can take the value from the diagonal element above and to the left (–1) and add the mismatch score (0), since the two nucleotides for this position (A and C) do not match, resulting in the value –1.

Since we take the maximum of these three choices, we place the value 0 in position (2,3).

Once the table has been completed, the value in the lower right represents the score for the optimal gapped alignment between the two sequences. For the example shown in Figure 2.7, we can see that the score for the optimal alignment will be 1. Note that we have determined this score without having to exhaustively score all possible alignments between the two sequences. Furthermore, now that we have the partial scores table, we can reconstruct the optimal alignment(s) between the two sequences. Sometimes we will find more than one alignment that achieves the optimal score, as is the case in this example.

To reconstruct the alignment from the scores table, we need to find a path from the lower rightmost entry in the table to the upper leftmost position. To form this path, we can move from our current position in the table to any other position that could legally have produced the score in our current position. As an example, look at the lower rightmost position in Figure 2.7. The score in this position is 2. Of the three choices for forming this score, only one could have produced a score of 2: taking the diagonal element, which has score 0, and adding the match penalty. Since this is the only possible way to obtain the 2 in the current column, we draw an arrow to the diagonal element, as shown in Figure 2.8. From this new position (7,5) there is likewise only one position from which the score could have been obtained, and again it is from the diagonal element. As before, we draw an arrow to this position. We continue this process until all possible paths are completed back to position (1,1). These paths now represent all the optimal alignments between the two sequences.

To convert a path to an alignment, we simply recall our original interpretation of the partial scores array. A vertical move represents a gap in the sequence along the top axis, a horizontal move represents a gap in the sequence along the left axis, and a diagonal move represents an alignment of the nucleotides from each sequence at the current position. For example, consider the path highlighted in Figure 2.8. The sequence of moves in this path, from lower right to upper left, is ↖↖↑↑↖↖. Using these moves we reconstruct the alignment "backwards," from right to left. The first arrow is diagonal, so we align the last two nucleotides:

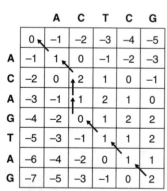

F I G U R E 2.8 *Arrows indicating all allowed paths from the lower right corner of the partial scores table to the upper left corner. Each path represents one of several equally optimal alignments.*

```
G
G
```

The next two arrows are also diagonal so we align the next two positions as well:

```
TCG
TAG
```

The next arrow is vertical, so we place a gap in the top sequence aligned with the next nucleotide from the left sequence:

```
-TCG
GTAG
```

Continuing in this manner, from right to left, we obtain the following optimal alignment, with an alignment score of 2:

```
AC--TCG
ACAGTAG
```

If other paths were present (Figure 2.8), we would know there were other optimal alignments, which also would receive a score of 2. By following all the paths in the partial scores table, we can reconstruct all possible optimal alignments between the two sequences.

Global and Local Alignments

Semiglobal Alignments

The basic alignment algorithm discussed so far performs a **global alignment.** That is, it compares two sequences in their entirety; the gap penalty is assessed regardless of whether gaps are located internally within a sequence, or at the end of one or both sequences. This is not always the most desirable way to align two sequences. For example, suppose we wish to search for the short sequence ACGT within the longer sequence AAACACGTGTCT. Of the several possible alignments between these two sequences, the one we are most interested in is:

```
AACACGTGTCT
---ACGT----
```

This is the most interesting alignment because it demonstrates that the shorter sequence appears in its entirety within the longer sequence. When searching for the best alignment between a short sequence and an entire genome, for example, we might wish to avoid penalizing for gaps that appear at one or both ends of a sequence. **Terminal gaps** are usually the result of incomplete data acquisition and do not have biological significance—hence it is appropriate to treat them differently than internal gaps. This approach is sometimes referred to as a **semiglobal alignment.** Fortunately, we can conduct such an alignment by making a few small changes to our basic dynamic programming algorithm.

Recall that in our original algorithm, a vertical move in the table was equivalent to a gap in the sequence on the topmost axis. It should be clear that by moving vertically to the bottom of the table, and then horizontally to the rightmost edge, we would produce the following alignment for the sequences in Figure 2.6:

```
-------ACTCG
ACAGTAG-----
```

From the top left corner of the table, each downward move adds an additional gap to the beginning of the first sequence in the alignment. Since each gap adds a gap penalty to the overall alignment score (remember, we are using simple, uniform gap penalties), we initialize the first column of the table with multiples of the gap penalty. Now, suppose we wish to allow initial gaps in the first sequence with no penalty. We can make this change quite easily by simply initializing the first column of the table to all zeros. Now each vertical move in the first column does not add a gap penalty to the alignment score. Likewise, by initializing the first row of the table to all zeros, we can allow initial gaps in the second sequence without penalty.

To allow gaps at the end of a sequence without penalty, we must change our interpretation of the table slightly. Suppose we have the following alignment:

```
ACACTGATCG
ACACTG----
```

If we use this alignment to construct a path through a partial alignment scores table, after the first six nucleotides are aligned, we would find ourselves at the bottom row of the table, as illustrated in Figure 2.9. To reach the lower right corner of the table, we need to make four horizontal moves in this row. Under our previous scoring strategy, each of these moves would incur a gap penalty for the alignment. We can easily rectify this by allowing horizontal moves in the bottom row of the table with no gap penalty. Likewise, we can allow end gaps in the first sequence by allowing vertical moves in the last column of the table without assessing a gap penalty. By initializing the first row and column of our partial scores table with zero values, and by allowing free horizontal and vertical moves in the last row and column of the table, respectively, we now have a modification of our Needleman and Wunsch algorithm that searches for semiglobal alignments.

		A	C	A	C	T	G	A	T	C	G
	0	0	0	0	0	0	0	0	0	0	0
A	0	1	0	1	0	0	0	1	0	0	0
C	0	0	2	1	2	1	0	0	1	1	0
A	0	1	1	3	2	2	1	1	0	1	1
C	0	0	2	2	4	3	2	1	1	1	1
T	0	0	1	2	3	5	4	3	2	1	1
G	0	0	0	1	2	3	6	6	6	6	6

F I G U R E 2.9 *The leftmost column and top row of this partial alignment scores table have been initialized to the value zero. Additionally, horizontal moves in the bottom row and vertical moves in the rightmost column are penalty free. This allow gaps at the start or end of either sequence to remain unpenalized.*

The Smith-Waterman Algorithm

Sometimes even semiglobal alignments do not afford the flexibility needed in a sequence search. For example, suppose you have a long sequence of DNA, and you would like to find any subsequences that are similar to any part of the yeast genome. For this sort of comparison, a semiglobal alignment will not suffice, since each alignment will be penalized for every nonmatching position. Even if there is an interesting subsequence that matches part of the yeast genome, all of the nonmatching residues are likely to produce an abysmal alignment score. The appropriate tool for this sort of search is a **local alignment,** which will find the best matching subsequences within the two search sequences. Consider, by way of example, the following two sequences: AACCTATAGCT and GCGATATA. Using our semiglobal alignment algorithm, and using a gap penalty of −1, a match bonus of +1, and a mismatch score of −1, we will obtain the following alignment:

```
AAC-CTATAGCT
-GCGATATA---
```

In one view, this is a fairly poor alignment; four of the first five positions in the alignment are mismatches or gaps, as are the last three positions. However, this alignment does reveal that there is a matching region in the center of the two sequences: the subsequence TATA. With minimal modifications, our dynamic programming method can be used to identify subsequence matches while ignoring mismatches and gaps before and after the matching region. The resulting algorithm was first introduced by F. Smith and M. Waterman in 1981, and is a fundamental technique in bioinformatics.

To perform a local alignment, we modify our global alignment algorithm by allowing a fourth option when filling in the partial scores table. Specifically, we can place a zero in any position in the table if all of the other methods result in scores lower than zero. Once the table is completed in this manner, we simply find the maximum partial alignment score in the entire table, and work backwards, as before, constructing our alignment until we reach a zero. The resulting local alignment will represent the best matching subsequence between the two sequences being compared. Figure 2.10 illustrates the partial scores matrix for the two sequences in our previous example. Recall that the global alignment illustrated the matching subsequence TATA. The maximal value in the partial alignment scores table in Figure 2.10 is 4. Starting with this position, and working backward until we reach a value of 0, we obtain the following alignment:

```
TATA
TATA
```

	A	A	C	C	T	A	T	A	G	C	T
0	0	0	0	0	0	0	0	0	0	0	0
G	0	0	0	0	0	0	0	0	1	0	0
C	0	0	0	1	1	0	0	0	0	2	1
G	0	0	0	0	0	0	0	0	1	0	1
A	0	1	1	0	0	0	1	0	1	0	0
T	0	0	0	0	0	1	0	2	1	0	1
A	0	1	1	0	0	0	2	0	3	2	1	0
T	0	0	0	0	0	1	1	3	2	2	1	2
A	0	1	1	0	0	0	2	2	4	3	2	1

F I G U R E 2.10 *By allowing the option of placing a zero in the partial scores table at any position where a positive value cannot be obtained, the dynamic programming method can be modified to search for local alignments. Here, the best local alignment between the sequences AACCTATAGCT and GCGATATA is represented by the maximal value (4) in the table.*

The local alignment algorithm has identified exactly the subsequence match that we identified from our previous semiglobal alignment. When working with long sequences of many thousands, or even millions, of nucleotides, local alignment methods can identify subsequence matches that would be impossible to find using global or semiglobal alignments.

Database Searches

While sequence alignments can be an invaluable tool for comparing two known sequences, a far more common use of alignments is to search through a database of many sequences to retrieve those that are similar to a particular sequence. If, for example, we had identified a region of the human genome that we believe is a previously unidentified gene, we might compare our putative gene with the millions of other sequences in the GenBank database at the National Center for Biological Information (NCBI). The search results, consisting of other sequences that align well with (and thus are similar to) our sequence, might give us an indication of the functional role of our newfound gene along with valuable clues regarding its regulation and expression and its relationship to similar genes in humans and other species.

In performing database searches, the size and sheer number of sequences to be searched (at the time of the writing of this text, there were more than 13 million sequences in GenBank) often precludes the obvious and direct approach of aligning a query sequence with each sequence in the database and returning the sequences with the highest alignment scores. Instead, various indexing schemes and heuristics must be used to speed the search process. Many of the commonly used database search algorithms are not guaranteed to produce the best match from the database, but rather have a high probability of returning most of the sequences that align well with the query sequence. Nevertheless, the efficiency of these tools in finding sequences similar to a query sequence from the vast repositories of available sequence data has made them invaluable tools in the study of molecular biology.

BLAST and Its Relatives

One of the most well known and commonly used tools for searching sequence databases is the BLAST algorithm, introduced by S. Altschul *et al.* in the early 1990s. The original BLAST algorithm searches a sequence database for maximal ungapped local alignments. In other words, BLAST finds subsequences from the database that are similar to subsequences in the query sequence. Several variations of the BLAST algorithm are available for searching protein or nucleotide sequence databases using protein or nucleotide query sequences. To illustrate the basic concepts of BLAST searches, we will discuss the BLASTP algorithm, which searches for protein sequence matches using PAM or BLOSUM matrices to score the ungapped alignments.

To search a large database efficiently, BLASTP first breaks down the query sequence into **words,** or subsequences of a fixed length (4 is the default word length). All possible words in the query sequence are calculated by sliding a window equal in size to the word length over the query sequence. For example, a protein query sequence of AILVPTV would produce four different words: AILV (4 characters, starting with the first character), ILVP (starting with the second character), LVPT, and VPTV. Once all of the words in the query sequence have been determined, words composed mostly of common amino acids will be discarded. The sequences in the database are then searched for occurrences of the search words. Each time a word match is found in the database, the match is extended in both directions from the matching word until the alignment score falls below a given threshold. Since the alignment is ungapped, the extension only involves adding additional residues to the matching region and recalculating the score according to the scoring matrix. The choice of the threshold value for continuing the extension is an important search parameter, because it determines how likely the resulting sequences are to be biologically relevant homologs of the query sequence. Figure 2.11 shows a simplified overview of the BLASTP search process for a simple polypeptide sequence.

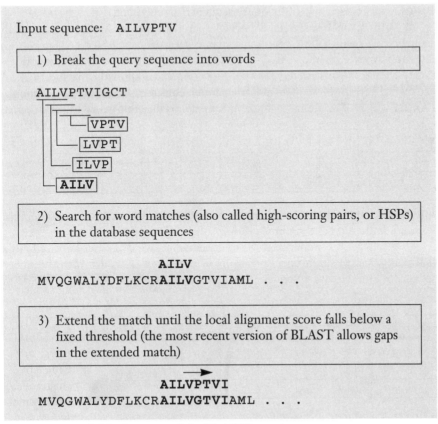

F I G U R E   2.11 *Overview of the BLASTP search process.*

Numerous sequence alignment and database search algorithms have been developed for various specific types of sequence searches. As mentioned previously, BLASTP searches protein sequence databases for polypeptide sequences. Other variations of BLAST, including BLASTN and BLASTX, allow searching of nucleotide sequence databases and translating from nucleotide sequences to protein sequences prior to searching, respectively. BLAST 2.0, the most recent version of BLAST, inserts gaps to optimize the alignment. PSI-BLAST, another member of the BLAST family, summarizes results of sequence searches into **position-specific scoring matrices,** which are useful for protein modeling and structure prediction.

FASTA and Related Algorithms

The FASTX algorithms are another commonly used family of alignment and search tools. FASTA and its relatives perform gapped local alignments between sequences. Since FASTX searches perform several detailed comparisons between the query sequence and each sequence in the database, FASTX searches generally require significantly more execution time than the BLAST searches. However, the FASTX algorithms are considered by some to be more sensitive than BLAST, particularly when the query sequence is repetitive.

As with BLAST searches, a FASTA search begins by breaking the search sequence into words. For genomic sequences a word size of 4 to 6 nucleotides is generally used, while 1 to 2 residues are generally used for polypeptides. Next, a table is constructed for the query sequence showing the locations of each word within the sequence. For example, consider the amino acid sequence FAMLGFIKYLPGCM. For a word size of 1, the following table would be constructed:

Word	A	C	D	E	F	G	H	I	K	L	M	N	P	Q	R	S	T	V	W	Y
Pos.	2	13			1	5		7	8	4	3		11							9
					6	12				10	14									

In this table, the column for phenylalanine (F) contains entries 1 and 6 because F occurs in the first and sixth positions of the query sequence.

To compare this sequence to a target sequence, we construct a second table that compares the amino acid positions in the target sequence with the query sequence. For the target sequence TGFIKYLPGACT this table would appear as follows:

1	2	3	4	5	6	7	8	9	10	11	12
T	G	F	I	K	Y	L	P	G	A	C	T
	3	-2	3	3	3	-3	3	-4	-8	2	
	10	3				3		3			

Consider position 2, a glycine (G) residue. Looking at the table for the query sequence, we can quickly see that glycines are present in positions 5 and 12 of the query sequence. The distance between 5 and 12 and the position of the first glycine in the target sequence (position 2) produces the two entries 3 and 10. For the second glycine, in position 9, we likewise subtract 9 from 5 and 12, obtaining entries –4 and 3. Amino acids, such as threonine (T), that are not found in the query sequence are not included in this table.

Note the large number of instances of the distance 3 in the second table. This suggests that by offsetting the target sequence by 3, we might obtain a reasonable alignment between the two sequences. In fact, we would obtain the following:

```
FAMLGFIKYLPGCM
   |||||||||
   TGFIKYLPGACT
```

By comparing the offset tables for two sequences, areas of identity can be found quickly. Once these areas are found, they are joined to form larger sequences, which are then aligned using a full Smith-Waterman alignment. However, because the alignment is constrained to a known region of similar sequence, FASTA is much faster than performing a complete dynamic programming alignment between the query sequence and all possible targets.

Alignment Scores and Statistical Significance of Database Searches

While a database search will always produce a result, the sequences found cannot be assumed to be related to the search sequence without more information. The primary indicator of how similar the search results are to a query sequence is the alignment score. Alignment scores, however, vary among the different database search algorithms, and are not, of themselves, a sufficient indicator that two sequences are related. Given a database search result with an alignment score S, an appropriate question to ask is "Given a set of sequences *not related* to the query sequence (or even random sequences), what is the probability of finding a match with alignment score S simply by chance?" To answer this question, database search engines generally provide a P score or an E score along with each search result. While they answer slightly different questions, the two scores are closely related, and often have very similar values. Given a database result with an alignment score S, the E score is the expected number of sequences of score $> = S$ that would be found by random chance. The P score is the probability that *one or more* sequences of score $> = S$ would have been found randomly. Low values of E and P indicate that the search result was unlikely to have been obtained by random chance, and thus is likely to bear an evolutionary relationship to the query sequence. While E values of 10^{-3} and below are often considered indicative of statistically significant results, it is not uncommon for search algorithms to produce matches with E values on the order of 10^{-50}, indicating a very strong likelihood of evolutionary relationship between the query sequence and the search results.

Multiple Sequence Alignments

While all of the alignment algorithms discussed thus far are designed to perform pairwise alignments, it is often necessary to simultaneously align a number of sequences. For example, when observing a number of sequences in order to determine substitution frequencies, a **multiple sequence alignment,** which aligns the gaps among all the sequences as much is possible, is often preferable to a set of pairwise alignments. Multiple sequence alignments are also vital for the creation of scoring matrices, such as the PAM and BLOSUM matrices, discussed earlier in this chapter.

The most straightforward techniques for performing multiple alignments are logical extensions of the dynamic programming methods we have discussed so far. For aligning n sequences, an n-dimensional array is used instead of the two-dimensional array used in the Needleman-Wunsch algorithms, but the algorithm is otherwise the same. Unfortunately, the computational complexity of multiple alignment methods grows rapidly with the number of sequences being aligned. Even using supercomputers or networks of workstations, multiple sequence alignment is an intractable problem for more than 20 or so sequences of average length and complexity. As a result, alignment methods using heuristics have been developed. These methods, including the well-known CLUSTAL algorithm, cannot guarantee an optimal alignment, but can find near-optimal alignments for larger numbers of sequences than would be possible with full dynamic programming techniques.

The CLUSTAL algorithm, first described by D. G. Higgins and P. M. Sharp in 1988, begins by aligning closely related sequences and then adds increasingly divergent sequences to produce a complete multiple sequence alignment. First, the algorithm constructs a phylogenetic tree (see Chapters 4 and 5) to determine the degrees of similarity among the sequences being aligned. Using this tree as a guide, closely related sequences are aligned two at a time using dynamic programming for the pairwise alignments.

Selection of a scoring matrix for alignments can present a significant problem in multiple sequence alignments. Some matrices, such as PAM-1 and BLOSUM-90, are appropriate for closely related sequences, while others, such as PAM-1000 and BLOSUM-35, might be more appropriate for very divergent sequences. Use of an inappropriate scoring matrix will generally result in a poor alignment. In CLUSTALW, the most recent version of the CLUSTAL algorithm, sequences are weighted according to how divergent they are from the most closely related pair of sequences, and the gap opening and gap extension penalties, as well as the scoring matrix selection, are based on the weight of each sequence.

An additional consideration for scoring multiple sequence alignments is that it is now possible for two sequences in the alignment to have a gap in the same position. A common strategy is to assign a score of zero for aligned gap positions.

Note also that, like pairwise methods, multiple sequence alignments are based solely on nucleotide or amino acid similarity between sequences. The goal of a multiple alignment is generally to align regions of similar structural or functional importance among sequences. While sequence similarity is an important indicator of related function, it is often the case that a molecular biologist has additional knowledge about the structure or function of a particular protein or gene. Information such as the locations of secondary structure elements, surface loop regions, and active sites are often used to tune multiple alignments by hand in order to produce biologically meaningful results.

Chapter Summary

An alignment between two or more genetic or amino acid sequences represents a hypothesis about the evolutionary path by which the two sequences diverged from a common ancestor. While the true evolutionary path cannot be inferred with certainty, sequence alignment algorithms can be used to identify alignments with a low probability of occurrence by chance. The selection of a scoring function has a significant bearing on the results of a sequence alignment. Various techniques are available to bias scoring functions to discover evolutionarily likely alignments, including the use of scoring matrices such as the PAM and BLOSUM matrices. The algorithm first described by Needleman and Wunsch for global sequence alignment and also the local alignment method of Smith and Waterman have become the cornerstones on which numerous database search algorithms, including the BLASTX and FASTX tools, have been built. These algorithms use indexing, heuristics, and fast comparison techniques to allow an entire database of sequences to be rapidly compared with a query sequence.

Readings for Greater Depth

The PAM matrix was first described in M. Dayhoff, R. M. Schwartz, and B. C. Orcutt, 1978, A model of evolutionary change in proteins, in *Atlas of Protein Sequence and Structure*, Vol. 5, pp. 345–352, National Biomedical Research Foundation, Silver Spring, MD.

Another approach to scoring alignments, the BLOSUM matrix, was introduced in S. Henikoff and J. G. Henikoff, 1992, Amino acid substitution matrices from protein blocks, *Proc. Nat. Acad. Sci. U.S.A.* **89**: 10915–10919.

Needleman and Wunsch's plenary algorithm for global sequence alignment was detailed in S. B. Needleman and C. D. Wunsch, 1970, A general method applicable to the search for similarities in the amino acid sequences of two proteins, *J. Mol. Biol.* **48**: 443–453.

Smith and Waterman's ubiquitous algorithm for local alignments is succinctly described in F. F. Smith and M. S. Waterman, 1981, Identification of common molecular subsequences, *J. Mol. Biol.* **147**: 195–197.

The well-known BLAST engine for database searching is described in S. F. Altschul, W. Gish, W. Miller, E. W. Myers, and D. J. Lipman, 1990, A basic local alignment search tool, *J. Mol. Biol.* **215**: 403–410.

FAST, an alternative sequence search and alignment method, was first detailed in D. J. Lipman and W. R. Pearson, 1985, Rapid and sensitive protein similarity search, *Science* **227**: 1435–1441.

The CLUSTAL algorithm for multiple sequence alignment was first described in D. G. Higgins and P. M. Sharp, 1988, CLUSTAL: A package for performing multiple sequence alignment on a microcomputer, *Gene* **73**: 237–244. CLUSTALW, a commonly used variant of the original algorithm, is described in J. D. Thompson, D. G. Higgins, and T. J. Gibson, 1994, CLUSTALW: Improving the sensitivity of progressive multiple sequence alignment through sequence weighting, positions-specific gap penalties and weight matrix choice, *Nucl. Acids Res.* **22**: 4673–4680.

MUSCA, an alternative multiple sequence alignment method from IBM's bioinformatics group, is described in L. Parida, A. Floratos, and I. Rigoutsos, 1999, An approximation algorithm for alignment of multiple sequences using motif discovery. *J. Combinatorial Optimization* **3**: 247–275.

MultAlin, another multiple sequence alignment method, is described in F. Corpet, 1988, Multiple sequence alignment with hierarchical clustering, *Nucl. Acids Res.* **16**: 10881–10890.

Questions and Problems

* **2.1** What are some situations in which a molecular biologist might wish to perform a pairwise sequence alignment? A multiple sequence alignment? A sequence database search?

2.2 For the following two sequences, construct a simple dot plot using graph paper. Place each sequence along one axis, and place a dot in the plot for each identical pair of nucleotides:

```
GCTAGTCAGATCTGACGCTA
GATGGTCACATCTGCCGC
```

Does your dot plot reveal any regions of similarity?

* **2.3** For the two sequences in Question 2.2, construct a dot plot using a sliding window of size 4 and a similarity cutoff of three nucleotides. Does this plot reveal any regions of similarity between the two regions?

2.4 Determine the alignment score for each of the following sequence alignments:

  a. Global alignment: match score = +1, mismatch score = 0, gap penalty = –1

```
TGTACGGCTATA
TC--CGCCT-TA
```

  b. Global alignment: match score = +1, mismatch score = 0, gap penalty = –1

```
--TCTGTACGCGATCATGT
TAGC-GTCCGATAT-A---
```

c. Global alignment: match score = +1, mismatch score = –1, origination penalty = –2, length penalty = –1

```
AGATAGAAACTGATATATA
AGA-A-A-ACAGAG-T---
```

d. Global alignment: match score = +1, mismatch score = –1, origination penalty = –2, length penalty = –1

```
AGATAGAAACTGATATATA
AG---AAAACAGAGT----
```

e. Semiglobal alignment: match score = +1, mismatch score = –1, origination penalty = –2, length penalty = –1

```
AGATAGAAACTGATATATA
AG---AAAACAGAGT----
```

* **2.5** Using the Needleman and Wunsch dynamic programming method, construct the partial alignment score table for the following two sequences, using the following scoring parameters: match score = +1, mismatch score = 0, gap penalty = –1.

```
ACAGTCGAACG
ACCGTCCG
```

What is the optimal global alignment between these sequences?

2.6 Using the same scoring parameters as in Question 2.5, use the modified Needleman and Wunsch method to compute the optimal semiglobal alignment for the two sequences in Question 2.5.

* **2.7** Using the Smith-Waterman method, construct the partial alignment scoring table for a local alignment of the following two sequences:

```
ACGTATCGCGTATA
GATGCTCTCGGAAA
```

Substitution Patterns

Nature, red in tooth
and claw.

Alfred Tennyson (1809–1892)

Patterns of Substitutions within Genes
Mutation rates
Functional constraint
Synonymous vs. nonsynonymous substitutions
Indels and pseudogenes
Substitutions vs. mutations
Fixation

Estimating Substitution Numbers
Jukes-Cantor model
Transitions and transversions
Kimura's two-parameter model
Models with even more parameters
Substitutions between protein sequences

Variations in Evolutionary Rates between Genes

Molecular Clocks
Relative rate test
Causes of rate variation in lineages

Evolution in Organelles

Comparisons of the nucleotide sequences from two or more organisms such as those described in the previous chapter frequently reveal that changes have accumulated at the level of their DNA even when the sequences are from functionally equivalent regions. In fact, it is not uncommon to find sequences that have become so different over the course of evolution that reliable sequence alignments are difficult to obtain. Analyses of both the number and nature of substitutions that have occurred are of central importance to the study of molecular evolution. Because the process of natural selection is very effective at removing harmful changes, such analyses also provide powerful clues to bioinformaticians interested in recognizing and characterizing the portions of genes that are most functionally important. This chapter explains how and why the rate of nucleotide substitutions differs within and between genes as well as across species boundaries.

Patterns of Substitutions within Genes

Alterations in DNA sequences can have dire consequences for living cells. Most genes are very close to being in an optimal state for an organism in its typical environment, and the axiom "if it's not broken, don't fix it" definitely applies. It should not be surprising then for cells to have developed elaborate mechanisms that ensure the accuracy of DNA replication and repair. Still, **mutations** (both exchanges of one nucleotide for another and insertion/deletion events) do occur and cells do not always pass on a perfect copy of their genetic instructions. Those who study molecular evolution divide those mistakes into three categories: (1) those that are disadvantageous or **deleterious,** (2) those that are advantageous, and (3) those that are effectively **neutral** (have no effect on the fitness of an organism). The relative abundance of changes that fall into each category is still an open question, but two things are well accepted: (1) Advantageous changes are in a substantial minority, and (2) some changes in nucleotide sequences have greater consequences for an organism than do others. Not all portions of a gene are created equal—at least not from the perspective of how closely they are scrutinized during the process of natural selection.

Mutation Rates

The number of substitutions two sequences have undergone since they last shared a common ancestor, K, can often be determined simply by counting the differences between them. When K is expressed in terms of the number of substitutions per site and coupled with a divergence time (T) it is easily converted into a rate (r) of substitution. Because substitutions are assumed to accumulate simultaneously and independently in both sequences, the substitution rate is obtained by simply dividing the number of substitutions between two homologous sequences by $2T$ as shown in this equation:

$r = K/(2T)$

Note that in order to estimate substitution rates data must always be available from at least two species. This simple equation can be quite powerful: If evolutionary rates between several species are similar, substitution rates can give insights into the dates of evolutionary events for which no other physical evidence is available. Comparisons of substitution rates within and between genes are even more commonly used to determine the roles of different genomic regions as described below.

Functional Constraint

Changes to genes that diminish an organism's ability to survive and reproduce are typically removed from the gene pool by the process of **natural selection.** Since proteins are responsible for carrying out most of the important work of cells, it should not be surprising that changes to the nucleotide sequence of genes that also change the catalytic or structural properties of proteins are especially subject to natural selection. Portions of genes that are especially important are said to be under **functional constraint** and tend to accumulate changes very slowly over the course of evolution. Many changes to the nucleotide sequence of a gene have no effect on the amino acid sequence or expression levels of proteins and are much less subject to correction by natural selection—changes of this type accumulate relatively quickly.

Numerous analyses have confirmed that different portions of genes do accumulate changes at widely differing rates that reflect the extent to which they are functionally constrained. An example of those differences is shown in Table 3.1 for the changes that have accumulated within the beta-like globin gene of four mammals since they last shared a common ancestor roughly 100 million years ago. Recall from our discussion of gene structure in Chapter 1 that a typical eukaryotic gene is made up of some nucleotides that specify the amino acid sequence of a protein (coding sequences) and other nucleotides that do not code

T A B L E 3.1 Average pairwise divergence among different regions of the human, mouse, rabbit, and cow beta-like globin genes.

Region	Length of Region (bp) in Human	Average Pairwise Number of Changes	Standard Deviation	Substitution Rate (substitutions/ site/10^9 years)
Noncoding, overall	913	67.9	14.1	3.33
Coding, overall	441	69.2	16.7	1.58
5' Flanking sequence	300	96.0	19.6	3.39
5' Untranslated sequence	50	9.0	3.0	1.86
Intron 1	131	41.8	8.1	3.48
3' Untranslated sequence	132	33.0	11.5	3.00
3' Flanking sequence	300	76.3	14.3	3.60

Note: No adjustment is made for the possibility that multiple changes may have occurred at some sites.

for amino acids in a protein (noncoding sequences). The roughly two-times higher rate of change in the noncoding sequences of beta-like globin genes suggests that, taken as a whole, they are not as functionally constrained as the adjacent coding sequences (3.33×10^{-9} changes/site/year vs. 1.58×10^{-9} changes/site/year). Noncoding sequences can be subdivided into many different categories including introns, leader regions and trailer regions that are transcribed but not translated, and 5' and 3' flanking sequences that are not transcribed (Figure 3.1). Each of those regions also tends to accumulate changes at different rates that are generally correlated with the extent to which their nucleotides are functionally constrained. For instance, it should not be surprising that one of the lowest substitution rates seen in Table 3.1 (1.86×10^{-9} substitutions/site/year) is associated with the 5' sequences of the gene that are transcribed but not translated because so many of the nucleotides in that region are functionally important for the appropriate translation of beta-like globin proteins. In contrast, the nucleotides that are downstream of the beta-like globin gene's polyadenylation signal appear to play little if any functional role and are free to accumulate substitutions at a relatively fast rate (3.60×10^{-9} substitutions/site/year).

The results reported in Table 3.1 come from a fairly small data set—an analysis of roughly 1.3 kb containing the beta-like globin gene in each of four different mammalian genomes. It is entirely reasonable to expect that other genes accumulate substitutions at different rates and even for beta-like globin genes to be under different levels of functional constraint in different species. However, Table 3.1 does illustrate a general trend: Changes accumulate most rapidly in introns and flanking sequences, next most rapidly in other regions that are transcribed but not translated, and least rapidly within coding sequences. Data from

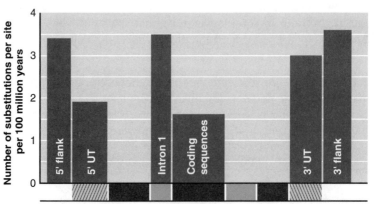

F I G U R E 3.1 *Structure and relative rate of change within the beta-like globin gene in four mammals. Three hundred base pairs of the 5' and 3' flanking sequences are shown as open boxes; the 5' transcribed but untranslated (5' UT) sequence is represented as a forward slash-filled box; the 3' transcribed but untranslated (3' UT) sequence is shown as a backward slash-filled box; exons are shown as black boxes; and introns are shown as gray boxes. Relative rates of change are taken from Table 3.1.*

the beta-like globin genes also give a general feel for the time frames in which nucleotide changes accumulate. While a 0.35% change in a nucleotide sequence per million years (the approximate rate for introns and flanking sequences) may seem inordinately slow from a human perspective, it is relatively fast when considered from the perspective of molecular evolution.

Synonymous vs. Nonsynonymous Substitutions

As was pointed out in Chapter 1, 18 of the 20 different amino acids are encoded by more than one triplet codon (Table 1.1). For example, four different codons (GGG, GGA, GGU, and GGC) all code for the amino acid glycine. Any change at the third position of a codon for glycine (changing GGG to GGC, for instance) results in a codon that still causes ribosomes to insert a glycine at that point in the primary structure of a protein. Changes such as these at the nucleotide level of coding sequences that do not change the amino acid sequence of the protein are reasonably called **synonymous substitutions.** In contrast, changes to the second position of a glycine codon would result in changes to the amino acid sequence of a protein and are therefore known as **nonsynonymous substitutions** (for example, GCG codes for the amino acid alanine).

If natural selection distinguishes primarily between proteins that function well and those that do not, then synonymous substitutions should be observed more frequently than nonsynonymous ones. However, of the 47 substitutions that have accumulated within the human and rabbit beta-like globin genes in the past 100 million years, 27 are synonymous substitutions and 20 are nonsynonymous substitutions. This is especially remarkable in light of the fact that there were almost three times as many opportunities for *nonsynonymous* substitutions within the coding sequence of that gene.

From the example of mutations to the glycine codons described above, it should be clear that not all positions within triplet codons are as likely to result in nonsynonymous substitutions. In fact, the nucleotides in triplet codons can be placed in one of three different categories on that basis. **Nondegenerate sites** are codon positions where mutations always result in amino acid substitutions (i.e., UUU codes for phenylalanine, CUU codes for leucine, AUU codes for isoleucine, and GUU codes for valine). **Twofold degenerate sites** are those codon positions where two different nucleotides result in the translation of the same amino acid, but the two other nucleotides code for a different amino acid (e.g., GAU and GAC both code for aspartic acid, whereas GAA and GAG both code for glutamic acid). **Fourfold degenerate sites** are codon positions where changing a nucleotide to any of the three alternatives has no effect on the amino acid that ribosomes insert into proteins (such as the third codon position of glycine described above). Again, if natural selection works primarily at the level of mutations that alter protein function, it should not be surprising that nucleotide changes should accumulate most rapidly at fourfold degenerate sites and least rapidly at nondegenerate sites. That is exactly what is observed for the substitutions that have accumulated in the coding sequence of the human and rabbit beta-like globin genes (Table 3.2). The substitution rate at fourfold degenerate sites

T A B L E 3.2 Divergence between different kinds of sites within the coding sequence of the human and rabbit beta-like globin genes.

Region	Number of Sites (bp)	Number of Changes	Substitution Rate (substitutions/ site/10^9 years)
Nondegenerate	302	17	0.56
Twofold degenerate	60	10	1.67
Fourfold degenerate	85	20	2.35

Note: Sequences used are available from GenBank (accession numbers V00497 and V00879, respectively). No adjustment is made for the possibility that multiple changes may have occurred at some sites. A divergence time of 100 million years is assumed.

often approaches that of 3′ flanking sequences and other regions that are relatively free of selective constraint.

Indels and Pseudogenes

All of the changes discussed to this point in this chapter have focused on those occurring within transcriptionally active genes. In such a setting there is a very strong bias against insertion and deletion (indel) events because of their tendency to alter the reading frame used by ribosomes. That bias against frameshift mutations in coding regions is so strong that DNA replication and repair enzymes in general appear to have evolved in a way that makes indels roughly 10 times less likely to occur in any region of the genome than simple exchanges of one base for another.

It is also interesting to consider substitution patterns in genes that once were under selective constraint but have become transcriptionally inactive. As will be discussed in greater detail in Chapter 6, genes with new functions are commonly derived from genes with existing, useful functions. Duplication of an entire gene allows one copy to provide the necessary function of the original and the other copy to accumulate substitutions in a way that is free of selective constraint. On occasion, the evolving copy of such a gene undergoes some changes that give it an important new function and it again becomes important to the fitness of the organism. More often, however, one of the copies of a duplicated gene becomes a **pseudogene** when it acquires mutations that make it nonfunctional and transcriptionally inactive. Mammalian genomes are littered with such pseudogenes, and their sequences tend to accumulate substitutions at a very fast rate—at an average of almost four substitutions per site per 100 million years and just a bit faster than the 3′ flanking sequences of genes within a species.

Substitutions vs. Mutations

Natural selection has an insidious effect on the data that are typically available for analysis by bioinformaticians. With only very rare exceptions, the only alleles available for characterization in naturally occurring populations of organisms are those that have not had a detrimental effect on fitness. The point here is that while all changes to the nucleotide sequence of a gene may be possible, not all are seen. An appreciation of this data-sampling problem gives rise to an interesting and subtle distinction between the use of the words *mutation* and *substitution* in molecular evolution studies. Mutations are changes in nucleotide sequences that occur due to mistakes in DNA replication or repair processes. **Substitutions** are mutations that have passed through the filter of selection on at least some level. Estimates of substitution rates are common in the field of molecular evolution. At the same time it is very difficult to estimate mutation rates reliably because natural selection can be so subtle and pervasive. This becomes a particularly important issue because comparisons between substitution and mutation rates give the best indication as to how functionally constrained a sequence actually is. Synonymous (and pseudogene) substitution rates (K_s), such as those shown in Table 3.3, are generally considered to be fairly reflective of the actual mutation rate operating within a genome because they are not subject to natural selection. Nonsynonymous substitutions rates (K_a) are not because they are subject to natural selection.

Fixation

Most naturally occurring populations of organisms harbor a substantial amount of genetic variation. Humans, for instance, differ from each other at an average of 1 base pair out of every 200. Different versions of any given gene within a species of organism are known as **alleles.** Differences among alleles cover a broad spectrum ranging from those that are relatively innocuous (i.e., a single difference in the nucleotide sequence of a 3' flanking sequence) to those that have very dramatic consequences (i.e., the presence of a premature stop codon that causes a truncated, nonfunctioning protein to be produced). Change in the relative frequencies of these different alleles is the essence of evolution.

With the exception of those that are introduced through migration or transfer across species boundaries, new alleles arise from mutations occurring to an existing allele within a single member of a population. As a result, new versions of genes typically begin at very low frequencies (q):

$$q = 1/2N$$

where N is the number of reproductively active diploid organisms within the population. As mentioned earlier, mutations that make organisms less likely to survive and reproduce tend to be removed from the gene pool through the process of natural selection and their frequencies eventually return to 0 (unless new mutations re-create the allele). The apparent rarity of mutations that dramatically increase the fitness of organisms suggests that most genes are at least fairly close to an optimal state for an organism's typical environment. However, when advantageous alleles do arise, their frequencies should move progressively toward 1.

Knowing that substitution rates are fairly low and that changes that alter fitness achieve a frequency of either 0 or 1 relatively quickly, what accounts for the

T A B L E 3.3 Ratios of synonymous differences per synonymous site (K_s) and nonsynonymous differences per nonsynonymous site (K_a) for a variety of mammalian genes.

Gene	Codons (in human)	Human/mouse K_s	K_a	Human/cow K_s	K_a	Human/rabbit K_s	K_a	Mouse/cow K_s	K_a	Mouse/rabbit K_s	K_a	Cow/rabbit K_s	K_a	Averages K_s	K_a
Erythropoietin	194	0.481	0.063	0.242	0.068	0.394	0.070	0.495	0.076	0.480	0.058	0.342	0.071	0.406	0.068
Growth hormone	217	0.321	0.100	0.236	0.106	0.220	0.113	0.380	0.046	0.396	0.027	0.244	0.048	0.299	0.073
Prolactin receptor	621	0.304	0.082	0.249	0.122	0.321	0.072	0.358	0.124	0.413	0.088	0.300	0.114	0.324	0.100
Prolactin	226	0.364	0.098	0.368	0.085	0.395	0.064	0.382	0.112	0.307	0.131	0.521	0.064	0.390	0.092
Serum albumin	610	0.528	0.062	0.329	0.067	0.324	0.075	0.477	0.065	0.500	0.065	0.327	0.067	0.414	0.067
Alpha globin	143	0.584	0.022	0.236	0.025	0.204	0.038	0.505	0.025	0.539	0.041	0.242	0.048	0.385	0.033
Beta globin	148	0.324	0.033	0.271	0.046	0.294	0.015	0.263	0.062	0.392	0.039	0.333	0.059	0.313	0.042
Prothrombin	608	0.033	0.687	0.033	1.040	0.075	1.602	0.196	0.887	0.037	1.442	0.078	0.318	0.075	0.996
Apolipoprotein E	317	0.199	0.148	0.132	0.117	0.108	0.114	0.187	0.160	0.165	0.144	0.125	0.126	0.153	0.135
Carbonic anhydrase I	336	0.255	0.159	0.203	0.149	0.207	0.138	0.338	0.113	0.284	0.115	0.187	0.117	0.246	0.132
P53	392	0.372	0.059	0.351	0.061	0.382	0.045	0.457	0.067	0.412	0.054	0.378	0.056	0.392	0.057
Histone 2A	115	0.967	0.057	1.110	0.057	0.174	0.034	0.298	0.006	1.176	0.025	1.192	0.025	0.820	0.033
Column averages		0.394	0.131	0.313	0.162	0.258	0.198	0.361	0.145	0.425	0.186	0.356	0.093	0.351	0.152

relatively high levels of variation seen within naturally occurring populations of organisms? Quite simply, much of the variation that is observed among individuals must have little beneficial or detrimental effect and be essentially **selectively neutral.** The probability (*P*) that any truly neutral variant of a gene will eventually be lost from a population is simply a matter of chance and is equal to $1 - q$, where *q* is the relative frequency of the allele in the population. By the same token, the probability that a particular neutral allele will be **fixed** (occur within a population at a frequency of 1) is equal to *q*, the current frequency of the gene in the population. Even though the chance of fixation for a new version of a gene might be small, neutral mutations can persist in populations for very long periods of time (even by molecular evolution standards), and the mean time for fixation for a new neutral mutation is effectively equal to the amount of time required for 4*N* generations to pass.

All of this has direct, practical implications for bioinformaticians interested in determining the functionality of genes. The variation between and especially within species seen in comparative sequence analyses such as those described above is almost always limited to those portions of a gene that are free of functional constraint. Analysis of such variation helps to distinguish between those regions of genomes that contain genes and those that do not (discussed in greater depth in Chapter 6). Comparative sequence analysis also goes a long way toward obviating the need for the time-consuming and experimentally grueling process of **saturation mutagenesis** in which molecular biologists make all possible changes to the nucleotide sequence of a gene to determine which alter its function. To a large extent, nature is performing a perpetual saturation mutagenesis experiment, and the majority of the variation available for us to observe corresponds to changes that do not significantly alter the function of genes.

Estimating Substitution Numbers

The number of substitutions (*K*) observed in an alignment between two sequences is typically the single most important variable in any molecular evolution analysis. If an optimal alignment suggests that relatively few substitutions have occurred between two sequences, then a simple count of the substitutions is usually sufficient to determine a value for *K*. However, even before the nucleotide sequences of any genes were available for analysis, T. Jukes and C. Cantor (1969) realized that alignments between sequences with many differences might cause a significant underestimation of the actual number of substitutions since the sequences last shared a common ancestor.

Jukes-Cantor Model

Where substitutions were common, there were no guarantees that a particular site had not undergone multiple changes such as those illustrated in Figure 3.2. To address that possibility, Jukes and Cantor assumed that each nucleotide was just as likely to change into any other nucleotide. Using that assumption, they

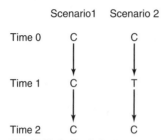

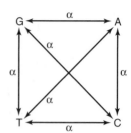

FIGURE 3.2 *Two possible scenarios where multiple substitutions at a single site would lead to underestimation of the number of substitutions that had occurred if a simple count were performed.*

FIGURE 3.3 *Diagram of the Jukes-Cantor model of nucleotide substitution. For their model, Jukes and Cantor assumed that all nucleotides changed to each of the three alternative nucleotides at the same rate, α.*

created a mathematical model (diagrammed in Figure 3.3) in which the rate of change to any one of the three alternative nucleotides was assumed to be α and the overall rate of substitution for any given nucleotide was 3α. In that model, if a site within a gene was occupied by a C at time 0, then the probability (P) that that site would still be the same nucleotide at time 1 would be $P_{C(1)} = 1 - 3\alpha$. Because a reversion (back mutation) to C could occur if the original C changed to another nucleotide in that first time span, at time 2 the probability, $P_{C(2)}$, would be equal to $(1 - 3\alpha)P_{C(1)} + \alpha [1 - P_{A(1)}]$. Further expansion suggested that at any given time (t) in the future, the probability that that site would contain a C was defined by the following equation:

$$P_{C(t)} = 1/4 + (3/4)e^{-4\alpha t}$$

Ten years later nucleotide sequence data became available for the first time and made it clear that Jukes's and Cantor's assumption of a global uniformity in substitution patterns was an oversimplification. Even still, their model continues to provide a useful framework for taking into account the actual number of substitutions per site (K) when multiple substitutions are possible. Through manipulations of the Jukes-Cantor equation above, we can derive a fairly simple equation that yields an estimate of the true number of substitutions that have occurred between two sequences when only a pairwise counting of differences is available:

$$K = -3/4 \ln[1 - (4/3)(p)]$$

In this equation p is the fraction of nucleotides that a simple count reveals to be different between two sequences. This equation is totally consistent with the idea that when two sequences have few mismatches between them, p is small and the chance of multiple substitutions at any given site is also small. It also suggests that when the observed number of mismatches is large, the actual number of substitutions per site will be larger than what is actually counted directly.

Transitions and Transversions

Nucleotides can be divided into two separate categories on the basis of the structure of their nitrogenous bases (see Figure 1.1). Guanine and adenine are called **purines** because their nitrogenous bases have a two-ring structure. In contrast, **pyrimidines** like cytosine, thymine, and uracil all have nitrogenous bases with only a one-ring structure. The first actual nucleotide sequence data, which became available in the 1970s, made it clear that exchanging one nucleotide for another within or between these classes occurred at significantly different rates. Specifically, **transitions** (exchanging one purine for another or exchanging one pyrimidine for another) occurred at least three times as frequently as **transversions** (exchanging a purine for a pyrimidine or vice versa).

Kimura's Two-Parameter Model

In 1980, M. Kimura developed a two-parameter model that took into account the different rates of transitions and transversions. In his model transitions were assumed to occur at a uniform rate of α and transversions at a different, uniform rate of β (diagrammed in Figure 3.4). With these parameters, if a site within a gene was occupied by a C at time 0, then the probability (P) that that site would still be the same nucleotide at time 1 would be $P_{CC(1)} = 1 - \alpha - 2\beta$. Back mutations could still occur between time 1 (t_1) and time 2 (t_2) and the probability that the site would still contain a C, $P_{CC(2)}$, is the sum of the probabilities associated with four different scenarios: (1) C remained unchanged at t_1 and at t_2; (2) C changed at t_1 and reverted by a transition to C at t_2; (3) C changed to a G at t_1 and reverted by a transversion to C at t_2; and (4) C changed to an A at t_1 and reverted by a transversion back to C at t_2 (Figure 3.5). Thus, for this model, the probability that the site is still occupied by a C at t_2 is

$$P_{CC(2)} = (1 - \alpha - 2\beta)P_{CC(1)} + \beta P_{GA(1)} + \beta P_{AC(1)} + \alpha P_{TC(1)}$$

As with the Jukes-Cantor model, further expansion suggested that at any given time (t) in the future, the probability that that site would contain a C is defined by this equation:

$$P_{CC(t)} = 1/4 + (1/4)e^{-4\beta t} + (1/2)e^{-2(\alpha + \beta)t}$$

The symmetry of the substitution scheme in both the Jukes-Cantor model and Kimura's two-parameter model results in all four nucleotides having an equal probability of being the same between time 0 and any point in the future ($P_{GG(t)} = P_{AA(t)} = P_{TT(t)} = P_{CC(t)}$). And, just as with the Jukes-Cantor one-parameter model, further manipulation of this equation and those for the other three nucleotides results in a useful equation that yields an estimate of the true number of substitutions that have occurred between two sequences when only a pairwise counting of differences is available:

$$K = 1/2 \ln[1/(1 - 2P - Q)] + 1/4 \ln[1/(1 - 2Q)]$$

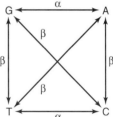

FIGURE 3.4 *Diagram of Kimura's two-parameter model of nucleotide substitution. Kimura assumed that nucleotide substitutions occurred at essentially two different rates: α for transitions (i.e., changes between G and A or between C and T), and β for transversions (changes between purines and pyrimidines).*

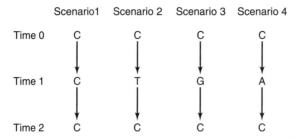

F I G U R E 3.5 *Four possible routes by which a site appears to have been unchanged after two time intervals have passed.*

In this equation P is the fraction of nucleotides that a simple count reveals to be transitions, and Q is the fraction that are transversions. If no distinction is made between transitions and transversions (i.e., $p = P + Q$), this equation reduces precisely to the equivalent Jukes-Cantor equation for estimating the number of substitutions that have occurred between two sequences.

Models with Even More Parameters

The large amounts of sequence data that have been generated since the early 1980s have revealed that Kimua's assumption that nucleotides change at two different rates is almost as much of an oversimplification as Jukes's and Cantor's assumption that all nucleotides had an equal probability of changing into any of the other three. Since each of the four nucleotides can change into any of the other three, 12 different types of substitutions are possible: $G \rightarrow A$; $G \rightarrow T$; $G \rightarrow C$; $A \rightarrow G$; $A \rightarrow T$; $A \rightarrow C$; $T \rightarrow G$; $T \rightarrow A$; $T \rightarrow C$; $C \rightarrow G$; $C \rightarrow A$; and $C \rightarrow T$.

Matrices such as the one shown in Table 3.4 can be generated that attach probabilities to each of those different types of mutation, which can then be used in a mathematically cumbersome 12-parameter model. A 13th parameter can also be invoked that compensates for differences in matrices like the one in Table 3.4 that are caused by substitution biases associated with regional genomic GC context. Although intimidating if being analyzed by hand, such complex models can be fairly easily implemented computationally. However, such complex models invoke more assumptions than the one- and two-parameter models described earlier (i.e., that the nucleotide sequences being studied were at an equilibrium state at the time of their divergence). Sampling errors due to the comparatively small number of instances of each kind of change are also compounded during the analysis. Consequently, simulation studies suggest that one- and two-parameter models often give more reliable results than more complex alternatives—and are themselves virtually indistinguishable when closely related sequences are studied.

T A B L E 3.4 Relative frequencies of nucleotide substitutions in Alu-Y (Sb) sequences throughout the human genome.

From	To				
	A	**T**	**C**	**G**	**Row Totals**
A	—	4.0	4.6	9.8	18.4
	—	(1.5)	(1.7)	(3.6)	(6.7)
T	3.3	—	10.4	2.7	16.4
	(1.2)	—	(3.8)	(1.0)	(6.0)
C	7.2	17.0	—	6.2	31.1
	(5.0)	(33.2)	—	(4.5)	(42.6)
G	23.6	4.6	6.0	—	34.2
	(37.7)	(3.2)	(3.7)	—	(44.7)
Column totals	34.1	26.3	21.0	9.0	
	(44.0)	(37.8)	(9.2)	(18.7)	

Note: Members of the *Alu* repeat family are approximately 260 base pairs in length. They are derived from one or a small number of ancestral sequences that have been duplicated almost 1 million times during primate evolution.

The relative frequencies of substitutions observed involving each of the four nucleotides within 403 Alu-Y (Sb) repeat sequences scattered throughout the human genome excluding those involving CpG dinucleotides. Values in parentheses were obtained when substitutions at CpG dinucleotides were not excluded. A total of 7,433 substitutions (2,713 of which were at sites other than CpG dinucleotides) were accumulated by the 403 Alu-Y (Sb) repeats included within this analysis since they were propagated roughly 19 million years ago.

Substitutions between Protein Sequences

The proportion (p) of different amino acids between two protein sequences can be calculated simply as

$$p = n/L$$

where n is the number of amino acids that differ between the two sequences, and L is the number of positions at which differences could be observed in the aligned sequences. However, refining estimates of the number of substitutions that have occurred between the amino acid sequences of two or more proteins is generally more difficult than the equivalent task for noncoding DNA sequences. Just as with DNA sequences, back mutations can result in significant undercounting of substitutions. And, in addition to the fact that some substitutions occur more frequently than others, the substitutional path from one amino acid to another is not always the same length. For instance, the CCC codon for proline can be converted to the CUC codon for leucine with just one mutation, but it is not possible to convert it to a codon for isoleucine (such as AUC) without at least two mutations. The problem is complicated even more by the fact that most amino acid substitutions do not have an equivalent effect on protein function, and effects can differ greatly from one context to another. One solution to these problems is to weight each amino acid substitution differently by using empirical data from a variety of different protein comparisons to generate a matrix such as the PAM matrix described in Chapter 2.

Variations in Evolutionary Rates between Genes

Just as variations in evolutionary rates are readily apparent in comparisons of different regions within genes, striking differences in the rates of evolution between genes have also been observed. If stochastic factors (like those arising from small population sizes due to sampling error) are ruled out, the difference in rates must be attributable to one or some combination of two factors: (1) differences in mutation frequency and/or (2) the extent to which natural selection affects the locus. While some regions of genomes do seem to be more prone to random changes than others, synonymous substitution rates rarely differ by more than a factor of 2. That difference is far from sufficient to account for the roughly 200-fold difference in nonsynonymous substitution rates observed between the different mammalian genes listed in Table 3.3. As was the case for variation in observed substitution rates within genes, variation of substitution rates between genes must be largely due to differences in the intensity of natural selection at each locus.

Specific examples of two classes of genes, histones and apolipoproteins, illustrate the effects of different levels of functional constraint (Table 3.3). Histones are positively charged, essential DNA binding proteins present in all eukaryotes. Almost every amino acid in a histone such as histone H2A interacts directly with specific chemical residues associated with negatively charged DNA. Virtually any change to the amino acid sequence of histone H2A affects its ability to interact with DNA. As a result, histones are one of the slowest evolving groups of proteins known, and it is actually possible to replace the yeast version of histone H2A with its human homolog with no effect despite hundreds of millions of years of independent evolution. Apolipoproteins, in contrast, accumulate nonsynonymous substitutions at a very high rate. They are responsible for nonspecifically interacting with and carrying a wide variety of lipids in the blood of vertebrates. Their lipid-binding domains are composed predominantly of hydrophobic amino acids. Any similar amino acid (i.e., leucine, isoleucine, and valine) appears to function in those positions just as well as another so long as it too is hydrophobic.

Also, while amino acid substitutions within many genes are generally deleterious, we should point out that natural selection actually favors variability within populations for some genes. The genes associated with the human leukocyte antigen (HLA), for instance, are actually under evolutionary pressure to diversify. As a result, the rate of nonsynonymous substitutions within the HLA locus is actually greater than that of synonymous substitutions (mean number of synonymous substitutions, K_s = 3.5%, and nonsynonymous substitutions, K_a = 13.3%, for the 57-amino-acid-long sequence of the antigen recognition site within five variants of the human HLA-A locus). The HLA locus contains a large multigene family whose protein products are involved with the immune system's ability to recognize foreign antigens. Within human populations, roughly 90% of individuals receive different sets of HLA genes from their parents, and a sample of 200 individuals can be expected to have 15 to 30 different alleles.

Such high levels of diversity in this region are favored by natural selection because the number of individuals vulnerable to infection by any single virus is likely to be substantially less than it would have been had they all had similar immune systems. At the same time that host populations are pressured to maintain diverse immune systems, viruses too are under pressure to evolve rapidly. Error-prone replication coupled with diversifying selection causes the rate of nucleotide substitutions within the influenza *NS* genes to be 1.9×10^{-3} nucleotide substitutions per site per year—roughly a million times greater than the synonymous substitution rate for representative mammalian genes such as those in Table 3.3.

Molecular Clocks

As described above, the differences in the nucleotide and amino acid replacement rates between nuclear genes can be striking but is likely to be due primarily to differences in the selective constraint on each individual protein. However, rates of molecular evolution for loci with similar functional constraints can be quite uniform over long periods of evolutionary time. In fact, the very first comparative studies of protein sequences performed by Emile Zuckerkandl and Linus Pauling in the 1960s suggested that substitution rates were so constant within homologous proteins over many tens of millions of years that they likened the accumulation of amino acid changes to the steady ticking of a **molecular clock.**

The molecular clock may run at different rates in different proteins, but the number of differences between two homologous proteins appeared to be very well correlated with the amount of time since speciation caused them to diverge independently, as shown in Figure 3.6 on page 72. This observation immediately stimulated intense interest in using biological molecules in evolutionary studies. A steady rate of change between two sequences should facilitate not only the determination of phylogenetic relationships between species but also the times of their divergence in much the same way that radioactive decay was used to date geological times.

Despite its great promise, however, Zuckerkandl and Pauling's molecular clock hypothesis has been controversial. Classical evolutionists argued that the erratic tempo of morphological evolution was inconsistent with a steady rate of molecular change. Disagreements regarding divergence times have also placed in question the very uniformity of evolutionary rates at the heart of the idea.

Relative Rate Test

Most divergence dates used in molecular evolution studies come from interpretations of the notoriously incomplete fossil record and are of questionable accuracy. To avoid any questions regarding speciation dates, Sarich and Wilson (1973)

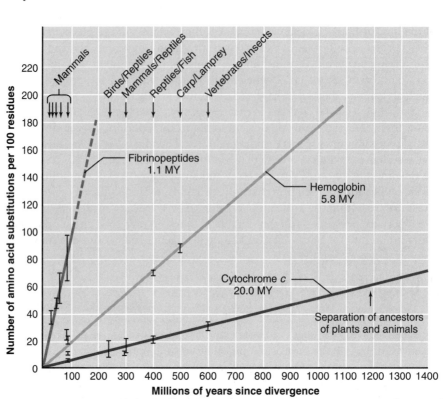

F I G U R E 3.6 *Numbers of amino acids replaced and species divergence times are well correlated for a number of proteins.*

devised a simple way to estimate the overall rate of substitution in different lineages that does not depend on specific knowledge of divergence times. For example, to determine the **relative rate** of substitution in the lineages for species 1 and 2 in Figure 3.7, we need to designate a less related species 3 as an **outgroup.** Outgroups can usually be readily agreed on; for instance, in this example, if species 1 and 2 are humans and gorillas, respectively, then species 3 could be another primate such as a baboon. In the evolutionary relationship portrayed in Figure 3.7, the point in time when species 1 and 2 diverged is marked with the letter "A." The number of substitutions between any two species is assumed to be the sum of the number of substitutions along the branches of the tree connecting them such that

$$d_{13} = d_{A1} + d_{A3}$$

$$d_{23} = d_{A2} + d_{A3}$$

$$d_{12} = d_{A1} + d_{A2}$$

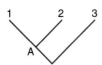

F I G U R E 3.7

Phylogenetic tree used in a relative rate test. Species 3 represents an outgroup known to have been evolving independently prior to the divergence of species 1 and species 2. "A" denotes the common ancestor of species 1 and species 2.

where d_{13}, d_{23}, and d_{12} are easily obtained measures of the differences between species 1 and 3, species 2 and 3, and species 1 and 2, respectively. Simple algebraic manipulation of those statements allows the amount of divergence that has taken place in species 1 and in species 2 since they last shared a common ancestor to be calculated using these equations:

$$d_{A1} = (d_{12} + d_{13} - d_{23})/2$$

$$d_{A2} = (d_{12} + d_{23} - d_{13})/2$$

By definition, the time since species 1 and species 2 began diverging independently is the same, so the molecular clock hypothesis predicts that values for d_{A1} and d_{A2} should also be the same.

The data available for testing the molecular clock's premise that the rate of evolution for any given gene is constant over time in all evolutionary lineages are increasing exponentially. Substitution rates in rats and mice have been found to be largely the same. In contrast, molecular evolution in humans and apes appears to have been only half as rapid as that which has occurred in Old World monkeys since their divergence. Indeed, relative rate tests performed on homologous genes in mice and humans suggest that rodents have accumulated substitutions at twice the rate of primates since they last shared a common ancestor during the time of the mammalian radiation 80 to 100 million years ago. Even a casual review of Table 3.3 shows that the rate of the molecular clock varies among taxonomic groups. Such departures from constancy of the clock rate pose a problem in using molecular divergence to date the times of existence of recent common ancestors. Before such inferences can be made, it is necessary to demonstrate that the species being examined have a uniform clock such as the one observed within rodents.

Causes of Rate Variation in Lineages

Several possible explanations have been put forward to account for the differences in evolutionary rates revealed by the relative rate tests. For instance, generation times in monkeys are shorter than those in humans, and the generation time of rodents is much shorter still. The number of germ line DNA replications should be more closely correlated with substitution rates than simple divergence times. Differences may also be due in part to a variety of other differences between two lineages since the time of their divergence, such as average repair efficiency, metabolic rate (and the related rate of generation of oxygen free radicals), and the necessity to adapt to new ecological niches and environments. Such parameters tend to be very difficult to quantify in a useful way: We know that at the time of divergence both groups of organisms had similar attributes, and we know the extent of their differences at the present time but typically have very little information about their relative differences at all other times during the course of their evolution.

Evolution in Organelles

The average length of mammalian mitochondrial DNA (often abbreviated mtDNA) is approximately 16,000 base pairs, while the chloroplast DNA (often abbreviated cpDNA) of vascular plants ranges in size from 120,000 to 220,000 base pairs. The single, circular chromosomes of both organelles contain several protein and RNA encoding genes that are essential for their function. The relatively small size of their chromosomes and unusual pattern of inheritance (i.e., in mammals, mitochondria are contributed only by the mother and never the father) have fostered a considerable amount of interest in the way in which they accumulate substitutions.

The high concentration of mutagens (particularly oxygen free radicals) present within mitochondria as a result of their metabolic activity appears to subject mtDNA to an almost 10-fold higher rate of mutation than that found in nuclear DNA. That higher rate of change results in a correspondingly higher rate of both synonymous and nonsynonymous substitutions in mitochondrial genes. As a result, comparisons of mtDNA are often used to study relationships between closely related populations of organisms (but are often less useful for species that have diverged for more than 10 million years due to the expectation of multiple substitutions at each site). Chloroplast DNA seems to accumulate substitutions at a much slower pace than mtDNA, and values for K_s and K_a actually tend to be only one-fourth to one-fifth the rates observed for nuclear genes in the same species.

Chapter Summary

DNA, like any molecule, accumulates chemical damage with time. When that damage or a DNA replication error results in a change to the information content of a DNA molecule, a mutation is said to have occurred. Mutations do not all affect the fitness of an organism to the same degree. As a result, natural selection causes many to be lost from the gene pool, and the changes that remain are referred to as substitutions. Substitution rate can be used as a measure of the functional importance of a gene or other portion of a genome. Several models that take into account the possibility of multiple substitutions at any given site have been made to estimate the true number of substitutions that have occurred between two nucleotide or amino acid sequences and, generally speaking, those with the fewest parameters perform the best. Just as some genes accumulate substitutions more quickly than others, relative rate tests show that some organisms have a faster rate of substitution than others even when genes with similar functional constraints are considered.

Readings for Greater Depth

A description of the original Jukes and Cantor model of substitutions is found in
    T. H. Jukes and C. R. Cantor, 1969, Evolution of protein molecules, in H. N.

Munro (ed.), *Mammalian Protein Metabolism*, pp. 21–123, Academic Press, New York.

Kimura's two-parameter model is described in detail in M. Kimura, 1980, A simple method for estimating evolutionary rates of base substitutions through comparative studies of nucleotide sequences, *J. Mol. Evol.* **16**: 111–120.

The molecular clock hypothesis was first suggested in E. Zuckerkandl and L. Pauling, 1965, Evolutionary divergence and convergence in proteins, in V. Bryson and H. J. Vogel (eds.), *Horizons in Biochemistry*, pp. 97–166, Academic Press, New York.

A comprehensive set of algorithms associated with substitution modeling can be found in R. F. Doolittle, 1990, *Molecular Evolution: Computer Analysis of Protein and Nucleic Acid Sequences*, Academic Press, San Diego, CA.

The relative rate test of Sarich and Wilson is described in detail in V. M. Sarich and A. C. Wilson, 1973, Generation time and genomic evolution in primates, *Science* **179**: 1144–1147.

The neutral theory of evolution (genetic differences within populations are maintained by a balance between the effects of mutation and random genetic drift) was first espoused in M. Kimura, 1968, Evolutionary rate at the molecular level, *Nature* **217**: 731–736.

A fascinating and thought-provoking consideration of the societal (as well as biological) implications of evolutionary theory can be found in R. Dawkins, 1976, *The Selfish Gene*, Oxford University Press, New York.

Questions and Problems

* **3.1** Given that there are currently 6 billion reproductively active humans on earth and that the average human generation time is roughly 30 years, how long would it take for a single, neutral mutation that occurs within you to be fixed within the human population?

3.2 Using the same data presented in Question 3.1, what is the probability that a single, new, neutral mutation in you will be fixed? How much more likely is it that it will be lost?

* **3.3** The following sequence is that of the first 45 codons from the human gene for preproinsulin. Using the genetic code (refer back to Table 1.1), determine what fraction of mutations at the first, second, and third positions of these 45 codons will be synonymous.

```
ATG GCC CTG TGG ATG CGC CTC CTG CCC CTG CTG GCG CTG CTG GCC
CTC TGG GGA CCT GAC CCA GCC GCA GCC TTT GTG AAC CAA CAC CTG
TGC GGC TCA CAC CTG GTG GAA GCT CTC TAC CTA GTG TGC GGG GAA
```

At which position is natural selection likely to have the greatest effect and are nucleotides most likely to be conserved?

3.4 The sequences shown below represent an optimum alignment of the first 50 nucleotides from the human and sheep preproinsulin genes. Estimate the number of substitutions that have occurred in this region since humans and sheep last shared a common ancestor using the Jukes-Cantor model.

Human: ATGGCCCTGT GGATGCGCCT CCTGCCCCTG CTGGCGCTGC TGGCCCTCTG

Sheep: ATGGCCCTGT GGACACGCCT GGTGCCCCTG CTGGCCCTGC TGGCACTCTG

* **3.5** Using the number of substitutions estimated in Question 3.4 and assuming that humans and sheep last shared a common ancestor 100 million years ago, estimate the rate at which the sequence of the first 50 nucleotides in their preproinsulin genes has been accumulating substitutions.

3.6 Would the mutation rate be greater or less than the observed substitution rate for a sequence of a gene such as the one shown in Question 3.4? Why?

* **3.7** If the rate of nucleotide evolution along a lineage is 1.0% per million years, what is the rate of substitution per nucleotide per year? What would be the observed rate of divergence between two species evolving at that rate since they last shared a common ancestor?

3.8 Assume that the sequence of the first 50 nucleotides from the chicken preproinsulin gene can be optimally aligned with the homologous sequences in the human and sheep used in Question 3.4, as shown below.

Human: ATGGCCCTGT GGATGCGCCT CCTGCCCCTG CTGGCGCTGC TGGCCCTCTG

Sheep: ATGGCCCTGT GGACACGCCT GGTGCCCCTG CTGGCCCTGC TGGCACTCTG

Chicken: ATGGCTCTAT GGACACGCCT TCTGCCTCTA CTGGCCCTGC TAGCCCTCTG

What are the relative rates of evolution within the human and sheep lineages since the time of the mammalian radiation for this region?

Distance-Based Methods of Phylogenetics

Nothing in biology makes sense except in the light of evolution.

Theodosius Dobzhansky
(1900–1975)

History of Molecular Phylogenetics

Advantages to Molecular Phylogenies

Phylogenetic Trees
Terminology of tree reconstruction
Rooted and unrooted trees
Gene vs. species trees
Character and distance data

Distance Matrix Methods
UPGMA
Estimation of branch lengths
Transformed distance method
Neighbor's relation method
Neighbor-joining methods

Maximum Likelihood Approaches

Multiple Sequence Alignments

The phylogenetic relationship between two or more sets of sequences is often extremely important information for bioinformatic analyses such as the construction of sequence alignments. It is not unreasonable to think of the kinds of molecular data discussed in the previous chapter as being something of a historical document that contains within it evidence of the important steps in the evolution of a gene. The very same evolutionary events (substitutions, insertions, deletions, and rearrangements) that are important to the history of a gene can also be used to resolve questions about the evolutionary history and relationships between entire species. In fact, the phylogenetic relationships among many kinds of organisms are difficult to determine in any other way. As a result, a variety of different approaches have been devised to reconstruct genealogies from molecular data not just for genes but for species of organisms as well. This chapter introduces the basic vocabulary of phylogenetics and focuses on cluster analysis, the oldest and most statistically based of those approaches commonly used to infer evolutionary relationships.

History of Molecular Phylogenetics

Taxonomists were naming and grouping organisms long before it was even suspected that evolutionary records might be retained within the sequence information of their genomes. Drawing heavily on studies in anatomy and physiology, the field of taxonomy has produced countless valuable insights, especially once Darwin's ideas caused Linnaeus's system of grouping and naming organisms to reflect evolutionary relationships. Those insights are largely responsible for such varied and dramatic accomplishments as the development of new crops for agriculture, the discovery of treatments for infectious diseases, and even the idea that all living things on this planet share a single common ancestor.

Consideration of similarities and differences at a molecular level seemed a natural addition to the tools commonly used by taxonomists when G. H. F. Nuttall demonstrated in 1902 and 1904 that the extent to which the blood of an organism generated an immune response when it was injected into a test organism was directly related to how evolutionarily related the two organisms were. Through such experiments he examined the relationship of hundreds of organisms and was among the first to correctly conclude that humans and apes shared a common ancestor with each other more recently than they did with other primates. Antibodies and their varying abilities to interact with other molecules are still used by some scientists today as a fast phylogenetic screening tool when working with organisms for which little or no DNA or protein sequence data are available.

It was not until the 1950s, though, that molecular data began to be used extensively in phylogenetic research. **Protein electrophoresis** allowed the separation and comparison of related proteins on the basis of somewhat superficial features such as their size and charge. Rates at which denatured genomes could cross-hybridize with each other gave indications of relatedness but worked best only when fairly closely related organisms were used. **Protein sequencing** also became possible for the first time though it was not until the 1960s that the complete amino acid sequences of proteins of even modest size could be easily generated. Taken together, these molecular approaches stimulated a significant change in terms of the types of organisms whose phylogenies could be studied. They also provided an abundance of parameters that could be measured and began to highlight the inadequacy of the largely intuitive approaches to data analysis that had sufficed for previous generations of taxonomists.

By the time that actual genomic information became available in the 1970s, first in the form of restriction enzyme maps and then as actual DNA sequence data, a flurry of interest in phylogenetic reconstruction had resulted in the generation of a variety of mathematically rigorous approaches for the molecular biologists who were generating exponentially increasing amounts of molecular data. For the first time it was possible to assign statistical confidences to phylogenetic groupings and it also became comparatively easy to formulate testable hypotheses about evolutionary processes.

Today, DNA sequence data are substantially more abundant than any other form of molecular information. Traditional taxonomic approaches based on anatomic differences continue to provide complementary data to evolutionary studies, and paleontological information provides irreplaceable clues about the actual time frames in which organisms accumulate differences and evolve. However, it is the ease with which molecular approaches such as PCR (described in Chapter 1) provide homologous sequence data that promises to deliver the raw materials needed to answer the most important outstanding questions regarding the history and relationships of life on this planet.

Advantages to Molecular Phylogenies

Because evolution is defined as genetic change, genetic relationships are of primary importance in the deciphering of evolutionary relationships. The greatest promise of the molecular clock hypothesis (see Chapter 3) is the implication that molecular data can be used to decipher the phylogenetic relationships between all living things. Quite simply, organisms with high degrees of molecular similarity are expected to be more closely related than those that are dissimilar. Before the tools of molecular biology were available to provide molecular data for such analyses, taxonomists were forced to rely on comparisons of **phenotypes** (how organisms looked) to infer their **genotypes** (the genes that gave rise to their physical appearance). If phenotypes were similar, it was assumed the genes that coded for the phenotypes were also similar; if the phenotypes were different, the genes were different. Originally the phenotypes examined consisted largely of gross anatomic features. Later, behavioral, ultrastructural, and biochemical characteristics were also studied. Comparisons of such traits were successfully used to construct evolutionary trees for many groups of plants and animals and, indeed, are still the basis of many evolutionary studies today.

However, relying on the study of such traits has limitations. Sometimes similar phenotypes can evolve in organisms that are distantly related in a process called **convergent evolution.** For example, if a naïve biologist tried to construct an evolutionary tree on the basis of whether eyes were present or absent in an organism, he might place humans, flies, and mollusks in the same evolutionary group, since all have light-detecting organs. In this particular case, it is fairly obvious that these three organisms are not closely related—they differ in many features other than the possession of eyes, and the eyes themselves are very different in their design. The point, though, is that phenotypes can sometimes be misleading about evolutionary relationships, and phenotypic similarities do not always reflect genetic similarities.

Another problem with relying on phenotypes to determine evolutionary relationships is that many organisms do not have easily studied phenotypic features suitable for comparison. For example, the study of relationships among bacteria has always been problematic, because bacteria have few obvious traits even when examined with a microscope, let alone ones that correlate with the degree of their genetic relatedness. A third problem arises when we try to compare distantly related organisms. What phenotypic features should be compared, for example, in an analysis of bacteria, worms, and mammals, which have so few characteristics in common?

Analyses that rely on DNA and protein sequences are often free of such problems because many homologous molecules are essential to all living things. Even though Chapter 3 warns that the relative rate of molecular evolution may vary from one lineage to another and molecularly inferred divergence times must be treated with caution, molecular approaches to generating phylogenies can usually be relied on to group organisms correctly. Many have argued that molecular phylogenies are more reliable even when alternative data (such as morphologic data) are available because the effects of natural selection are generally less pronounced at the sequence level. On those occasions when differences between molecular and morphological phylogenies are found, they usually create valuable opportunities to examine the effect of natural selection acting at the level of phenotypic differences.

Phylogenetic Trees

Central to most studies of phylogeny is the concept of a **phylogenetic tree**— typically a graphical representation of the evolutionary relationship among three or more genes or organisms. These trees truly can be pictures that are worth a thousand words, and it is possible for them to convey not just the relatedness of data sets but also their divergence times and the nature of their common ancestors.

Terminology of Tree Reconstruction

Sometimes also referred to as a dendrogram, phylogenetic trees are made by arranging **nodes** and **branches** (Figure 4.1). Every node represents a distinct taxonomical unit. Nodes at the tips of branches (**terminal nodes**) correspond to a gene or organism for which data have actually been collected for analysis, while **internal nodes** usually represent an inferred common ancestor that gave rise to two independent lineages at some point in the past. For example, in Figure 4.1, nodes I, II, III, IV, and V are terminal nodes that represent organisms for which sequence data are available. In contrast, the internal nodes A, B, C, and D represent **inferred ancestors** (of I and II, III and IV, A and B, and C and V, respectively) for which empirical data are no longer available. Computer programs often convey this basic information about the structure of a phylogenetic tree in a series of nested parentheses called the **Newick format.** For instance, the Newick format would describe the tree in Figure 4.1 as (((I, II), (III, IV)), V).

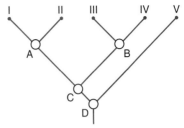

F I G U R E 4.1 *A phylogenetic tree illustrating the evolutionary relationships among five species (I, II, III, IV, and V). Filled circles represent terminal nodes while open circles correspond to internal nodes. Inferred common ancestors to the species for which sequence data are available are labeled with letters (A, B, C, and D). The root of the tree corresponds to D.*

The internal nodes of most trees have only two lineages that descend from them and are said to be **bifurcating** as a result, although it is also possible for internal nodes to be **multifurcating** and have three or more descendant lineages. Multifurcating nodes can be interpreted in one of two ways: (1) An ancestral population simultaneously gave rise to three or more independent lineages, or (2) two or more bifurcations occurred at some point in the past but limitations in the data available make it impossible to distinguish the order in which they happened. Just as the branching patterns of a phylogenetic tree can be used to convey information about the sequence in which evolutionary events occurred, the length of branches is sometimes used to indicate the extent to which different data sets have diverged. **Scaled trees** are ones in which branch lengths are proportional to the differences between pairs of neighboring nodes. In the best of cases, scaled trees are also **additive,** meaning that the physical length of the branches connecting any two nodes is an accurate representation of their accumulated differences. In contrast, **unscaled trees** line up all terminal nodes and convey only their relative kinship without making any representation regarding the number of changes that separate them.

Rooted and Unrooted Trees

Another important distinction in phylogenetics is that between trees that make an inference about a common ancestor and the direction of evolution and those that do not (Figure 4.2). In **rooted trees** a single node is designated as a common ancestor, and a unique path leads from it through evolutionary time to any other node. **Unrooted trees** only specify the relationship between nodes and say nothing about the direction in which evolution occurred. Roots can usually be assigned to unrooted trees through the use of an **outgroup**—species that have unambiguously separated the earliest from the other species being studied. In the case of humans and gorillas when baboons are used as an outgroup, the root of the tree can be placed somewhere along the branch connecting baboons to the

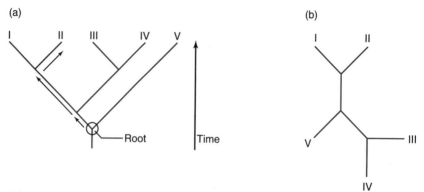

FIGURE 4.2 *(a) Rooted and (b) unrooted trees. Arrows indicate a unique path leading from the root to species D in the rooted tree. No inferences regarding the direction in which evolution occurred can be made from the unrooted tree.*

common ancestor of humans and gorillas. In a situation where only three species are being considered, three rooted trees are possible, but only one unrooted tree, as shown in Figure 4.3.

Contemplating all possible rooted and unrooted trees that might describe the relationship among three or four different species is not very difficult. However,

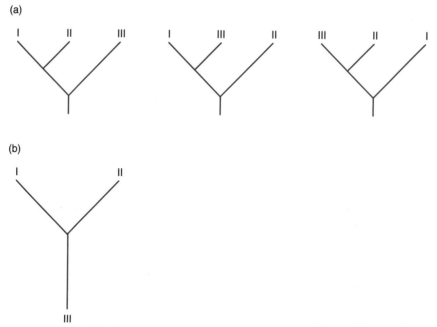

FIGURE 4.3 *All possible (a) rooted and (b) unrooted trees when only three species are considered.*

T A B L E 4.1 Number of possible rooted and unrooted trees that can describe the possible relationships among fairly small numbers of data sets.

Number of Data Sets	Number of Rooted Trees	Number of Unrooted Trees
2	1	1
3	3	1
4	15	3
5	105	15
10	34,459,425	2,027,025
15	213,458,046,767,875	7,905,853,580,625
20	8,200,794,532,637,891,559,375	221,643,095,476,699,771,875

the number of possible trees quickly becomes staggering as more species are considered, as shown in Table 4.1. The actual number of possible rooted (N_R) and unrooted (N_U) trees for any number of species (n) can be determined with the following equations:

$$N_R = (2n - 3)!/2^{n-2}(n - 2)!$$
$$N_U = (2n - 5)!/2^{n-3}(n - 3)!$$

The reader should appreciate that the value for n can be profoundly large (conceivably every species or even every individual organism or copy of a gene that has ever been). Evaluating the relative merits of all possible trees is something that not even the fastest of computers can be expected to accomplish once more than a few dozen sequences or species are considered. Numerous shortcuts (some of which are described at the end of this chapter and also in Chapter 5) have been devised that focus only on those trees most likely to be reflective of the true relationship between the data sets.

Despite the staggering number of rooted and unrooted trees that can describe the relationships among even a small number of data sets (Table 4.1), only one of all possible trees can represent the true phylogenetic relationship among the genes or species being considered. Because the true tree is usually only known when artificial data are used in computer simulations, most phylogenetic trees generated with molecular data are referred to as **inferred trees.**

Gene vs. Species Trees

We would also like to point out that a phylogenetic tree based on the divergence observed within a single homologous gene is more appropriately referred to as a **gene tree** than a **species tree**. Such trees may represent the evolutionary history of a gene but not necessarily that of the species in which it is found. Species trees are usually best obtained from analyses that use data from multiple genes. For example, a recent study on the evolution of plant species used more than 100 different genes to generate a species tree for plants. While this may sound like an

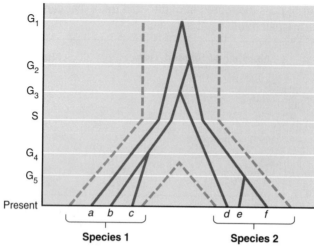

F I G U R E 4.4 *Individuals may actually appear to be more closely related to members of a species other than their own when only one gene is considered. Gene divergence events (G₁ through G₅) often occur before as well as after speciation events (S). The evolutionary history of gene divergence resulting in the six alleles denoted* a *through* f *is shown in solid lines; speciation (i.e., population splitting) is shown by broken lines. Individual* d *would actually appear to be more closely related to individuals in species 1 if only this locus were considered even though it is a member of species 2.*

unnecessary demand for more data, it has proven to be important due to the fact that evolution occurs at the level of *populations* of organisms, not at the level of individuals. Divergence within genes typically occurs prior to the splitting of populations that occurs when new species are created. For the locus being considered in Figure 4.4, some individuals in species 1 may actually be more similar to individuals in species 2 than they are to other members of their own population. The differences between gene and species trees tend to be particularly important when considering loci where diversity within populations is advantageous such as the human leukocyte antigen (HLA) locus described in Chapter 3. If HLA alleles alone were used to determine species trees, many humans would be grouped with gorillas rather than other humans because the origin of the polymorphism they carry predates the split that gave rise to the two lineages.

Character and Distance Data

The molecular data used to generate phylogenetic trees fall into one of two categories: (1) **characters** (a well-defined feature that can exist in a limited number of different states) or (2) **distances** (a measure of the overall, pairwise difference between two data sets). Both DNA and protein sequences are examples of data that describe a set of discrete character states. Other examples of character data sets are those more commonly encountered in anatomically or behaviorally based taxonomy such as an organism's color or how long it takes to respond to a particular stimulus. As mentioned earlier, DNA sequence data are now so abundant that it is uncommon to find data sets that begin as distance measures such as those that can be generated by DNA–DNA hybridization studies among the genomes of organisms.

Character data can be fairly easily converted to distance data once criteria for determining the similarities among all possible character states have been established. For instance, a single value for the overall distance (D) between two genes from two species can be determined simply by generating an optimal pairwise alignment for the sequences, tallying the number of matching nucleotides (m), and dividing by the total number of sites at which matches could have been detected (t): $D = m/t$. Adjustments can be made for the possibility of multiple substitutions at any given site (see Chapter 3), and many biologists normalize distance values by expressing them in terms of "number of changes per 100 nucleotides." Protein distances can be calculated in the same way when amino acid sequences are aligned. However, a great deal of potentially important biological information can be lost in such conversions. For instance, it has long been appreciated that some kinds of substitutions are more likely to occur within nucleotide and protein sequences than others. Given that a C is replaced with a T almost three times as often as it is replaced with a G or an A within mammalian genomes, a reasonable argument could be made that C/T mismatches in pairwise alignments not be as heavily weighted as C/G or C/A mismatches when calculating the pairwise distance of DNA sequences. The situation can be much more complicated in protein comparisons where not only are some amino acids more likely to be replaced by others due to the chemical activity of their functional groups, but the number of substitutions at the DNA level to exchange one amino acid for another can also differ.

Mathematically based approaches to phylogenetic reconstruction (such as UPGMA, described later) generally discount the importance of such biological subtleties in data sets. **Pheneticists** tend to prefer these methods because they place a greater emphasis on the relationships among data sets than the paths they have taken to arrive at their current states. **Cladists,** however, are generally more interested in evolutionary pathways and patterns than relationships and tend to prefer the more biologically based approaches to tree generation (like maximum parsimony) discussed in Chapter 5. While disputes between the champions of the two approaches have often been surprisingly intense, it is fair to say that both approaches are widely used and work well with most data sets.

Distance Matrix Methods

Distinguishing which of all possible trees is most likely to be the true tree can be a daunting task and is typically left to high-speed computers. Pairwise distance matrices, tabular summaries of the differences between all data sets to be analyzed, are the raw material used by many popular phylogenetic tree reconstruction algorithms. A basic understanding of the logic behind these approaches should give the reader an understanding of exactly what information phylogenetic trees convey and what sort of molecular data are most useful for their generation. It should also make it easier to appreciate the circumstances that make using a variant approach advisable.

UPGMA

The oldest distance matrix method is also the simplest of all methods for tree reconstruction. Originally proposed in the early 1960s to help with the evolutionary analysis of morphological characters, the **unweighted-pair-group method with arithmetic mean (UPGMA)** is largely statistically based and, like all distance-based methods, requires data that can be condensed to a measure of genetic distance between all pairs of taxa being considered. In general terms, the UPGMA method requires a distance matrix such as one that might be created for a group of four taxa called A, B, C, and D. Assume that the pairwise distances between each of the taxa are given in the following matrix:

Species	A	B	C
B	d_{AB}	—	—
C	d_{AC}	d_{BC}	—
D	d_{AD}	d_{BD}	d_{CD}

In this matrix, d_{AB} represents the distance (perhaps simply the number of nonmatching nucleotides divided by the total number of sites where matches could have been found) between species A and B, while d_{AC} is the distance between taxa A and C, and so on.

UPGMA begins by clustering the two species with the smallest distance separating them into a single, composite group. In this case, assume that the smallest value in the distance matrix corresponds to d_{AB} in which case species A and B are the first to be grouped (AB). After the first clustering, a new distance matrix is computed with the distance between the new group (AB) and species C and D being calculated as $d_{(AB)C} = 1/2(d_{AC} + d_{BC})$ and $d_{(AB)D} = 1/2(d_{AD} + d_{BD})$. The species separated by the smallest distance in the new matrix are then clustered to make another new composite species. The process is repeated until all species have been grouped. If scaled branch lengths are to be used on the tree to represent the evolutionary distance between species, branch points are positioned at a distance halfway between each of the species being grouped (i.e., at $d_{AB}/2$ for the first clustering).

A practical example using UPGMA with actual sequence data will help illustrate the general approach just described. Consider the alignment between five different DNA sequences presented in Figure 4.5. Pairwise comparisons of the five different sequences yield a distance matrix such as the one shown in Table 4.2. Notice that because all five sequences are the same length and there are no gaps, the distance matrix in this case can simply be the number of nonmatching nu-

	10	20	30	40	50
A:	GTGCTGCACGG	CTCAGTATA	GCATTTACCC	TTCCATCTTC	AGATCCTGAA
B:	ACGCTGCACGG	CTCAGTGCG	GTGCTTACCC	TCCCATCTTC	AGATCCTGAA
C:	GTGCTGCACGG	CTCGGCGCA	GCATTTACCC	TCCCATCTTC	AGATCCTATC
D:	GTATCACACGA	CTCAGCGCA	GCATTTGCCC	TCCCGTCTTC	AGATCCTAAA
E:	GTATCACATAG	CTCAGCGCA	GCATTTGCCC	TCCCGTCTTC	AGATCTAAAA

F I G U R E 4.5 *A five-way alignment of homologous DNA sequences.*

T A B L E 4.2 A pairwise distance matrix that summarizes the number of nonmatching nucleotides between all possible pairs of sequences shown in Figure 4.5.

Species	A	B	C	D
B	9	—	—	—
C	8	11	—	—
D	12	15	10	—
E	15	18	13	5

cleotides observed in each pairwise comparison (i.e., the number of nonmatching nucleotides between A and B, d_{AB}, is 9).

The smallest distance separating any of the two sequences in the multiple alignment corresponds to d_{DE}, so species D and species E are grouped (Figure 4.6a). A new distance matrix is then made in which the composite group (DE) takes the place of D and E (Table 4.3). Distances between the remaining species and the new group are determined by taking the average distance between its two members (D and E) and all other remaining species [i.e., $d_{(DE)A} = 1/2(d_{AD} + d_{AE})$ so $d_{(DE)A} = 1/2(12 + 15) = 13.5$], as shown in Table 4.3.

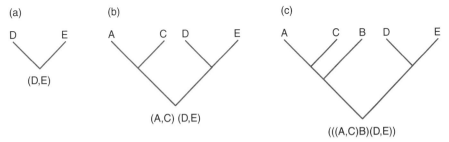

(a) D E (D,E)

(b) A C D E (A,C) (D,E)

(c) A C B D E (((A,C)B)(D,E))

F I G U R E 4.6 *A phylogenetic tree as it is constructed using the UPGMA method. (a) The first grouping (D,E) is between species D and E, which are connected by a single bifurcating branch. (b) The second grouping (A,C) is between species A and C, which are also connected to each other by a single bifurcating branch. (c) The last grouping ((A,C)B) unambiguously places the branching point for species B between that of the common ancestors of (A,C) and (D,E).*

T A B L E 4.3 The distance matrix that results when species D and E of Table 4.2 are combined and considered as a single group.

Species	A	B	C
B	9	—	—
C	8	11	—
DE	13.5	16.5	11.5

T A B L E 4.4 The distance matrix that results when species A and C of Table 4.3 are combined and considered as a single group.

Species	B	AC
AC	10	—
DE	16.5	12.5

The smallest distance separating any two species in this new matrix is the distance between A and C, so a new combined species, (AC), is created (Figure 4.6b). Another distance matrix using this new grouping then looks like the one shown in Table 4.4. In this last matrix the smallest distance is between species (AC) and B (d_{DE} = 10) so they are grouped as ((AC)B). One way to symbolically represent the final clustering of species is shown in Figure 4.6c. Alternatively, in the standard Newick format it could be described as (((A,C)B)(D,E)). In many cases, generating the distance matrix needed for the UPGMA method is the most tedious and time-consuming step in the entire process of inferring a phylogenetic tree. While small data sets can be analyzed by hand, computer programs can easily analyze data sets that are large in terms of both the number and the lengths of the sequences involved.

Estimation of Branch Lengths

Remember that in addition to describing the relatedness of sequences it is possible for the **topology** of phylogenetic trees to convey information about the relative degree to which sequences have diverged. Scaled trees that convey that information, often referred to as **cladograms,** do so by having the length of branches correspond to the inferred amount of time that the sequences have been accumulating substitutions independently.

Determining the relative length of each branch in a cladogram can also be easily calculated using the information in a distance matrix. If rates of evolution are assumed to be constant in all lineages, then internal nodes should simply be placed at equal distances from each of the species they give rise to on a bifurcating tree. For instance, using the sequences and distance matrix from Figure 4.5 and Table 4.2, respectively, the distance between species D and E (d_{DE}) is 5, and the pair of branches connecting each of those species to their common ancestor should each be $d_{DE}/2$ or 2.5 units long on a tree with scaled branch lengths. Similarly, A and C should be connected to their common ancestor by branches that are $d_{AC}/2$ or 4 units long, and the branch point between (AC) and (DE) should be connected to (AC) and (DE) by branches that are both $d_{(AC)(DE)}/2$ or 6.25 units long, as shown in Figure 4.7. This very simple approach to estimating branch lengths actually allows UPGMA to be one of only a very small number of approaches that intrinsically generate rooted phylogenetic trees.

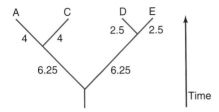

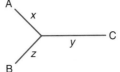

FIGURE 4.7 *A scaled tree showing the branch lengths separating four of the species depicted in Figure 4.6. Branch lengths are shown next to each branch. Branches are also drawn to scale to reflect the amount of differences between all species. If evolution has occurred at a constant rate for all of these lineages, then branch length also corresponds to divergence time.*

FIGURE 4.8 *The simplest tree whose branch lengths might have some meaningful information. Each of the three branches on this tree can be represented as a single variable (x, y, and z).*

Determining branch lengths for a scaled tree is only slightly more complicated when it cannot be assumed that evolutionary rates are the same for all lineages. The simplest tree whose branch lengths might have some meaningful information is one with just three species and one branch point, such as the one shown in Figure 4.8. On such a tree, the length of each of the three branches can be represented by a single letter (x, y, and z) for which we know the following must be true:

$$d_{AC} = x + y$$
$$d_{AB} = x + z$$
$$d_{BC} = y + z$$

Simple algebraic manipulation of those equations can then be used to give equations for each branch length simply in terms of the values in a pairwise distance matrix:

$$x = (d_{AB} + d_{AC} - d_{BC})/2$$
$$y = (d_{AC} + d_{BC} - d_{AB})/2$$
$$z = (d_{AB} + d_{BC} - d_{AC})/2$$

Branch lengths for more complicated trees (ones with more than one branch point) can be estimated by continuing to consider just three branches at a time. Two of those branches, x and z in Figure 4.8, are the ones that connect the two most closely related species in the distance matrix, and one, y in Figure 4.8, connects their common ancestor to the common ancestor of all others in the distance matrix. For instance, for a distance matrix for five species (1, 2, 3, 4, and 5) in which UPGMA groups species 1 and 2 first, the values for d_{AC} and d_{BC} in the earlier equations are just the average values for the distance between those species and all other species taken together:

$$d_{AC} = (d_{13} + d_{14} + d_{15})/3$$
$$d_{BC} = (d_{23} + d_{24} + d_{25})/3$$

Transformed Distance Method

One strength of distance matrix approaches in general is that they work equally well with morphological and molecular data and even combinations of the two. They also take into consideration all of the data available for a particular analysis, whereas the alternative parsimony approaches described in Chapter 5 discard so-called uninformative sites.

One particular weakness of the UPGMA approach is that it assumes a constant rate of evolution across all lineages—something that the relative rate tests (Chapter 3) tell us is not always the case. Variations in rates of substitutions can be a serious problem for the UPGMA method and can easily cause it to produce trees with incorrect topologies. In fact, one indication that that is not the case for the set of five DNA sequences used to illustrate the UPGMA method (Figure 4.5) is that the branch lengths of the resulting tree are not additive (for example, the scaled tree shown in Figure 4.7 suggests that $d_{AE} = 4 + 6.25 + 6.25 + 2.5 = 19$ while the distance matrix in Table 4.2 tells us that the actual value for d_{AE} is 15).

Several distance matrix–based alternatives to UPGMA take the possibility of different rates of evolution within different lineages into account. The oldest and simplest of those is the **transformed distance method.** This approach, first described by J. Farris in 1977, takes full advantage of the power of an **outgroup**— a species that is known to have diverged from the common ancestor of all other species represented in a distance matrix prior to all other species being considered (the **ingroups**).

Using the same data set shown in Figure 4.5, assume that species D is known to be an outgroup to species A, B, and C. Also assume that the true relationship between these species is the one depicted in Figure 4.9 [(((A,B)C)D) in the Newick format]. If the numbers beside each of the branches in Figure 4.9 correspond to the number of mutations within the 50 base pairs of the sequence shown in Figure 4.5 that have accumulated along each lineage during each stage of its evolution, then the pairwise evolutionary distances are shown in Table 4.5 (an abbreviated version of Table 4.2). In this situation, D can be used as an external reference to transform the distances that separate the other species using this equation:

$$d'_{ij} = (d_{ij} - d_{iD} - d_{jD})/2 + \bar{d}_D$$

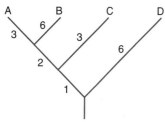

FIGURE 4.9 *The true phylogenetic relationship and branch lengths of four species: A, B, C, and D.*

where d'_{ij} is the transformed distance between species i and j, and $\bar{d}_D$ is the average distance between the outgroup and all ingroups (in this case: $d_D = (d_{AD} + d_{BD} + d_{CD})/3 = 37/3$). The term $\bar{d}_D$ is introduced simply to ensure that all transformed distance

T A B L E 4.5 Pairwise evolutionary distances for the four species depicted in Figure 4.7, assuming that the tree is additive as it should be.

Species	A	B	C
B	9	—	—
C	8	11	—
D	12	15	10

T A B L E 4.6 Transformed distance matrix for the three ingroups of Table 4.5 when D is used as an outgroup.

Species	A	B
B	10/3	—
C	16/3	16/3

values are positive values since negative distances are not possible from an evolutionary perspective. Using this value for d'_D and the distances in Table 4.5, a transformed distance matrix for species A, B, and C can be generated (Table 4.6). The basic UPGMA approach can then be used with this new distance matrix; since d'_{AB} is the smallest value, A and B are the first to be clustered (A,B). Species C is added to the tree next and D, the outgroup, is added last to give a tree with the true topology: (((A,B)C)D).

The power of the transformed distance matrix approach comes from an insight that is so simple it is easy to miss: Ingroups only evolve separately from each other *after* they diverge, and any differences in the number of substitutions they have accumulated must have occurred since that time. In this situation, outgroups simply provide an objective frame of reference for comparing those rates of substitution.

As was the case in the example above, the transformed distance matrix approach is typically better at determining the true topology of a tree than the UPGMA method alone. It can also be applied in those situations where it is not possible to independently determine which species is an outgroup. Any ingroup can also provide a frame of reference suitable for use in transforming a distance matrix. The principal advantage of outgroups over ingroups for this purpose is that outgroups alone allow a root to be placed on the phylogenetic tree.

Neighbor's Relation Method

Another popular variant of the UPGMA method is one that emphasizes pairing species in such a way that a tree is created with the smallest possible branch lengths overall. On any unrooted tree, pairs of species that are separated from each other by just one internal node are said to be **neighbors.** The topology of a phylogenetic tree such as the one in Figure 4.10 gives rise to some useful algebraic relationships between neighbors. If the tree in Figure 4.9 is a true tree for which additivity holds, then the following should be true:

$$d_{AC} + d_{BD} = d_{AD} + d_{BC} = a + b + c + d + 2e = d_{AB} + d_{CD} + 2e$$

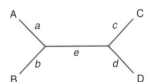

F I G U R E 4.10 *A generic phylogenetic tree with four species (A, B, C, and D) and each branch uniquely labeled (a, b, c, d, and e).*

where *a*, *b*, *c*, and *d* are the lengths of the terminal branches and *e* is the length of the single central branch. The following conditions, known together as the **four-point condition,** will also be true:

$$d_{AB} + d_{CD} < d_{AC} + d_{BD}$$

and

$$d_{AB} + d_{CD} < d_{AD} + d_{BC}$$

It is in this way that a **neighborliness approach** considers all possible pairwise arrangements of four species and determines which arrangement satisfies the four-point condition. An important assumption of the four-point condition is that branch lengths on a phylogenetic tree should be additive and, while it is not especially sensitive to departures from that assumption, data sets that are not additive can cause this method to generate a tree with an incorrect topology.

In 1977, S. Sattath and A. Tversky suggested a way to use the neighborliness approach for trees that described the relationship between more than four species. They begin by generating a distance matrix and using the values in that matrix to generate three values for the first four species: (1) $d_{AB} + d_{CD}$; (2) $d_{AC} + d_{BD}$; and (3) $d_{AD} + d_{BC}$. Whichever sum is the smallest causes both pairings to be assigned a score of 1, while the four other pairings are given a score of 0. This process is repeated for all possible sets of four species in the data set, and a running tally of the scores is maintained. The single pair of species with the highest score at the end of the analysis is grouped—these species are as neighbors—and a new distance matrix is generated as was done for UPGMA. The new distance matrix is then used in another scoring process until only three species remain (at which time the topology of the tree is unambiguously determined). While manageable when considering the relationship between only five or six species, this approach can become very computationally intensive for more complex trees.

Neighbor-Joining Methods

Other neighborliness approaches are also available including several variants called **neighbor-joining methods.** These methods start with a star-like tree with all species coming off a single central node regardless of their number. Neighbors are then sequentially found that minimize the total length of the branches on the tree. The principal difference between the neighbor-joining methods is the way in which they determine the sum of all branch lengths with each reiteration of the process. N. Saitou and M. Nei originally proposed in 1987 that the tree's total branch length be determined with this formula:

$$S_{12} = (1/(2(N-2)))(\Sigma(d_{1k} + d_{2k}) + (1/2)d_{12} + (1/N-2)(\Sigma d_{ij})$$

where any pair of species can take positions 1 and 2 in the tree, *N* is the number of species represented in the distance matrix, *k*, is an accepted outgroup, and d_{ij} is the distance between species *i* and *j*. J. Studier and K. Keppler advocated a computationally faster algorithm in 1988:

$$Q_{12} = (N-2)d_{12} - \Sigma d_{1i} - \Sigma d_{2i}$$

All possible pairs of species are considered in each round of the process, and the pairing that makes a tree with the overall smallest branch lengths (the smallest values for S or Q) is grouped so that a new distance matrix can be generated.

Both the S and Q criteria have since been shown to be theoretically related. Both the neighbor-joining and neighbor's relation approach described above have also been shown to be theoretically equivalent in that they are fundamentally dependant on the four-point condition and the assumption of additivity. As a result, both neighbor-joining and neighbor's relation approaches tend to generate trees with very similar, if not identical, topologies.

Maximum Likelihood Approaches

Maximum likelihood approaches represent an alternative and purely statistically based method of phylogenetic reconstruction. With this approach, probabilities are considered for every individual nucleotide substitution in a set of sequence alignments. For instance, we know from Chapter 3 that transitions (exchanging one purine for another or one pyrimidine for another) are observed roughly three times as often as transversions (exchanging a purine for a pyrimidine or vice versa). In a three-way alignment where a single column is found to have a C, a T, and a G, it can be reasonably argued that a greater likelihood exists that the sequences with the C and T are more closely related to each other than they are to the sequence with a G. Calculation of probabilities is complicated by the fact that the sequence of the common ancestor to the sequences being considered is generally not known. They are further complicated by the fact that multiple substitutions may have occurred at one or more of the sites being considered and that all sites are not necessarily independent or equivalent. Still, objective criteria can be applied to calculating the probability for every site *and* for every possible tree that describes the relationship of the sequences in a multiple alignment. The number of possible trees for even a modest number of sequences (Table 4.1) makes this a very computationally intensive proposition, yet the one tree with the single highest aggregate probability is, by definition, the most likely to reflect the true phylogenetic tree.

The dramatic increase in the raw power of computers has begun to make maximum likelihood approaches feasible, and trees inferred in this way are becoming increasingly common in the literature. Note, however, that no one substitution model is as yet close to general acceptance and, because different models can very easily lead to different conclusions, the model used must be carefully considered and described when using this approach.

Multiple Sequence Alignments

As described in Chapter 2, sequence alignments are easiest when the sequences being aligned are very similar and have not experienced many insertion and deletion events. Simultaneous alignment of more than two sequences is a natural extension of the two-sequence case. As in pairwise alignments, sequences in a multiple alignment are customarily placed in a vertical list so that characters (or gaps) in corresponding positions occupy the same column. The major difficulty in aligning multiple sequences is computational. For instance, the insertion of a single nucleotide in one sequence requires that a gap be added to every other sequence in a multiple alignment and can easily wreak havoc with static scoring of gap insertion and length penalties. Several studies have also shown that the order in which sequences are added to a multiple alignment can significantly affect the end result.

Given that similar sequences can be aligned both more easily and with greater confidence, it is not surprising that the alignment of multiple sequences should take into consideration the branching order of the sequences being studied. If the phylogeny of the sequences being aligned is known before the alignment is made, sequences are generally added one at a time to the growing multiple alignment with the most related sequences being added first and the least related being added last. It is increasingly common, however, for analyses of the sequences themselves to be the way in which phylogenetic relationships are determined. In those cases, an integrated or unified approach is generally adopted that simultaneously generates an alignment and a phylogeny. This approach typically requires many rounds of phylogenetic analysis and sequence alignment and can be very computationally intensive. For instance, a common strategy of several popular multiple sequence aligning algorithms is to (1) generate a pairwise distance matrix based on all possible pairwise alignments between the sequences being considered, (2) use a statistically based approach such as UPGMA to construct an initial tree, (3) realign the sequences progressively in order of their relatedness according to the inferred tree, (4) construct a new tree from the pairwise distances obtained in the new multiple alignment, and (5) repeat the process if the new tree is not the same as the previous one.

Chapter Summary

The true relationship between homologous sequences is hardly ever known aside from computer simulation experiments. The numbers of alternative phylogenetic trees to choose among quickly become daunting even for relatively small numbers of sequences. A variety of approaches are available for inferring the most likely phylogenetic relationship between genes and species using nucleotide and amino acid sequence information. Distance-based approaches to phylogenetic reconstruction draw attention to just a few (and, often, just one) of those many possible trees by considering the overall similarities between available sequences and progressively grouping those that are most alike. Maximum likelihood approaches are computationally intensive but strive to draw attention to the phylogenetic relationship that is statistically most likely to represent the true relationship.

Readings for Greater Depth

The general utility of molecular data in phylogenetic studies is succinctly reviewed in T. A. Brown and K. A. Brown, 1994, Using molecular biology to explore the past, *BioEssays* **16**:719–726.

The simplest method for tree reconstruction, UPGMA, was first applied in R. R. Sokal and C. D. Michener, 1958, A statistical method for evaluating systematic relationships, *Univ. Kansas Sci. Bull.* **28**: 1409–1438.

The algorithm underlying the neighbor-joining approach as well as a comparison to the neighbor's relation method are described in detail in N. Saitou and M. Nei, 1987, The neighbor-joining method: A new method for reconstructing phylogenetic trees, *Mol. Biol. Evol.* **4**: 406–425.

A detailed description and review of the maximum likelihood approach (as well as references to papers describing different substitution models and algorithms) can be found in J. P. Huelsenbeck and K. A. Crandall, 1997, Phylogeny estimation and hypothesis testing using maximum likelihood, *Annu. Rev. Ecol. Syst.* **28**: 437–466.

Questions and Problems

* **4.1** What are some of the advantages of using molecular data to infer evolutionary relationships?

4.2 As suggested by the popular movie *Jurassic Park*, organisms trapped in amber have proven to be a good source of DNA from tens and even hundreds of millions of years ago. However, when using such sequences in phylogenetic analyses it is usually not possible to distinguish between samples that come from evolutionary "dead ends" and those that are the ancestors of organisms still alive today. Why would it not be possible to use information from ancient DNA in a standard UPGMA analysis?

* **4.3** Draw the phylogenetic tree that corresponds to the one described in the standard Newick format as (((A,B)C)(D,E))F.

4.4 Draw all possible rooted and unrooted trees for four species: A, B, C, and D.

* **4.5** What is the chance of randomly picking the one rooted phylogenetic tree that describes the true relationship between a group of eight organisms? Are the odds better or worse for randomly picking among all possible unrooted trees for those organisms?

4.6 Why is it easier to convert character data into distance data than vice versa? Which type of data would be preferred by a pheneticist or a cladist?

* **4.7** Using the five-way sequence alignment shown in Figure 4.5, construct a distance matrix by weighting transversions (A's or G's changing to C's or T's) twice as heavily as transitions (C's changing to T's, T's changing to C's, A's changing to G's, or G's changing to A's).

4.8 Use UPGMA to reconstruct a phylogenetic tree using the following distance matrix:

Species	A	B	C	D
B	3	—	—	—
C	6	5	—	—
D	9	9	10	—
E	12	11	13	9

* **4.9** Using the same distance matrix provided for Question 4.8 and assuming that species D is an outgroup, reconstruct a phylogenetic tree with the transformed distance method. Does the topology of this tree differ from the one you generated with UPGMA alone?

4.10 Using the same distance matrix provided for Question 4.8 and assuming that species F is an outgroup, reconstruct a phylogenetic tree with the transformed distance method. Does the topology of this tree differ from the one you generated using D as an outgroup?

* **4.11** Assume that the rate of evolution is not the same for all lineages in the tree you generated for Question 4.10. What are the relative lengths of each of the branches in the tree?

Character-Based Methods of Phylogenetics

> There is grandeur in this view of life, . . . from so simple a beginning endless forms most beautiful and most wonderful have been, and are being, evolved.
>
> *Charles Darwin (1809–1882)*

Parsimony

Informative and uninformative sites
Unweighted parsimony
Weighted parsimony

Inferred Ancestral Sequences

Strategies for Faster Searches

Branch and bound
Heuristic searches

Consensus Trees

Tree Confidence

Bootstrapping
Parametric tests

Comparison of Phylogenetic Methods

Molecular Phylogenies

The tree of life
Human origins

While an understanding of the relationships between sequences and species has been the basis of profound advances in disciplines as varied as agriculture and medicine, bioinformaticians are generally more interested in using the relationships just as clues for other analyses such as those involved in multiple sequence alignments. Bioinformaticians tend to be more like the pheneticists described in the previous chapter than the pathway and evolutionary process–oriented cladists. At the same time, though, there is no denying that distance-based methods "look at the big picture" and pointedly ignore much potentially valuable information. All of that additional information is at the heart of what excites cladists and poses demanding (but solvable) computational problems that have intrigued many programmers. Of course, much can be learned about relationships from a consideration of the path taken in the process of divergence. Because the analyses employed by the distance- and character-based methods are so fundamentally different, agreement of their conclusions regarding relationships is considered to be particularly strong support for a phylogenetic tree—a very valuable commodity for bioinformaticians.

Parsimony

The concept of **parsimony** is at the very heart of all character-based methods of phylogenetic reconstruction. The term itself is borrowed from the English language and was popularly used in the United States during the 1930s and 1940s to somewhat derogatorily describe someone who was especially careful with the spending of their money. In a biological sense, it is used to describe the process of attaching preference to one evolutionary pathway over another on the basis of which pathway requires the invocation of the smallest number of mutational events. As described in the two previous chapters, phylogenetic trees represent theoretical models that depict the evolutionary history of three or more sequences. The two premises that underlie biological parsimony are quite simple: (1) Mutations are exceedingly rare events and (2) the more unlikely events a model invokes, the less likely the model is to be correct. As a result, the relationship that requires the fewest number of mutations to explain the current state of the sequences being considered is the relationship that is most likely to be correct.

Informative and Uninformative Sites

Before considering how it is that parsimony is used to infer phylogenetic relationships, it is necessary to consider what sites within a multiple sequence alignment might have useful information content for a parsimony approach. The short four-way multiple sequence alignment shown in Figure 5.1 contains positions that fall into two categories in terms of their information content for a parsimony analysis: those that have information (are **informative**) and those that do not (are **uninformative**). The relationship between four sequences can be described by

Sequence	Position					
	1	2	3	4	5*	6*
1	G	G	G	G	G	G
2	G	G	G	A	G	T
3	G	G	A	T	A	G
4	G	A	T	C	A	T

F I G U R E 5.1 *An alignment of four homologous sequences, each of which is six nucleotides long. Asterisks (*) indicate the two columns within the alignment that correspond to informative sites. The four remaining sites are uninformative.*

only three different unrooted trees (as described in Chapter 4 and shown in Figure 5.2), and informative sites are those that allow one of those trees to be distinguished from the other two on the basis of how many mutations they must invoke. For the first position in the alignment in Figure 5.1, all four sequences have the same character (a "G") and the position is therefore said to be **invariant.** Invariant sites are clearly uninformative because each of the three possible trees that describe the relationship of the four sequences (Figure 5.2.1) invokes exactly the same number of mutations (0). Position 2 is similarly uninformative from a parsimony perspective because one mutation occurs in all three of the possible trees (Figure 5.2.2). Likewise, position 3 is uninformative because all three trees require two mutations (Figure 5.2.3), and position 4 is uninformative because all three trees require three mutations (Figure 5.2.4). In contrast, positions 5 and 6 are both informative because for both of them, one of the three trees invokes only one mutation and the other two alternative trees both require two (Figures 5.2.5 and 5.2.6).

In general, for a position to be informative regardless of how many sequences are aligned, it has to have at least two different nucleotides, and each of these nucleotides has to be present at least twice. All parsimony programs begin by applying this fairly simple rule to the data set being analyzed. Notice that four of the six positions being considered in the alignment shown in Figure 5.1 are simply discarded and not considered any further in a parsimony analysis. All of those sites would have contributed to the pairwise similarity scores used by a distance-based approach, and this difference alone can generate substantial differences in the conclusions reached by both types of approaches.

Unweighted Parsimony

Once uninformative sites have been identified and discarded, implementation of the parsimony approach in its simplest form can be straightforward. Every possible tree is considered individually for each informative site. A running tally is maintained for each tree that keeps track of the minimum number of substitutions required for each position. After all informative sites have been considered, the tree (or trees) that needs to invoke the smallest total number of substitutions

F I G U R E 5.2 *Three possible unrooted trees that describe the possible relationships between the four sequences at all 6 positions shown in Figure 5.1. Each position is numbered as in Figure 5.1. The Newick format description of each of the trees is also shown. The two internal nodes of each tree contain a possible common ancestor's sequence, and lineages where mutations must have occurred are highlighted with arrows.*

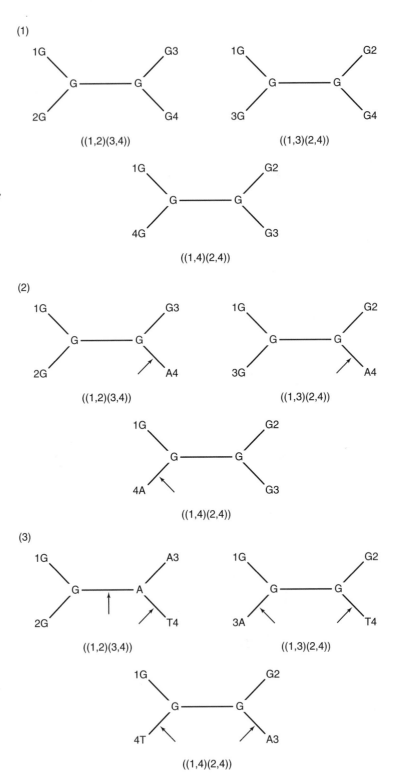

(4)

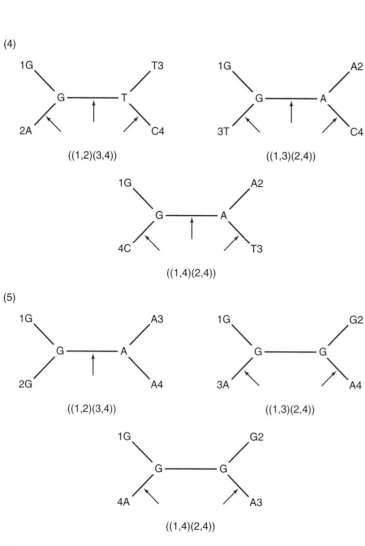

((1,2)(3,4))   ((1,3)(2,4))

((1,4)(2,4))

(5)

((1,2)(3,4))   ((1,3)(2,4))

((1,4)(2,4))

(6)

((1,2)(3,4))   ((1,3)(2,4))

((1,4)(2,4))

is labeled the most parsimonious. The example presented in Figures 5.1 and 5.2 for a four-way sequence alignment is the simplest case possible. In an analysis involving only four sequences, each informative site can favor only one of the three alternative trees, and the tree supported by the largest numbers of informative sites must also be the most parsimonious.

Evaluation of data sets with five or more sequences is substantially more complicated due to three important differences. First, the number of alternative unrooted trees that need to be considered increases dramatically as the number of sequences in an alignment becomes greater than just four (Table 4.1). Even when only a small number of informative sites are being evaluated, applying the unmodified parsimony approach by hand is virtually unimaginable when as few as just seven or eight sequences are being considered. Second, the situation is further complicated by the fact that in analyses involving more than four sequences, individual informative sites can support more than one alternative tree (see Figures 5.3a and b), and the tree of maximum parsimony for the entire data

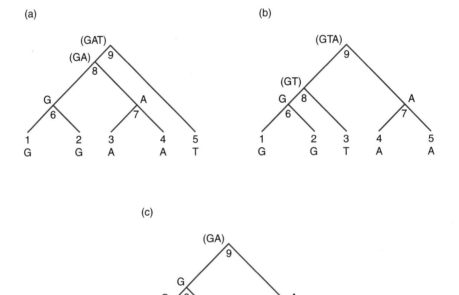

FIGURE 5.3 *Three of 15 unrooted trees that illustrate the relationship between five different taxonomic units. All three trees are equally parsimonious in that they each require a minimum of two substitutions. Terminal nodes are labeled 1 through 5 while the four internal nodes are labeled 6 through 9. The most likely candidates for inferred ancestral nucleotides according to the parsimony rule are shown at each internal node.*

set is not necessarily the one supported by the largest number of informative sites. Third, calculating the number of substitutions invoked by each alternative tree becomes considerably more difficult when five or more sequences are considered.

Figure 5.3 shows three of the possible 15 unrooted trees that describe the possible relationship between five different sequences. Determining the number of substitutions invoked by each tree requires inferring the most likely nucleotide at each of the four internal nodes from the nucleotides known to exist at each of the five terminal nodes. The parsimony rule makes inference of the ancestral nucleotide at node 6 in Figure 5.3a quite easy—the ancestral nucleotide must be a "G" or a substitution would have had to have occurred in the lineages leading to *both* terminal node 1 and terminal node 2. Identical reasoning can be used to justify assigning an "A" to node 7 in Figure 5.3a. The ancestral nucleotide at node 8 cannot be determined unambiguously for this tree but must be either a "G" or an "A" according to the parsimony rule. In the same way, the most parsimonious candidate nucleotides for node 9 are "G," "A," and "T." Consider also the alternative scenario involving nodes 6 and 8 in the tree shown in Figure 5.3c. In this case, nodes 1 and 2 suggest that the ancestral nucleotide at node 6 is "G" *or* "T." However, node 3 also casts a vote for "G" being the candidate nucleotide at node 8. By assigning a "G" as the ancestral nucleotide for nodes 6 and 8, only one substitution (along the lineage leading from node 6 to node 2) must be invoked for this portion of the tree. The three alternatives (assigning a "T" at node 6, a "T" at node 8, or a "T" at nodes 6 and 8) all require at least two substitutions for this portion of the tree.

From a mathematical (and programming) perspective the algorithm for assigning ancestral positions is as follows: The set of most likely candidate nucleotides at an internal node is the intersection of the two sets at its immediate descendant nodes if the intersection is not empty; otherwise it is the union of the sets at the descendant nodes. When a union is required to form a nodal set, a nucleotide substitution must have occurred at some point within the lineage leading to that position. The number of unions is therefore also the minimum number of substitutions required to account for the nucleotides at the terminal nodes since they all last shared a single common ancestor.

Of course, the method described above applies only to the informative sites and not to the uninformative sites discarded in the first step of a typical parsimony analysis. Calculating the minimum number of substitutions that any given tree invokes at an uninformative site is actually very easy. The minimum number is simply the number of different nucleotides present at the terminal nodes minus one. For example, if the nucleotides at a particular position in a five-way alignment are G, G, A, G, and T, then the minimum number of substitutions is 3 − 1 = 2 regardless of the tree topology. Uninformative sites contribute an equal number of steps to all alternative trees and are often excluded entirely from parsimony analyses. However, when the total number of substitutions required at both informative and uninformative sites is reported for any particular tree, that value is referred to as the tree's **length.**

Weighted Parsimony

While the general principle that "mutations are rare events" is definitely sound, its suggestion that all mutations are equivalent should be an obvious oversimplification. We have already seen in Chapters 2, 3, and 4 that insertions and deletions are less likely than exchanging one nucleotide for another; long insertions and deletions are less common than short ones; some point substitutions are more likely than others (i.e., transitions vs. transversions); and mutations with functional consequences are less likely to occur than those that are inconsequential. If values can be attached to the relative likelihood of each of these kinds of mutations, those values can be translated into weights used by parsimony algorithms.

Unfortunately, it is not possible to arrive at a single set of likelihood-based weights that apply to all (or even a large fraction) of data sets. A very incomplete list of the problems that underlie determining a universal set of relative likelihoods includes (1) some sequences (such as noncoding sequences and especially those containing short, tandem repeats) are more prone to indels than others; (2) functional importance definitely differs from gene to gene and often from species to species even for homologous genes; and (3) subtle substitution biases (such as those that act to change the relative abundance of GC and AT base pairs or the relative abundance of one triplet codon over another that codes for the same amino acid) usually vary between genes and between species.

As a result, the best weighting schemes usually come from analyses of empirical data sets. And the best empirical data set available in terms of general equivalency is typically the one that is actually being analyzed. Assume, for instance, that for a particular multiple sequence alignment comparisons between each individual sequence and a consensus sequence suggest that transitions are three times more common than transversions. A parsimony analysis of the same set of sequences could then attach a value of 1 to every substitution that results in a transversion and a value of 0.33 to every one that results in a transition. The tree with the lowest score after all sites have been considered is then presented as the most likely at the end of the analysis.

Inferred Ancestral Sequences

A remarkable by-product of the parsimony approach is the inferred ancestral sequences that are generated during the course of analysis. Even though the common ancestor of sequences 1 and 2 in Figure 5.1 may have been extinct for tens of millions of years, the parsimony approach makes a fairly strong prediction that the nucleotide found at the fifth position of its sequence was a "G." This may seem trivial in the context of single nucleotides, but when considered over the course of entire genes or genomes, it can provide irreplaceable insights into evolutionary processes and pressures from long ago. When the structure and function of a protein are particularly well understood, amino acid replacements can even provide stunning insights into the day-to-day physiology and environment of truly ancient organisms. (The prototypical review of this kind of analysis remains the one by M. Perutz cited at the end of this chapter.)

Creationists often deride the theory of evolution because of the numerous gaps in the fossil record, and anthropologists frequently fall into the trap of responding by finding "missing links" (which in turn replaces the one original gap in the fossil record with two new ones—one on both sides of the missing link). Thanks to the inferred ancestors generated by parsimony analyses, the study of molecular evolution has no missing links, and intermediary states can be objectively inferred from the sequences of living descendants.

In technical terms, informative sites that support the internal branches in the inferred tree are deemed to be **synapomorphies** (a derived state that is shared by several taxa). All other informative sites are considered to be **homoplasies** (a character that has arisen in several taxa independently through convergence, parallelism, and reversals rather than being inherited from a common ancestor).

Strategies for Faster Searches

The underlying principle and rules of parsimony remain the same for both the simplest case of just a four-way alignment and for the more complex cases of deeper alignments. Still, using an unmodified parsimony approach quickly becomes impossible to do by hand for deep alignments even when the number of informative sites is relatively small. By the time 10 sequences are to be analyzed, more than 2 million trees must be considered (Table 4.1), and even the fastest computers cannot be expected to conduct an **exhaustive search** (an evaluation of every alternative unrooted tree) when as few as 12 sequences are aligned. Data sets are usually tens or even hundreds of times larger than these practical limitations allow, and a variety of algorithms have been developed that facilitate reliable determination of the most parsimonious trees without the need to consider all possible alternatives.

Branch and Bound

A clever and efficient means of streamlining the search for trees of maximum parsimony is the **branch and bound method** first proposed by Hardy and Penny in 1982. As the name suggests, the branch and bound method consists of two essentially different steps. The first step in applying the method is the determination of an upper bound, L, to the length of the most parsimonious tree for the data set. The value for L could be obtained from any randomly chosen tree that describes the relationship of all sequences being considered, but the method is most efficient if a reasonable approximation of what will be the most parsimonious tree is used to establish the upper bound (i.e., one obtained from a computationally fast method such as UPGMA described in Chapter 4).

The second step in the branch and bound method is the process of incrementally "growing" a tree by adding branches one at a time to a tree that describes the relationship of just a few of the sequences being considered (Figure 5.4). What

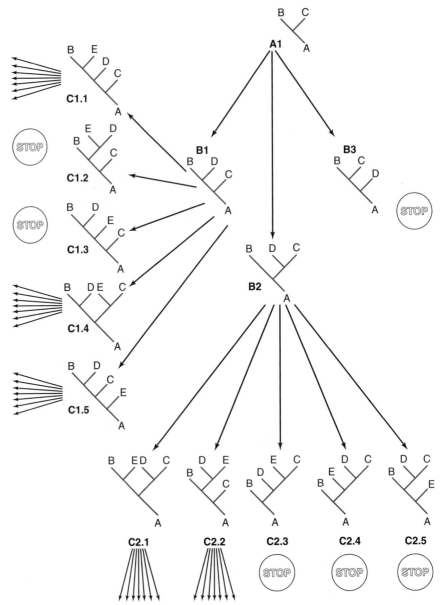

FIGURE 5.4 *A diagrammatic representation of the branch and bound approach for maximum parsimony analysis. Only one tree can describe the relationship between three sequences (A, B, and C) and it is used as a starting point (tree A1). A fourth sequence (D) from the data set can be added to tree 1 in only three different ways to give rise to trees B1, B2, and B3. If the length of one of those trees is greater than that of the upper bound, then that tree is discarded and no additional branches are added to it in subsequent steps. An additional (fifth) branch is then added to all remaining trees and the process is repeated until a branch has been added for all sequences being analyzed.*

makes the process so effective is the fact that any tree made from a subset of the data that requires more substitutions than L must become longer still as branches corresponding to the remaining sequences are added to the tree. In other words, no tree that contains that particular branching pattern can possibly be the most parsimonious tree since a more parsimonious tree for the complete data set has already been found. If, during the course of the analysis, trees are found that require fewer substitutions than the tree that was used to establish the initial upper bound, the value of L can then be changed accordingly and the remainder of the analysis of the data set will be even more efficient.

Like exhaustive searches, the branch and bound method guarantees that no more parsimonious trees have been missed when the analysis is complete. It also has the substantial advantage of typically being several orders of magnitude faster than an exhaustive search. As a result, it can reasonably be used when as many as 20 sequences are being analyzed, but is typically not sufficient for analyses where more than 1×10^{21} unrooted trees are possible.

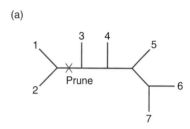

(a)

Heuristic Searches

Sequence information is increasingly abundant, however, and it is quite common for multiple alignments to be greater than 20 sequences deep. In such situations, algorithms that might not always find the most parsimonious tree must be employed. Several trial-and-error, self-educating techniques have been proposed but most of these **heuristic methods** are based on the same general assumption: Alternative trees are not all independent of each other. Because the most parsimonious trees should have very similar topologies to trees that are only slightly less parsimonious, heuristic searches all begin by constructing an initial tree and using it as a starting point for finding shorter trees.

As with the branch and bound approach, heuristic searches work best if the starting tree is a good approximation of the most parsimonious tree (i.e., one generated by UPGMA). Rather than building up all of the alternative trees branch by branch, though, most heuristic searches generate complete trees with topologies similar to the starting tree by **branch swapping** subtrees and grafting them onto other portions of the best tree found at that point of the analysis (Figure 5.5). Hundreds of new trees are typically generated from the starting tree in the first round of these analyses. All of the new trees that are shorter than the original are then pruned and grafted in the second round of the analysis. This process is repeated until a round of branch swapping fails to produce a tree that is equal to or shorter than the one generated in the previous round of pruning and grafting.

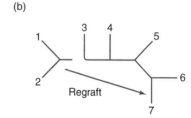

(b)

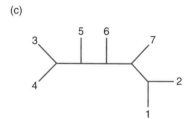

(c)

F I G U R E 5.5 *An example of branch swapping for an unrooted tree that describes the relationship between seven sequences labeled 1 through 7. The branch containing sequences 1 and 2 is randomly chosen for pruning and then randomly placed between terminal nodes 6 and 7 to generate a new tree with a topology that is similar to the original.*

Heuristic algorithms deal with the impossibility of examining even a small fraction of the astronomical number of alternative unrooted trees for deep alignments by placing an emphasis on branch swapping of increasingly more parsimonious trees. This can result in the algorithm stalling in tree topologies that do not necessarily invoke the smallest number of substitutions. In other words, if the most parsimonious tree is actually not similar to the tree used at the very start of the branch swapping process, it might not be possible to arrive at it without making some rearrangements that first *increase* the number of substitutions. Of course, algorithms can be allowed to occasionally explore paths that increase the length of trees in the hope of getting past such local minima but such provisions can come at substantial cost in terms of required computations.

Since it is the depths of alignments and not their lengths that pose the greatest computational problems, an often better alternative is to divide deep alignments into several shallower batches of alignments. For instance, the relationship between a large number of homologous mammalian sequences can be fairly easily broken into parts: one part that contains several different primate sequences to ascertain the relationships at the tip of the primate trunk of the tree, another part that contains several different rodent sequences to determine the relationships at the tip of the rodent trunk of the tree, and another that contains representatives from a variety of other mammalian orders like artiodactyls (cows) and lagomorphs (rabbits) as well as a few primates and rodents to examine the older divergences and the final placement of the more detailed primate and rodent trunks. Prior knowledge of the general relationships of the sequences (i.e., that all primates are more closely related to each other than they are to any other mammal) is certainly helpful when such a strategy is adopted. It is not essential, however, since a heuristic algorithm could also be asked to consider separately any cluster of sequences that exceeds a particular threshold of pairwise similarity.

Consensus Trees

It is quite common for parsimony approaches to yield more than one equally parsimonious tree. Deep data sets of closely related sequences often produce hundreds or even thousands of trees—far too many to be useful as a summary of the underlying phylogenetic information. In such cases, a simple alternative is the presentation of a single **consensus tree** that summarizes a set of trees (i.e., all those that are most parsimonious). Branching points where all the trees being summarized are in agreement are presented in consensus trees as bifurcations. Points of disagreement between trees are collapsed into internal nodes that connect three or more descending branches. In a **strict consensus tree,** all disagreements are treated equally even if only one alternative tree is not consistent with hundreds of others that are in agreement regarding a particular branching point (Figure 5.6a). A commonly used alternative to so stringent a definition of "agreement between trees" is a **50% majority-rule consensus** where any internal node that is supported by at least half of the trees being summarized is portrayed as a simple bifurcation and those nodes where less than half of the trees agree are shown as multifurcations (Figure 5.6b). Of course, the threshold for what constitutes significant disagreement is a parameter that can be changed to any value from > 0% to 100% (a strict consensus tree).

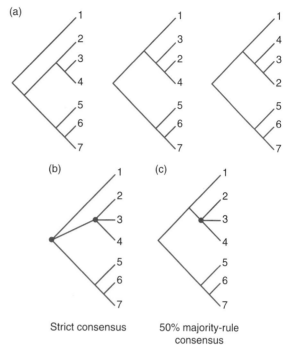

Strict consensus   50% majority-rule consensus

FIGURE 5.6 *Three trees (a) inferred from a single data set can be summarized in a single consensus tree using either (b) strict consensus criteria or (c) 50% majority-rule consensus criteria.*

Tree Confidence

All phylogenetic trees represent hypotheses regarding the evolutionary history of the sequences that make up a data set. Like any good hypothesis, it is reasonable to ask two questions about how well it describes the underlying data: (1) How much confidence can be attached to the overall tree and its component parts (branches)? and (2) How much more likely is one tree to be correct than a particular or randomly chosen alternative tree? While a variety of approaches have been proposed to address these two questions, a powerful resampling technique called bootstrapping has become the predominant favorite for addressing the first question, and a simple parametric comparison of two trees is typical of those used to address the second. Both are described below.

Bootstrapping

It is possible for portions of inferred trees to be determined with varying degrees of confidence. **Bootstrap tests** allow for a rough quantification of those confidence levels. The basic approach of a bootstrap test is straightforward: A subset of the original data is drawn (with replacement) from the original data set and a tree is inferred from this new data set, as illustrated in Figure 5.7. In a physical sense, the process is equivalent to taking the print out of a multiple alignment; cutting it up into pieces, each of which contains a different column from the alignment; placing all those pieces into a bag; randomly reaching into the bag and drawing out a piece; copying down the information from that piece before returning it to the bag; then repeating the drawing step until an artificial data set has been created that is as long as the original alignment. This whole process is repeated to create hundreds or thousands of resampled data sets, and portions of

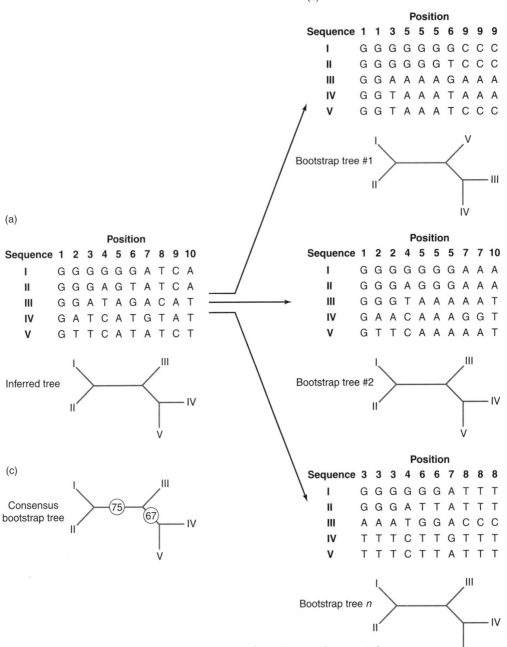

FIGURE 5.7 *Illustration of a boostrap test for a data set that is 10 characters long (positions are labeled 1 through 10) and five sequences (labeled I through V) deep. (a) The original data set and its most parsimonious tree is also shown. A random number generator chooses 10 times from the original 10 positions and creates the three resampled data sets with their corresponding trees (b). A consensus tree (c) for the three resampled data sets is shown with circled values indicating the fraction of bootstrapped trees that support the clustering of sequences I and II and sequences IV and V.*

the inferred tree that have the same groupings in many of the repetitions are those that are especially well supported by the entire original data set. Numbers that correspond to the fraction of bootstrapped trees yielding the same grouping are often placed next to the corresponding nodes in phylogenetic trees to convey the relative confidence in each part of the tree. Bootstrapping has become very popular in phylogenetic analyses even though some methods of tree inference can make it very time consuming to perform.

Despite their often casual use in the scientific literature, bootstrap results need to be treated with some caution. First, bootstrap results based on fewer than several hundred iterations (rounds of resampling and tree generation) are not likely to be reliable—especially when large numbers of sequences are involved. Simulation studies have also shown that bootstrap tests tend to underestimate the confidence level at high values and overestimate it at low values. And, since many trees have very large numbers of branches, there is often a significant risk of succumbing to "the fallacy of multiple tests," in which some results may appear to be statistically significant by chance simply because so many groupings are being considered. Still, some studies have suggested that commonly used solutions to these potential problems (i.e., doing thousands of iterations; using a correction method to adjust for estimation biases; collapsing branches to multifurcations wherever bootstrap values do not exceed a very stringent threshold) yield trees that are closer representations of the true tree than the single most parsimonious tree.

Parametric Tests

Since parsimony approaches often yield large numbers of trees that have the same minimum number of steps, it should not be surprising that alternative trees that invoke just a few additional substitutions can also be very common. Again, the underlying principle of parsimony suggests that the tree that invokes the smallest number of substitutions is the one that is most likely to depict the true relationship between the sequences. There is no limit to how many steps a most parsimonious tree might invoke, though, and data sets that are deep or involve dissimilar sequences can easily invoke many thousands of substitutions. In such cases it is reasonable to ask if a tree that is already so unlikely that it needs to invoke 10,000 substitutions is significantly more likely than an alternative that invokes 10,001. A common, related question is "How much more likely is the most parsimonious tree than a particular alternative that has previously been put forward to describe the relationship between these taxa?" One of the first parametric tests devised to answer such questions for parsimony analyses is that of H. Kishino and M. Hasegawa (1989). Their test assumes that informative sites within an alignment are both independent and equivalent and uses the difference in the minimum number of substitutions invoked by two trees, D, as a test statistic. A value for the variance, V, of D is determined by considering each of the informative sites separately as follows:

$$V = n/(n - 1)\Sigma[D_i - (1/n)(\Sigma D_k)]^2$$

where n is the number of informative sites. A paired t-test with $n-1$ degrees of freedom can then be used to test the null hypothesis that the two trees are not different from each other:

$$t = (D/n)/[(V)^{1/2}n^{1/2}]$$

Alternative parametric tests are available not just for parsimony analyses but for distance matrix and maximum likelihood trees as well.

Comparison of Phylogenetic Methods

Neither the distance- nor the character-based methods of phylogenetic reconstruction make any guarantee that they yield the one true tree that describes the evolutionary history of a set of aligned sequences. This chapter and the one that precedes it have introduced just a few of the numerous variations on each approach that have been suggested, and massive simulation studies have been performed to compare the statistical reliability of virtually all tree-constructing methods. The results of these simulations are easy to summarize: Data sets that allow one method to infer the correct phylogenetic relationship generally work well with all of the currently popular methods. However, if many changes have occurred in the simulated data sets or rates of change vary among branches, then none of the methods works very reliably. As a general rule, if a data set yields similar trees when analyzed by the fundamentally different distance matrix and parsimony methods, that tree can be considered to be fairly reliable.

Molecular Phylogenies

Countless interesting and important examples of evolutionary relationships being deciphered from sequence analyses have accumulated during the past 30 years. Such studies often have important implications for medicine (i.e., a drug that effectively treats one kind of infection is likely to also prove effective in treating infections by related organisms), agriculture (i.e., it is often easiest to transfer disease resistance factors between closely related species), and conservation (i.e., is a population of organisms sufficiently distinct to qualify as a separate species and therefore deserves special protection?). Examples of just two such areas of analysis are described below.

The Tree of Life

One of the most striking cases where sequence data have provided new information about evolutionary relationships is in our understanding of the primary divisions of life. Many years ago, biologists divided all of life into two major groups, the plants and the animals. As more organisms were discovered and their features examined in more detail, this simple dichotomy became unworkable. It was later recognized that organisms could be divided into prokaryotes and eukaryotes on the basis of cell structure. More recently, several primary divisions of life have been recognized, such as the five kingdoms (prokaryotes, protista, plants, fungi, and animals) proposed by Whittaker. All along, though, negative evidence such as the *absence* of internal membranes (the primary distinction of prokaryotes) has been recognized as a notoriously bad way to group organisms taxonomically.

Beginning in the late 1970s, RNA and DNA sequences were used to uncover for the first time the primary lines of evolutionary history among all organisms. In one study, Carl Woese and his colleagues constructed an evolutionary tree of life based on the nucleotide sequences of the 16S rRNA, which all organisms (as well as mitochondria and chloroplasts) possess. As illustrated in Figure 5.8, their evolutionary tree revealed three major evolutionary groups: the Bacteria (the traditional prokaryotes as well as mitochondria and chloroplasts), the Eucarya

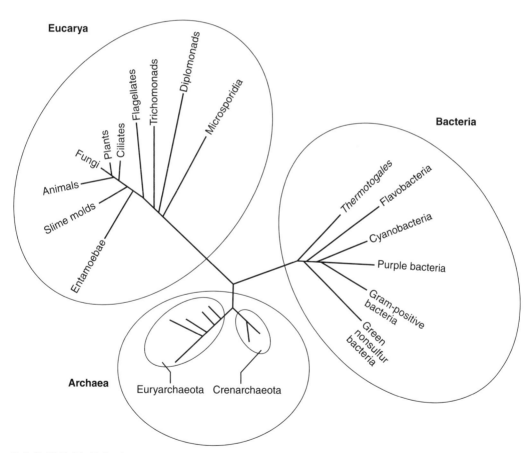

F I G U R E 5.8 *An unrooted "tree of life" as determined by parsimony and distance matrix approaches using sequence data from 16S ribosomal RNA genes. The three main lines of descent are Eucarya, Bacteria, and Archaea. (Adapted from C. R. Woese, 1996. Phylogenetic trees: Whither microbiology?* Curr. Biol. *6: 1060–1063.*

(eukaryotic organisms like plants, animals, and fungi), and the Archaea (including thermophilic bacteria and many other relatively little known organisms, some of which are only known through their rRNA sequences). Archaea and Bacteria, although both prokaryotic in that they had no internal membranes, were found to be as different genetically as Bacteria and Eucarya. The deep evolutionary differences that separate the Archaea and Bacteria were not obvious on the basis of phenotype, and the fossil record was absolutely silent on the issue. The differences became clear only after their nucleotide sequences were compared. Sequences of other genes, including 5S rRNAs, large rRNAs, and the genes coding for some fundamentally important proteins, have since been shown to also lend strong support to the idea that living organisms are best placed in three major evolutionary groups in this way.

Human Origins

Another field in which DNA sequences are being used to study evolutionary relationships is human evolution. In contrast to the extensive variation that is observed in size, body shape, facial features, skin color, etc., genetic differences among human populations are relatively small. Analysis of mtDNA sequences shows that the mean difference in sequence between two human populations is about 0.33%. Other primates exhibit much larger differences. For example, the two subspecies of orangutan differ by as much as 5%. This indicates that all human groups are closely related. Nevertheless, some genetic differences do occur among different human groups.

Surprisingly, the greatest differences are not found among populations located on different continents, but are seen among human populations residing in Africa. All other human populations show fewer differences than we find among the African populations. Many experts interpret these findings to mean that humans experienced their origin and early evolutionary divergence in Africa. After a number of genetically differentiated populations had evolved in Africa, it is hypothesized that a small group of humans may have migrated out of Africa and given rise to all other human populations. This hypothesis has been termed the "out-of-Africa theory." Sequence data from both mitochondrial DNA and the nuclear Y chromosome (the male sex chromosome) are consistent with this hypothesis.

Further interpretation of these data suggests that all people alive today have mitochondria that came from a "mitochondrial Eve" and that all men have Y chromosomes derived from a "Y chromosome Adam" roughly 200,000 years ago. Although the out-of-Africa theory is not universally accepted, DNA sequence data are playing an increasingly important role in the study of human evolution and indeed in the study of the evolution of many lineages.

Chapter Summary

Character-based methods of phylogenetic reconstruction are based primarily on the principle of parsimony—substitutions are rare events and the phylogeny that invokes the fewest number of substitutions is the one that is most likely to reflect the true relationship of the sequences being considered. In addition to providing insights into relationships between sequences, parsimony approaches also make potentially useful inferences regarding the sequences of long extinct ancestors to living organisms. Parsimony analyses can be very computationally intensive, however, especially when multiple alignments involving 20 or more sequences are considered. Data sets often yield several trees that are equally parsimonious, and consensus trees can be used to summarize them. Several methods are available for determining the robustness of parsimony trees including bootstrap and parametric tests, though no guarantees can be made that a tree created with either a character- or distance-based approach represents the true relationship between the sequences being considered.

Readings for Greater Depth

Every scientist should be able to point to a single paper that is their favorite. This one is ours. A thoroughly intimate understanding of the function of hemoglobin and an abundance of data that can be used to infer ancestral states are combined to produce a masterwork in the field of molecular evolution in M. Perutz, 1983, Species adaptation in a protein molecule, *Mol. Biol. Evol.* **1**: 1–28.

The most commonly used program for parsimony analysis has been and continues to be D. L. Swofford, 1993, *PAUP: Phylogenetic Analysis Using Parsimony*, Sinauer Associates, Sunderland, MA.

An efficient and popular method for calculating the substitution number associated with a specific tree is described in mathematical terms in W. Fitch, 1971, Toward defining the course of evolution: Minimum change for a specific tree topology, *Syst. Zool.* **20**: 406–416.

One of the first and largest simulation studies designed to put character- and distance-based methods of phylogenetic reconstruction to the test is described in J. Sourdis and M. Nei, 1988, Relative efficiencies of the maximum parsimony and distance-matrix methods in obtaining the correct phylogenetic tree. *Mol. Biol. Evol.* **5**: 298–311.

The possible existence of a mitochondrial Eve remains controversial among anthropologists while an African origin for humans is generally better accepted. The two hypotheses are related and both are discussed in E. Watson, P. Forster, M. Richards, and H. J. Bandelt, 1997, Mitochondrial footprints of human expansions in Africa. *Am. J. Hum. Genet.* **61**: 691–704.

Kishino's and Hasegawa's parametric test for parsimony analyses is described in H. Kishino and M. Hasegawa, 1989, Evolution of the maximum likelihood estimate of the evolutionary tree topologies from DNA sequence data, and the branching order in Hominoidae, *J. Mol. Evol.* **29**: 170–179.

Questions and Problems

* **5.1** What sites in the following alignment would be informative for a parsimony analysis? How many sites are invariant?

1	GAATGCTGAT	ATTCCATAAG	TCACGAGTCA	AAAGTACTCG
2	GGATGGTGAT	ACTTCGTAAG	TCCCGAGTCG	AAAGTACTCG
3	GGATGATGAT	ACTTCATAAG	TCTCAAATCA	AAGGTACTTG
4	GGATGCTGAC	ACTTCATAAG	TCGCGAGTCA	AAAGTACTTG
5	GGATGCTGAC	ACTCCGTAAG	TCCCGAGTCA	AATGTACTCG

5.2 Draw the 3 alternative unrooted trees for four taxa whose nucleotides at a position under consideration are T, T, C, and C. Label each of the internal nodes with the most likely candidates for inferred ancestral sequences.

* **5.3** How many of the 3 possible unrooted trees for the taxa used in the previous question are equally parsimonious in that they invoke a minimum of one substitution? How many invoke a minimum of two substitutions? Do any invoke more than a minimum of two substitutions?

5.4 Draw any 3 of the 105 alternative tree topologies that describe the relationship between six sequences. Using those 3 trees that you have drawn, infer the most likely ancestral sequences at each internal node if the terminal nodes are G, G, A, T, G, C. What is the minimum number of substitutions required by each of your 3 tree topologies?

* **5.5** Draw a strict consensus tree for the same 3 trees that you drew for Question 5.4. What would a strict consensus of all possible 105 trees look like?

5.6 What factor would have the greatest impact on the number of computations needed to complete a bootstrap analysis: doubling the depth or doubling the length of an alignment? Why?

C H A P T E R

6

Genomics and Gene Recognition

Now we see through
a glass, darkly.

New Testament,
1 Corinthians xiii, 12

Prokaryotic Genomes

Prokaryotic Gene Structure
Promoter elements
Open reading frames
Conceptual translation
Termination sequences

GC Content in Prokaryotic Genomes

Prokaryotic Gene Density

Eukaryotic Genomes

Eukaryotic Gene Structure
Promoter elements
Regulatory protein binding sites

Open Reading Frames
Introns and exons
Alternative splicing

GC Content in Eukaryotic Genomes
CpG islands
Isochores
Codon usage bias

Gene Expression
cDNAs and ESTs
Serial analysis of gene expression
Microarrays

Transposition

Repetitive Elements

Eukaryotic Gene Density

In previous chapters, an analogy has been drawn between written texts and genomes. Letters correspond roughly to nucleotides, sentences are akin to genes, and the individual volumes in a set of encyclopedias are something like an organism's individual chromosomes. The analogy is a good one in many respects, but deciphering the information content within a genome is much more difficult than determining the meaning of a paragraph—even when the written language is unfamiliar. Unannotated genomic sequences have no obvious equivalent to the indentation that marks the beginning of a new paragraph or to the period we expect to find at the end of a sentence. The problem is further compounded in eukaryotes by the fact that our genomes are cluttered with a surprisingly large amount of "junk DNA" that appears to have little or no important information content at all. Still, like any useful information storage system, genomes do contain signals that allow cells to determine the beginnings and ends of genes and when it is appropriate to express them. One of the greatest challenges of bioinformatics to date has been the task of discovering those signals. This chapter describes the underlying biology that bioinformaticians use to begin making sense of the bewildering array of G's, A's, T's, and C's that constitute typical raw genomic sequence data. The challenges of incorporating these signals into useful gene-detecting algorithms are also addressed. Interestingly, the development of gene-finding tools has drawn attention to previously unsuspected biological mechanisms responsible for the regulation of gene expression.

Prokaryotic Genomes

Central to the very concept of being alive is the ability to respond to stimuli. As the simplest free-living organisms, prokaryotes represent an excellent opportunity to determine the molecular basis for those responses. From a prokaryotic perspective, appropriate responses to stimuli invariably involve at least some alteration of gene expression levels.

The newly acquired ability to analyze complete bacterial genomes provided particularly useful insights into the minimum requirements for life. It has become increasingly clear that much of the information content of prokaryotic genomes is dedicated simply to the maintenance of a cell's basic infrastructure such as its ability to make and replicate its DNA (requiring not more than 32 genes), its ability to make new proteins (requiring between at least 100 to 150 genes), and its ability to obtain and store energy (requiring a minimum of approximately 30 genes). Some very simple prokaryotes such as *Haemophilus influenzae* (the first to have its genome sequence completely determined) have been found to have relatively little beyond that minimal set of between 256 and 300 genes. Other prokaryotes with more genes use their additional information content to more efficiently utilize a wider array of resources that might be found in their environments.

As described in Chapter 1, the basic methodology of DNA sequencing has been essentially unchanged since the mid-1980s and rarely yields contiguous sets of data that are more than 1,000 nucleotides long. It is useful to consider just how daunting a task it is to determine the complete sequence of a typical prokaryote's genome. With a single, circular chromosome 4.60 million nucleotides in length, *Escherichia coli*'s genome requires a minimum of 4,600 sequencing reactions to be performed in order to obtain complete coverage. Substantially more than that minimum number of reactions is required in order to assemble **contigs** (continuous runs of nucleotides longer than what can be obtained from any single sequencing reaction) by detecting overlap between the data from multiple sequencing reactions (Figure 6.1). Also, what has become a standard approach to genome sequencing efforts usually begins with a random assortment of subclones (corresponding to subsets of the genome sequence data) from the genome of interest. There are no guarantees that each portion of the genome is represented at least one time unless it is also accepted that some regions are represented multiple times. From a statistical perspective, the chance of "covering" any given nucleotide in a 4.60-Mb genome with a single 1,000-bp-long clone is only 1,000/4,600,000. Similarly, the chance for a specific region to *not* be covered is 4,599,000/4,600,000. Assuming a large enough sample of subclones in a library, 95% coverage is likely to be achieved when N clones are sequenced where:

$$(4{,}599{,}000/4{,}600{,}000)^N = 0.05$$

As a result, if a genome is 4.60 million nucleotides long (one **genome equivalent**), it is necessary to begin with a set of subclones that actually contains more than 20 million nucleotides (a little more than four genome equivalents) in order to have at least a 95% chance of having every individual sequence represented at least once.

Despite the logistical difficulties associated with the experimental and computational aspects of genome sequencing, over 60 prokaryotic genomes have been completely sequenced since the mid-1990s. Some laboratories such as The Institute of Genetic Research (TIGR) have made bacterial genome sequencing

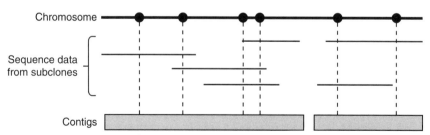

F I G U R E 6.1 *Diagram illustrating the principle of contig assembly. The results of numerous sequencing reactions are examined for regions of significant overlap. Various unique points within the genome that may have been previously sequenced (often STSs, sequence tagged sites, or even ESTs, expressed sequence tags) are shown as dark circles on the chromosome and can be used to help order the sequence information. Contigs of the sequencing information are assembled and, in this case, the STSs and ESTs can be grouped into two contigs that are separated by a comparatively short gap.*

T A B L E 6.1 Partial list of the many prokaryotic genomes that have been sequenced to date.

Organism	Genome size (Mb)	Gene number	Web site
Mycoplasma genitalium	0.58	470	http://www.tigr.org/tigr-scripts/CMR2/GenomePage3.spl?database=gmg
Helicobacter pylori	1.66	1,590	http://www.tigr.org/tigr-scripts/CMR2/GenomePage3.spl?database=ghp
Haemophilus influenzae	1.83	1,727	http://www.tigr.org/tigr-scripts/CMR2/GenomePage3.spl?database=ghi
Bacillus subtilis	4.21	4,100	http://www.pasteur.fr/Bio/SubtiList.html
Escherichia coli	4.60	4,288	http://www.genome.wisc.edu/k12.htm
Mesorhizobium loti	7.04	6,752	http://www.kazusa.or.jp/rhizobase/

Note: Genome sizes (in megabases) and predicted numbers of genes are based on complete genome sequence data maintained at the listed web sites.

into something of a cottage industry. TIGR's infrastructure of hundreds of high-throughput automated DNA sequencing machines that feed data directly to contig-assembling computers is now capable of completely characterizing several complete bacterial genome sequences every year. Examples of the types of prokaryotic organisms that have been studied by TIGR and other laboratories including their genome sizes and predicted numbers of genes are listed in Table 6.1. A more complete (and continuously updated) list as well as links to the actual sequence data themselves can be found at the TIGR web site (http://www.tigr.org). Bacterial genome sequencing has become so efficient that the U.S. Centers for Disease Control and Prevention (CDC) was able to perform complete genome comparisons of the anthrax strains used in the bioterrorism mailings in the United States in late 2001 within just weeks of their delivery to intended victims. (They consistently differed from the strain used by U.S. military labs at only four positions out of millions.)

Prokaryotic Gene Structure

The structure of prokaryotic genes is generally fairly simple, as shown in Figure 6.2. Just as you find yourself relying on simple, recurring punctuation marks as an aid to deciphering the information content of a written textbook, the proteins that are responsible for gene expression look for a recurring set of signals associated with every gene. Those genomic punctuation marks and the sometimes subtle variations between them allow distinctions to be made between genes that should be expressed and those that should not; the identification of the beginnings and ends of regions to be copied into RNA; and the demarcation of the beginnings and ends of regions of RNA that ribosomes should translate into proteins.

F I G U R E 6.2 *The structure of a typical prokaryotic gene. A promoter region where RNA polymerase initiates transcription is shown as a gray box while an operator sequence (sometimes found to overlap or precede the promoter for some genes) to which a regulatory protein might bind is shown a darker gray box. Protein coding regions are shown as a black box, while transcription and translation start and stop sites are labeled with arrows.*

Like all other information content within genomes, these signals are conveyed in relatively short strings of nucleotides. They typically make up only a small fraction of the hundreds or thousands of nucleotides needed to code for the amino acid sequence of a protein.

Promoter Elements

As described in Chapter 1, the process of gene expression begins with transcription—the making of an RNA copy of a gene by an RNA polymerase. Prokaryotic RNA polymerases are actually assemblies of several different proteins that each play a distinct and important role in the functioning of the enzyme. All prokaryotic RNA polymerases rely on a protein called β' (beta-prime) for their ability to bind to DNA templates, β (beta) to link one nucleotide to another, α (alpha) to hold all subunits together, and σ (sigma) to be able to recognize the specific nucleotide sequences of promoters. The proteins β', β, and α are evolutionarily well conserved and are often very similar from one bacterial species to another. The subunit responsible for promoter recognition, σ, tends to be less well conserved, and several significantly different variants of it are often found in any given cell.

The ability to make RNA polymerases from significantly different σ factors is directly responsible for a cell's ability to turn on or off the expression of whole sets of genes. *E. coli* has 7 different σ factors though other closely related bacteria like *Bacillus subtilis* have as many as 10. A list of *E. coli*'s σ factors and the −35 and −10 sequences (see Chapter 1) that they help RNA polymerases bind to are shown in Table 6.2. When it is appropriate for *E. coli* to express those genes that are involved with responding to heat shock, RNA polymerases containing σ^{32} seek out and find those genes with "σ^{32} promoters." By the same token, the roughly 70% of *E. coli* genes that need to be expressed at all times during normal growth and development are transcribed by RNA polymerases containing σ^{70}.

T A B L E 6.2 The seven σ factors known to be used by *E. coli.*

σ factor	Gene family	−35 sequence	−10 sequence
σ^{70}	General	TTGACA	TATAAT
σ^{32} (σ^{H})	Heat shock	TCTCNCCCTTGAA	CCCCATNTA
σ^{54} (σ^{N})	Nitrogen stress	CTGGCAC	TTGCA
σ^{28} (σ^{F})	Flagella synthesis	CTAAA	CCGATAT
σ^{38} (σ^{S})	Stationary phase genes	CGTCAA	CTNNTATAAT
σ^{20} (σ^{FecI})	Iron-dicitrate transport	TGGAAA	TGTAAT
σ^{24} (σ^{E})	Extracytoplasmic proteins	GAACTTC	TCTGA

Note: Consensus nucleotides associated with the −35 and −10 sequences of *E. coli*'s promoters are shown (*N* = any nucleotide). The names of the σ factors are derived from their molecular weights measured in terms of kilodaltons (i.e., the molecular weight of σ^{70} is 70 kDa). Alternative, commonly used names for *E. coli*'s σ factors are also shown. Some −35 and −10 sequences have not yet been well characterized (n.a.).

How well an RNA polymerase recognizes a gene's promoter is directly related to how readily it initiates the process of transcription. The −35 and −10 sequences recognized by any particular σ factor are usually described as a **consensus sequence**—essentially the set of most commonly found nucleotides at the equivalent positions of other genes that are transcribed by RNA polymerases containing the same σ factor. The better any given gene's −35 and −10 sequences match those consensus sequences, the more likely it is for an RNA polymerase to initiate transcription at that promoter.

The protein products of many genes are only useful when they are used in conjunction with the protein products of other genes. It is very common for the expression of genes with related functions to actually share a single promoter within prokaryotic genomes and to be arranged in an **operon.** This provides an elegant and simple means of ensuring that when one gene is transcribed, all others with similar roles are also transcribed. A classic example is that of the lactose operon—a set of three genes (beta-galactosidase, lactose permease, and lactose transacetylase) involved with the metabolism of the sugar lactose in bacterial cells. Transcription of the operon results in the synthesis of just one long **polycistronic** RNA molecule that contains the coding information needed by ribosomes to make all three proteins.

As mentioned in Chapter 1, individual regulatory proteins also facilitate bacterial gene expression responses to specific environmental circumstances at a much finer scale than different σ factors with affinities for a handful of different promoters could provide. The lactose operon, for instance, has a promoter that is recognized by RNA polymerases containing σ^{70} but is most efficiently expressed only when a cell's environment is rich in lactose and also poor in glucose (a preferred sugar that is more efficiently utilized than lactose). Responsiveness to lactose levels is mediated through a **negative regulator** called the lactose repressor protein (pLacI). When lactose levels are low, pLacI binds to a specific nucleotide sequence found only once in any given prokaryotic genome—the lactose operon's **operator sequence** located immediately downstream of the –10 sequence of the operon's promoter (Figure 6.3). When pLacI is bound to the operon's operator, it effectively acts as a roadblock that prevents RNA polymerases from transcribing any of the downstream coding sequences.

The protein encoded by the *LacI* gene (pLacI) is also capable of specifically binding to lactose. When lactose is bound to pLacI, the negative regulator's affinity for the operator is dramatically decreased (thereby making it is possible for the genes of the operon to be expressed). The lactose operon's sensitivity to glucose levels is accomplished through the action of a **positive regulator** called cyclic-AMP receptor protein (CRP). The –35 and –10 sequences of the lactose operon's promoter (5'-TTTACA-3' and 5'-TATGTT-3', respectively) are actually poor matches to those of the consensus sequences best recognized by RNA polymerases with the σ factor (see Table 6.2). As a result, the lactose operon is not expressed at high levels even when pLacI is not bound to the operator. The presence of CRP bound to a promoter is sufficient to make up for those deficiencies to an RNA polymerase, however. CRP does bind to the specific nucleotide sequences associated with the lactose operon's promoter but only when glucose levels within a cell are low.

There is much about prokaryotic promoter sequences and structures that is of interest to bioinformaticians. Computer programs can easily search a nucleotide sequence for a string of characters (though perfect matches are not required) known to be associated with the –35 and –10 sequences of different RNA polymerases. Attaching penalties to each nonmatching nucleotide within a putative promoter sequence allows different operons to be ranked in terms of which are most likely to be expressed at high levels in the absence of any positive regulators. Promoter recognition algorithms also allow the operons of an organism's newly sequenced genome to be organized in terms of their general expression

```
-81            -71            -61            -51            -41
   A A C G C A A T T A A T G T G A G T T A G C T C A C T C A T T A G G C A C C C
-40            -30            -20            -10            -1
   A G G C T T T A C A C T T T A T G C T T C C G G C T C G T A T G T T G T G T G G
 1              10             20             30             40
   A A T T G T G A G C G G A T A A C A A T T T C A C A C A G G A A A C A G C T a t
 41             51             61             71             81
   g a c c a t g a t t a c g g a t t c a c t g g c c g t c g t t t t a c a a c g t
```

F I G U R E 6.3 *Actual nucleotide sequence of the promoter region of* E. coli's *lac operon (GenBank accession #AE000141). Nucleotides associated with the –35 and –10 sequences are italicized; those associated with the binding site for pLacI are underlined; those for the binding site of CRP are double underlined. The transcriptional start site (+1) is shown in boldface italics as are the nucleotides associated with the operon's Shine-Delgarno sequence. The start codon for the beta-galactosidase gene and its downstream ORF are shown in lowercase letters.*

patterns. At the same time, many regulatory proteins (like CRP) have been discovered by first observing that a particular string of nucleotides other than –35 and –10 sequences is found to be associated with more than one operon's promoter.

Open Reading Frames

As described in Chapter 1, ribosomes translate a triplet genetic code in the RNA copy of a gene into the specific amino acid sequence of a protein. Of the 64 possible different arrangements of the four nucleotides in sets of three, three (UAA, UAG, and UGA) functionally act as periods to translating ribosomes in that they cause translation to stop. Most prokaryotic proteins are longer than 60 amino acids in length. (Within *E. coli*, the average length of a protein-coding region is 316.8 codons long, and less than 1.8% of the genes are shorter than 60 codons long.) Since stop codons are found in uninformative nucleotide sequences, approximately once every 21 codons (3 out of 64), a run of 30 or more triplet codons that does not include a stop codon (an **open reading frame** or an ORF) is in itself good evidence that the region corresponds to the coding sequence of a prokaryotic gene. In a statistical sense, if all codons can be expected to occur at the same frequency within a random DNA sequence, the chance of a sequence that is N codons long not containing a stop codon is $(61/64)^N$. A 95% confidence regarding the significance of the length of an ORF is equivalent to only a 5% likelihood of a "random" hit [$(61/64)^N = 0.05$] where N (the number of codons in a significantly long ORF) equals 60. Many gene mapping algorithms for prokaryotic organisms rely heavily on this single criterion.

Just as three codons of the genetic code are reserved as **stop codons,** one triplet codon is usually used as a **start codon.** Specifically, the codon AUG is used both to code for the amino acid methionine as well as to mark the precise spot along an RNA molecule where translation begins. (AUG is the first codon of 83% of *E. coli*'s genes; UUG and GUG make up the entirety of the remaining 17%.) If no likely promoter sequences are found upstream of a start codon at the beginning of the ORF before the end of the preceding ORF, then it is commonly assumed that the two genes are part of an operon whose expression is controlled at a further upstream promoter.

One other hallmark of prokaryotic genes that is related to their translation is the presence of the set of sequences around which ribosomes assemble at the 5' end of each open reading frame. Often found immediately downstream of transcriptional start sites and just upstream of the first start codon, ribosome loading sites (sometimes called **Shine-Delgarno sequences**) almost invariably include the nucleotide sequence 5'-AGGAGGU-3'. Point mutations in a gene's Shine-Delgarno sequence can prevent an mRNA from being translated. In some bacterial mRNAs where there are very few nucleotides between ORFs, translation between adjacent coding regions in a polycistronic mRNA is directly linked because ribosomes gain access to the start codon of the downstream ORF as they complete translation of the first ORF. The norm though is that each legitimate start codon has its own Shine-Delgarno sequence.

Conceptual Translation

In the 1960s and 1970s it was much easier to determine the amino acid sequence of a protein than the nucleotide sequence of the gene that coded for it. The advent of improved DNA sequencing methodologies in the 1980s and the success of numerous genome sequencing projects have changed that balance to the point where now the vast majority of protein sequences are inferred only from predicted gene sequences. The process of **conceptual translation** of gene sequences into the corresponding amino acid sequences of proteins using the genetic code (Table 1.1) is easily done by computers (see Appendix 3). Amino acid sequences in turn can be evaluated for structural tendencies such as the propensity to form alpha helices or beta sheets as described in the next chapter. Protein structure prediction from amino acid sequences rarely allows more than a guess at a particular gene's function, however. Comparisons with the amino acid sequences of proteins from other, better characterized organisms as well as the promoter sequences and genomic context of a gene often provide much more reliable clues about a protein's role. In the end, there is still no good substitute for the often laborious task of physically purifying and characterizing an enzyme using some of the biochemical approaches described in Appendix 2.

Termination Sequences

Just as RNA polymerases begin transcription at recognizable transcriptional start sites immediately downstream from promoters, the vast majority (greater than 90%) of prokaryotic operons also contain specific signals for the termination of transcription called **intrinsic terminators.** Intrinsic terminators have two prominent structural features: (1) a sequence of nucleotides that includes an inverted repeat (i.e., the sequence 5'-CGGATG|CATCCG-3' contains an inverted repeat centered at the "|" because "5'-CGGATG-3'" reads "5'-CATCCG-3'" on its complementary strand), and (2) a run of roughly six uracils immediately following the inverted repeat.

While RNA molecules are typically thought of as being single stranded, it is possible for them to adopt stable secondary structures due to intramolecular base pairing within their inverted repeats. The stability of an RNA secondary structure is directly related to the length of the (often imperfect) inverted repeats that base pair with each other and to the number of G's and C's relative to A's and T's within those repeats (as is described in greater detail in Chapter 8). For intrinsic terminators, each inverted repeat is typically 7 to 20 nucleotides long and rich in G's and C's.

The formation of secondary structures like the one shown in Figure 6.4 in an RNA molecule during its transcription has been experimentally proven to cause RNA polymerases to pause for an average of 1 minute (a very long time considering that prokaryotic RNA polymerases typically incorporate roughly 100 nucleotides a second otherwise). If the RNA polymerase pauses just as it is synthesizing a run of uracils in the new RNA, the unusually weak base pairing that occurs between uracils in the RNA and adenines in the DNA template allows the two polynucleotides to dissociate and effectively terminate transcription. The

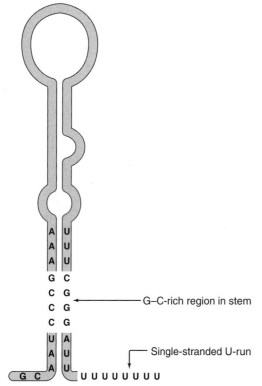

G–C-rich region in stem

Single-stranded U-run

F I G U R E 6.4 *Molecular structure of a prokaryotic intrinsic terminator of transcription. Intrinsic terminators include palindromic sequences that vary in length from 7 to 20 bp and tend to be rich in G's and C's. The stem-loop structure that results from intramolecular base pairing is immediately followed by a run of uracils in the RNA*

normal processivity (essentially, their molecular momentum) of RNA polymerases usually allows them to transcribe such runs of adenines in DNA templates. But, when coupled with the pause in synthesis caused by secondary structure in the RNA, the instability of uracil/adenine base pairing effectively and fairly precisely results in transcriptional termination.

GC Content in Prokaryotic Genomes

Base pairing rules require that for every G within a double-stranded DNA genome there be a complementary C, but the only physical constraint on the fraction of nucleotides that are G/C as opposed to A/T is that the two values add to 100%. The abundance of G and C nucleotides relative to A and T nucleotides has long been recognized as a distinguishing attribute of bacterial genomes. Measuring genomic **GC content** has proven to be a particularly useful means of identifying bacterial species due simply to the fact that it can vary so dramatically across prokaryotic species with values ranging from 25% to 75% GC (with corresponding values for AT spanning 75% to 25%, respectively).

The GC content of each bacterial species seems to be independently shaped by mutational biases of its DNA polymerases and DNA repair mechanisms working over long periods of time. As a result, the relative ratios of G/C to A/T base pairs are generally uniform throughout any bacteria's genome. As more and more prokaryotic genomes are being completely sequenced, analyses of their GC content has revealed that much of bacterial evolution occurs through large-scale acquisitions of genes (corresponding to tens and even hundreds of thousands of nucleotides in length) from other organisms through a process called **horizontal gene transfer.** Since bacterial species often have widely differing genomic GC contents, genes that have been recently acquired in this way often have GC contents that differ significantly from those that have resided within the genome for longer time periods. Those differences in GC content in turn give rise to significantly different codon usage biases (not all triplet codons are used with the same frequency within a genome's coding sequences as described below) and even amino acid utilizations between genes that have been recently acquired and those that have been long time residents within its genome. In short, many bacterial genomes appear to be patchworks of regions with distinctive GC contents that reflect the evolutionary history of the bacteria as the essences of their ecological and pathogenic characters have changed.

Prokaryotic Gene Density

The density of genes within prokaryotic genomes is remarkably high. Completely sequenced bacterial and archaea chromosomes suggest that between 85% and 88% of the nucleotides are typically associated with the coding regions of genes. In the specific case of *E. coli*, a total of 4,288 genes with average coding sequence lengths of 950 bp are separated by an average of just 118 bp. The ability to reproduce quickly appears to be important to the evolutionary success of bacteria. It has been speculated that maximizing the coding efficiency of their chromosomes may be the result of a need to minimize the potentially rate-limiting step of DNA replication during cell division.

More recent studies that have used GC-content analyses as a means of deciphering the evolutionary history of bacterial genomes have suggested an alternative explanation. These studies indicate that deletions of large regions of chromosomes may be just as common as their acquisition. The only sequences likely to be left behind in the genomes of successful bacterial species (such as those whose genomes get sequenced) are the regions that are absolutely essential such as the coding regions of important genes. Regardless of the underlying cause, the fact remains that finding a gene in prokaryotic genomes is comparatively easy by considering a fairly small number of characteristics:

- Long open reading frames (60 or more codons in length),
- Matches to simple promoter sequences (small numbers of sigma factors help RNA polymerases recognize the −35 and −10 sequences of promoters),
- Recognizable transcriptional termination signal (inverted repeats followed by a run of uracils), and
- Comparisons with the nucleotide (or amino acid) sequences of known protein coding regions from other organisms.

Chances are extremely good that any randomly chosen nucleotide will be associated with the coding sequences or promoter of an important gene. Prokaryotic genomes have very little in the way of wasted space.

Eukaryotic Genomes

Eukaryotic organisms are exceptionally more complex than prokaryotes in virtually every respect. First, their internal membrane-bound compartments allow them to maintain a wide variety of chemical environments within each cell. Second, unlike prokaryotes, almost all eukaryotes live as multicellular organisms and each cell type usually has a distinctive pattern of gene expression even though every cell within the organism has the very same set of genetic instructions. Third, there seems to be relatively little constraint regarding the size of eukaryotic genomes and, as a result, they exhibit an enormously greater tolerance for what is arguably dispensable, "junk" DNA. The demands associated with these three factors alone have forced eukaryotic genomes themselves and the gene expression apparatus that interprets them to be much more complicated and flexible than what is found in even the most sophisticated of prokaryotes. Those two features, complexity and flexible rules of interpretation, have caused the analysis and annotation of eukaryotic genomes to be one of the most challenging ongoing problems for bioinformaticians.

Obtaining the complete nucleotide sequence of any eukaryote's genome is definitely a major undertaking. Unlike prokaryotes with their single copies of typically circular chromosomes, eukaryotic nuclei usually contain two copies of each of at least several different linear chromosomes. Most human cells, for instance, have two copies of a total of 22 different chromosomes (these autosomes are named 1 through 22) and two sex chromosomes (two X chromosomes in females or an X and a Y in males), with the shortest being 55,000,000 bp (55 mega base pairs or 55 Mb) long and the longest being 250,000,000 bp (250 Mb) long and an overall genome size of approximately 3,200,000,000 bp (3,200 Mb). The overall size of a eukaryotic genome is actually difficult for most people to contemplate let alone analyze and annotate. If the nucleotide sequence of the human genome were spelled out using the same font size seen in most encyclopedias, it would require 10 times the number of pages in the complete 32-volume set of the 2002 edition of the *Encyclopedia Britannica!*

The same problems encountered in the sequencing of prokaryotic genomes described earlier in this chapter definitely apply and are compounded significantly by the much larger size of even the simplest and most streamlined eukaryotic genome. The computational problems of finding overlaps between the very large number of contigs that are created in the course of standard genome sequencing approaches necessitate the use of more than just sequence similarities between clones. An extremely useful additional strategy has included establishing correspondence between physical maps (like the STSs and ESTs shown in Figure 6.1 and described in greater detail below) and genetic maps (inferred by examining the combination of traits seen in the progeny of mating experiments). Among the first eukaryotic genomes where these strategies proved to be helpful are those of yeast, *Drosophila melanogaster* (fruit flies), *Arabidopsis thaliana* (a mustard plant), and even humans. As presented in Table 6.3, the genomes of these eukaryotes are all orders of magnitude larger than those of the prokaryotes listed in Table 6.1. Comparisons of gene number estimates between prokaryotic and eukaryotic organisms are very difficult due to lack of confidence in the ability to accurately predict eukaryotic genes simply from an examination of DNA sequence information, as will be described below. Still, the best estimates of gene numbers listed in Table 6.3 are consistent with the idea that in most cases, eukaryotes are more complex than any prokaryotic counterpart.

T A B L E 6.3 Partial list of eukaryotic genome sequencing projects.

Organism	Genome size (Mb)	Gene number	Web site
Saccharomyces cerevisiae (yeast)	13.5	6,241	http://genome-www.stanford.edu/Saccharomyces
Caenorhabditis elegans	100	18,424	http://www.sanger.ac.uk/Projects/C_elegans/
Arabidopsis thaliana (thale cress)	130	25,000	http://www.tair.org
Drosophila melanogaster (fruit flies)	180	13,601	http://flybase.bio.indiana.edu
Danio rerio (zebrafish)	1,700	na	http://zfish.uoregon.edu/
Homo sapiens (humans)	3,000	45,000	http://www.ncbi.nlm.nih.gov/genome/guide/

Note: Genome sizes (in megabases) and predicted numbers of genes are based on data maintained at the listed web sites.

Eukaryotic Gene Structure

The size of a eukaryotic genome alone has caused many people to liken the process of finding genes within their reams of sequence data to looking for a needle in a haystack. That old analogy actually falls very far short of conveying the enormity of the problem. A typical 2-gram needle in a 6,000-kilogram haystack would actually be 1,000 times easier to find, and that is only if genes were as different from the remainder of genomic DNA as a needle is from a piece of straw. Unfortunately, recognizing eukaryotic genes is substantially more difficult than the equivalent task in prokaryotic nucleotide sequences. The striking landmarks of prokaryotic open reading frames with statistically significant lengths used earlier are not found in eukaryotic genes due to the abundant presence of introns as described below. Eukaryotic promoters, like their prokaryotic counterparts, do have some conserved sequence features that gene-finding algorithms can search for but they tend to be much more diffuse and located far away from a gene's start codon.

In short, the problem of recognizing eukaryotic genes in genomic sequence data is a major challenge and promises to be one of the greatest open questions for bioinformaticians in the next several decades. The best attempts at solutions to date (programs such as Grail EXP and GenScan available on the web) have relied on **neural network** and **dynamic programming** techniques. Neural networks look for statistical similarities in characterized data sets (i.e., the sequences of known human genes) to predict the properties of related but uncharacterized data sets (i.e., raw sequence data from the human genome project). As described in Chapter 2, dynamic programming allows computers to efficiently explore all possible solutions to some kinds of complex problems. With correct predictions being made less than 50% of the time, current algorithms are a good start but not particularly reliable. Algorithms using these approaches scan sequences looking for a variety of features in appropriate orientations and relative positions.

Any one feature by itself might occur as the result of random chance, but the co-occurrence of several such as a likely promoter, a series of intron/exon boundaries, and a putative ORF with a favorable codon usage bias all lend weight to the prediction that a region may correspond to a gene. The biological significance of these features and what makes them distinctive are described below.

Promoter Elements

All of the information that a liver cell needs to be a liver cell is also present in a muscle or a brain cell. Regulation of gene expression is the only practical way to account for their differences and, as was the case for prokaryotes, the initiation of transcription represents one of the most efficient places to regulate expression. It should not be surprising then that eukaryotes have very elaborate mechanisms for regulating the initiation of transcription. At one level the added challenges of gene expression for eukaryotes are reflected simply in the number of different RNA polymerases they use. Unlike prokaryotes with a single RNA polymerase made from a handful of different proteins, all eukaryotic organisms employ three different kinds of RNA polymerase made of at least 8 to 12 proteins.

Each of the three eukaryotic RNA polymerases recognizes a different set of promoters, and each is used to transcribe different kinds of genes (Table 6.4). RNA polymerases I and III make RNA molecules that are themselves functionally important and needed at fairly constant levels in all eukaryotic cells at all times. RNA polymerase II is exclusively responsible for the transcription of the eukaryotic genes that code for proteins. The variety of promoter sequences RNA polymerase II recognizes definitely reflects the complexity of distinguishing between genes that should and should not be expressed at any given time in any given type of cell.

As with prokaryotes, eukaryotic promoters are the nucleotide sequences that are important for the initiation of transcription of a gene. Unlike prokaryotic operons where multiple genes share a single promoter, every eukaryotic gene has its own promoter. Most RNA polymerase II promoters contain a set of sequences known as a **basal promoter** where an RNA polymerase II **initiation complex** is assembled and transcription begins. The promoters of most RNA polymerase II transcribed genes also include several additional **upstream promoter elements** to which proteins other than RNA polymerase II specifically bind. Given a typical eukaryote's number of genes and cell types, it has been estimated that a minimum

T A B L E 6.4 The three eukaryotic RNA polymerases.

RNA polymerase	Promoter location	Promoter complexity	Transcribed genes
RNA polymerase I	−45 to +20	Simple	Ribosomal RNAs
RNA polymerase II	Far upstream to −25	Very complex	Protein-coding genes
RNA polymerase III	+50 to +100	Simple	tRNAs, other small RNAs

Note: Positions of promoter sequences relative to the transcriptional start site, the complexity of sequences, and the types of genes they transcribe are listed.

of five upstream promoter elements are required to uniquely identify any particular eukaryotic protein coding gene and ensure that it is expressed in an appropriate fashion. Assembly of initiation complexes on a core promoter can occur in the absence of the proteins associated with any or all upstream elements but only in an inefficient way.

A fundamental difference between the initiation of transcription in prokaryotes and eukaryotes is that RNA polymerase II does not directly recognize the basal sequences of promoters. Instead, **basal transcription factors** including a TATA-binding protein (TBP) and at least 12 TBP-associated factors (TAFs) seek out and bind to the nucleotide sequences of the promoter in a specific order and then facilitate the binding of the catalytic unit of RNA polymerase II, as shown in Figure 6.5. As with prokaryotes, eukaryotic promoters include a TATA box (the consensus sequence in eukaryotes is actually 5'-TATAWAW-3' where "W" means either "A" or "T" is present at equal frequency) at −25 instead of −10 relative to the transcriptional start site (+1). In eukaryotes the +1 position is associated with an **initiator (Inr) sequence** (with a consensus of 5'-YYCARR-3' where "Y" means "C" or "T" and "R" means "G" or "A"). The +1 nucleotide is almost always the highly conserved A within the Inr sequence but other nucleotides can be consistently used for some genes.

Subtle differences in basal transcription factors are known to exist among different cell types in eukaryotic organisms and are likely to recognize slightly different sequences as promoters. These transcription factor differences ultimately play an important role in the tissue-specific expression of some genes. Still, the presence of a strong TATA box and Inr sequence in the appropriate relative orientation and position is a useful indicator to bioinformaticians that a eukaryotic genomic sequence is associated with a downstream protein-coding region.

Regulatory Protein Binding Sites

The initiation of transcription in eukaryotes is fundamentally different from what occurs in prokaryotes. In bacteria, RNA polymerases have a high affinity for promoters, and an emphasis is placed on negative regulation (such as that achieved by pLacI described earlier) by proteins that prevent gene expression from occurring at inappropriate times. In eukaryotes, RNA polymerases II and III do not assemble around promoters very efficiently, and the basal rate of transcription is very low regardless of how well a promoter matches consensus sequences. As a result, eukaryotes place a much greater emphasis on additional proteins acting as positive regulators. Some of these positive regulators are essentially **constitutive** in that they work on many different genes and do not seem to respond to external signals. Other proteins are more **regulatory** in that they play a role for a limited number of genes and do respond to external signals. The distinction between constitutive and regulatory activating proteins (often referred to as "transcription factors") in eukaryotes is far from precise but the concept still provides a useful framework for discussion.

The majority of transcription factors are sequence-specific DNA-binding proteins (Table 6.5). Some, like CAAT transcription factor and the CP family of

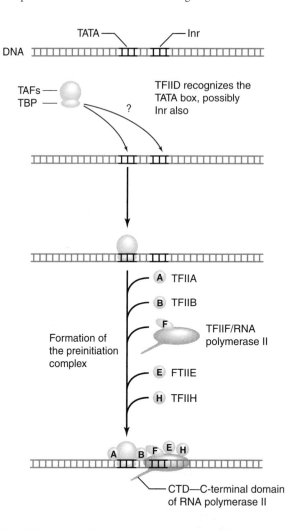

F I G U R E 6.5 *Assembly of the RNA polymerase II preinitiation complex. Assembly of the preinitiation complex begins with recognition of the TATA box and possibly the Inr sequence by TBP (probably in conjunction with TAFs). Other components of the preinitiation complex assemble in the order shown and with known protein contacts in place. (Based on Roeder, 1996.)*

proteins, recognize consensus sequences relatively close to transcriptional start sites like the **CAAT box** found in the same orientation and in the vicinity of –80 in most eukaryotic genes. Others like Sp1 are called **enhancers** because they work equally well in either orientation and over a wider range relative to the start site (usually from –500 to +500). Enhancers also tend to work cumulatively when multiple binding sites are present. Some eukaryotic enhancers are known to work at distances as great as many tens of thousands of nucleotides upstream of tran-

T A B L E 6.5 Examples of several eukaryotic transcription factors.

Protein factor	Consensus sequence	Role
Constitutive factors		
CAAT transcription factor	5'-GCCAATCT-3'	Ubiquitous
CP family	5'-GCCAATCT-3'	Ubiquitous
Sp1	5'-GGGCGG-3'	Ubiquitous
Oct-1	5'-ATGCAAAT-3'	Ubiquitous
Response factors		
Heat shock factor	5'-CNNGAANNTCCNNG-3'	Response to heat shock
Serum response factor in serum	5'-CCATATTAGG-3'	Response to growth factors
Cell-specific factors		
GATA-I	5'-GATA-3'	Only in erythroid cells
Pit-I	5'-ATATTCAT-3'	Only in pituitary cells
MyoDI	5'-CANNG-3'	Only in myoblast cells
NF-kB	5'-GGGACTTTCC-3'	Only in lymphoid cells
Developmental regulators		
Bicoid	5'-TCCTAATCCC-3'	Early embryo organization
Antennapedia	5'-TAATAATAATAATAA-3'	Embryonic head development
Fushi tarazu	5'-TCAATTAAATGA-3'	Embryonic segment pairing

Note: Examples include the sequences that the transcription factors specifically interact with and their roles. "N" means that all four nucleotides occur with roughly the same frequency.

scriptional start sites and have their effect by bending the DNA into a specific shape that brings other transcription factors into contact with each other to form structures called **enhanceosomes.** Still other transcription factors are available only under special circumstances and help mediate the response of eukaryotic cells to stimuli such as exposure to heat or allow genes to be expressed only in specific tissues or times during development.

Open Reading Frames

The nuclear membrane of eukaryotic cells provides a physical barrier that separates the process of transcription and translation in a way that never occurs in prokaryotes where translation by ribosomes typically begins as soon as an RNA polymerase has begun to make an RNA copy of a coding region.

Eukaryotes take advantage of the resulting delay in the initiation of translation that transport out of the nucleus necessitates to extensively modify their RNA polymerase II transcripts. Known as **hnRNAs** (heterogeneous RNAs) prior to processing, RNA polymerase II transcripts are capped, spliced, and polyadenylated as they are converted into mRNAs suitable for translation by ribosomes.

Capping refers to a set of chemical alterations (including methylation) at the 5' end of all hnRNAs. **Splicing** involves the wholesale and precise removal of often very large segments from the interior of hnRNAs. **Polyadenylation** describes the process of replacing the 3' end of an hnRNA with a stretch of approximately 250 A's that are not spelled out in the nucleotide sequence of a gene.

Each of the three kinds of modification just described can occur differently in different cell types. Variation in splicing in particular is a great boon to eukaryotic organisms in terms of their ability to meet the demands of tissue-specific gene expression without paying an inordinate cost in genome complexity. At the same time, though, splicing represents a serious problem for gene recognition algorithms. In short, the DNA sequences of eukaryotic genes do not have to possess the statistically significant long ORFs associated with DNA sequences of prokaryotic genes because the process of splicing typically removes countless stop codons that interrupt the ORFs in the DNA sequences of eukaryotic genes. If gene recognition algorithms can accurately model the splicing process, then the ORFs of eukaryotic mRNAs could be every bit as useful in gene recognition as they are in prokaryotes. The tissue-specific variability in splicing rules described below, however, makes this a very difficult problem to solve.

Introns and Exons

The genetic code (Table 1.1) was experimentally deciphered long before it was possible to determine the nucleotide sequence of genes. It came as quite a surprise in 1977, when the first eukaryotic genomic sequences were obtained, that many genes contained "intervening sequences" (**introns**) that interrupt the coding regions that were ultimately linked together in processed mRNAs (Figure 6.6).

At least eight distinctly different kinds of introns have since been found in eukaryotic cells though only one of those types, the one that conforms to a **GU-AG rule,** is predominantly associated with eukaryotic protein-coding genes. The GU-AG rule gets its name from the fact that the first two nucleotides at the 5' end of the DNA sequence of all of these introns are invariably 5'-GU-3' and the last two at the 3' end of the intron are always 5'-AG-3'. Additional nucleotides associated with these 5' and 3' splice junctions as well as an internal "branch site" located 18 to 40 bp upstream of the 3' splice junction are also scrutinized by the splicing machinery as indicated in the consensus sequences shown in Figure 6.6.

From an information storage perspective, it is worth noting that most of the sequences being scrutinized by the splicing apparatus actually lie within the intron itself and do not constrain the information content of the typically protein-coding **exon** sequences on either side that end up being linked as hnRNAs are processed into mRNAs. Introns must have a minimal length of about 60 bp simply to accommodate these splicing signals, although there appears to be no practical constraint on the upper bound of their length (a large number of human introns are many tens of thousands of base pairs long). Similarly, exon lengths also span a wide range of sizes in vertebrates with most being about 450 bp in length, although some are less than 100 bp long and others are known to be greater than 2,000 bp long.

(a)

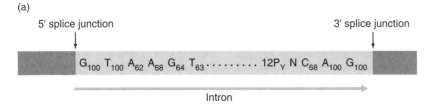

(b)

Correct splicing removes 3 introns by pairwise recognition of the junctions

F I G U R E 6.6 *A diagram representing the intron/exon structure of a eukaryotic gene and the mRNA it gives rise to after processing of an hnRNA transcript. (a) Conserved sequences associated with the 5′ and 3′ splice junctions of yeast introns are shown. Subscript numbers beside each consensus nucleotide indicate the frequency with which the nucleotide occurs in the introns of all known yeast genes. "Y" means that the consensus nucleotide is either a C or a T while "N" means that no one nucleotide is found at higher than expected frequency. (b) Splice junctions are recognized in pairwise recognition of the splice junctions by spliceosomes to give rise to mRNAs ready for translation by ribosomes.*

No strictly followed rules appear to govern the distribution of these introns though they are generally less common in simpler eukaryotes (i.e., the 6,000 genes of the yeast genome have a total of only 239 introns while some individual genes in humans are known to have 100 or more). Introns are a very common feature in the genes of most vertebrates, and almost 95% of all human genes have at least one (Table 6.6). Aside from the sequences required for splicing, the length and nucleotide sequences of introns appear to be under very little selective constraint. In contrast, the position of introns within any given gene does seem to be evolutionarily conserved in that they are often in identical positions in alignments of the sequences of homologous genes.

Alternative Splicing

All 5′ splice junctions appear to be functionally equivalent to the splicing apparatus, as do all 3′ splice junctions. Still, in usual circumstances splicing occurs only between the 5′ and 3′ sites of the *same* intron. The molecular basis for differentiating between splice junctions of the same and different introns appears to be more complex than simple scanning of the hnRNA sequence by the splicing machinery for adjacent sites and remains an important unanswered question for

T A B L E 6.6 Intron/exon structure of some human genes.

Gene (GenBank Acc. #)	Intron #	Coding sequence (bp)	Intron length (bp)
Histone H3 (X83550)	0	410	0
α-Globin (J00153)	2	426	261
β-Globin (AF083883)	2	441	982
Insulin (J00265)	2	332	963
Keratin, type I (Y16787)	6	1,248	2,267
Alpha albumin (U51243)	13	1,797	20,273
Phosphofructokinase (AJ005577)	14	1,512	17,421
RECQL4 helicase (AB026546)	20	3,624	2,592
Factor VIII (M14113)	25	7,053	≈179,000
Cystic fibrosis TR (AH006034)	26	4,440	≈226,000
Hyperion protein (AJ010770)	49	11,733	≈160,000
Dystrophin (M18533)	78	11,057	≈2,400,000
Type VII collagen (NM_000094)	117	8,833	21,932

Note: The number of introns in each gene are shown as well as the total length of each gene's coding region and the total length of its intron sequences.

molecular biologists. The majority of eukaryotic genes appear to be processed into a single type of spliced mRNA (i.e., introns and exons are recognized in the same way in all cell types). However, it has been conservatively estimated that 20% of human genes give rise to more than one type of mRNA sequence due to **alternative splicing.** In one extreme example of alternative splicing, a single human gene has been shown to generate up to 64 different mRNAs from the same primary transcript.

As mentioned earlier, the processing of hnRNAs into mRNAs does not happen in exactly the same way in different eukaryotic cell types and under all circumstances (Figure 6.7). For instance, exons 2 and 3 of the mouse troponin T gene are mutually exclusive; exon 2 is used in smooth muscle while exon 3 is used in all other tissues as illustrated in Figure 6.7b. Smooth muscle cells possess a protein that binds to repeated sequences present on either side of the exon in the gene's hnRNA and apparently mask the splice junctions that must be recognized to include it in the mRNA.

It is also worth considering that the splicing apparatus itself is made from a variety of small nuclear RNAs (snRNAs) as well as several proteins—each of which may differ from one cell type to another. Much of the variability observed in the consensus sequences of the splice junctions and branch sites may actually reflect the specific recognition of different splicing signals in different eukaryotic tissues. Single genes do not necessarily give rise to single proteins in eukaryotic systems, and the development of useful computational splicing models remains a major challenge at the heart of gene recognition algorithms. A catalog of known splicing variants is maintained on the web at the intron database (http://www.introns.com/front.html).

(a) *D. melanogaster tra* splices a 5' site to alternative 3' sites

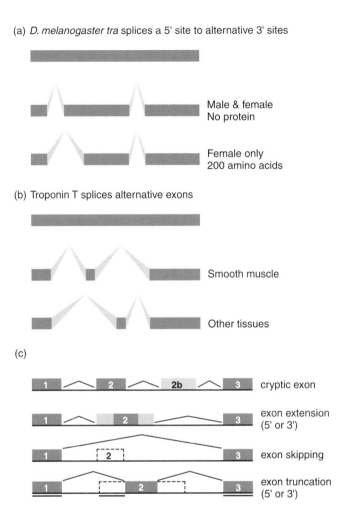

Male & female
No protein

Female only
200 amino acids

(b) Troponin T splices alternative exons

Smooth muscle

Other tissues

(c)

cryptic exon

exon extension
(5' or 3')

exon skipping

exon truncation
(5' or 3')

F I G U R E 6.7 *Possible products of alternative splicing of a eukaryotic gene. (a) Alternative splicing of the* tra *gene in* D. melanogaster *is responsible for sex determination in fruit flies. (b) Alternative splicing of troponin T leads to distinctly different protein products in human smooth muscle cells relative to other tissues. (c) Many variants on the theme of alternative splicing are known.*

GC Content in Eukaryotic Genomes

Overall genomic GC content does not show the same variability between eukaryotic species as is observed in prokaryotes. It does seem to play a much more important role in gene recognition algorithms, though, for at least two reasons: (1) Eukaryotic ORFs are much harder to recognize, and (2) large-scale variation of GC content *within* eukaryotic genomes underlies useful correlations between genes and upstream promoter sequences, codon choices, gene length, and gene density.

CpG Islands

One of the first bioinformatics analyses ever performed on DNA sequence data was a statistical evaluation of the frequency that all possible pairs of nucleotides (GG, GA, GT, GC, AG, etc.) were observed in generic sequences from the human

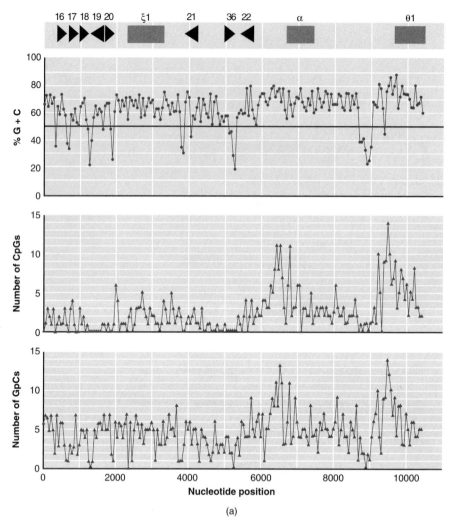

(a)

F I G U R E 6.8 *Gene map, dinucleotide frequency, and GC content of the rabbit alpha- and beta-like globin gene clusters. (a) The rabbit alpha-like globin gene cluster: a set of tissue-specific genes in a GC-rich portion of the human genome. Regions corresponding to genes are shown as filled boxes while copies of the predominant SINE in rabbits (C repeats) are numbered and shown as filled arrows. The number of occurrences of the dinucleotide 5'-CG-3' in a sliding window of 200 bp is shown in the panel immediately below the gene map. A CpG island can be seen to be associated with the 5' ends of both the alpha- and theta$_1$-globin genes. The number of occurrences of the dinucleotide 5'-GC-3' in a 200-bp window such as those shown is generally higher than those for CpGs because only CpGs are hypermutable due to methylation. The bottom panel simply shows what fraction (%) of nucleotides within the same sliding window of 200 bp is either G or C. (b, opposite) The rabbit beta-like globin gene cluster: tissue-specific genes in a GC-poor portion of the human genome. Genes and repeated sequences are shaded as for the alpha-globin gene cluster of part (a). Occurrences of CpGs are placed above those of GpCs and overall GC content using the same 200-bp window as part (a).*

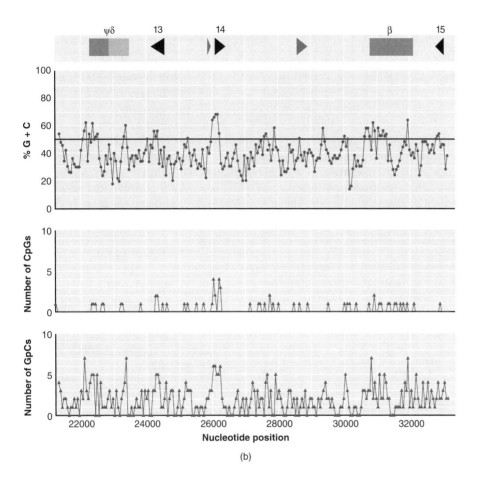

(b)

genome. A striking observation was made: CG dinucleotides (often called CpGs to reflect the phosphodiester bond that connects the two nucleotides) were found with only 20% of the frequency that should have occurred by chance (Figure 6.8). No other pair of nucleotides was found to be unusually over- or underrepresented.

An interesting exception to the general paucity of CpGs was found to be associated with stretches of 1–2 kb at the 5' ends of many human genes. These **CpG islands** typically span from about –1,500 to +500 and have densities of CpGs at the levels predicted by chance. Many of the individual CpGs appear to be involved with binding sites for known transcriptional enhancers such as Sp1 (see Table 6.5). Analysis of the complete human genome sequence indicates that there are approximately 45,000 such islands and that about half of them are associated with every known **housekeeping gene** (genes that are expressed at high levels in all tissues and at all times in development). Many of the remaining CpG islands appear to be associated with promoters of tissue-specific genes (like human α-globin shown in Figure 6.8a), although less than 40% of known tissue-specific genes have them (like human β-globin shown in Figure 6.8b). CpG islands are only rarely found in gene-free regions or with genes that have accumulated inactivating mutations.

CpG islands are intimately associated with an important chemical modification of DNA in most eukaryotes, **methylation.** A specific enzyme, DNA methylase, is known to attach methyl groups to the nitrogenous base cytosine as shown in Figure 6.9 but only when it occurs in 5'-CG-3' dinucleotides. Methylation itself seems to be responsible for the rarity of CpGs in the genome as a whole since methylated cytosines are known to be especially prone to mutation (particularly to TpGs and CpAs). High levels of DNA methylation in a region are associated with low levels of acetylation of histones (important DNA packaging proteins in eukaryotes) and vice versa. Low levels of DNA methylation and high levels of histone acetylation are also strongly correlated with high levels of gene expression. In the human γ-globin (gamma-globin) gene, for example, the presence of methyl groups in the region between –200 and +90 effectively suppresses transcription. Removal of the three methyl groups found upstream of the transcriptional start site or of the three methyl groups located downstream does not allow transcription to begin. However, removal of all six methyl groups allows the promoter to function. While there are some exceptions to this rule, transcription appears to require a methyl-free promoter region. Methylation patterns differ significantly from one cell type to another, and the γ-globin gene sequence is generally only free of methyl groups in erythroid cells. While the presence of CpG islands alone is a strong indication that a eukaryotic gene is nearby, methylation patterns of DNA are somewhat difficult to determine experimentally and are rarely reported in the context of genomic sequence data.

Histones are unusually positively charged, well-conserved proteins found within eukaryotes that have a high affinity for negatively charged DNA molecules. The roughly equal mixture (by mass) of DNA and closely associated histones within eukaryotic nuclei is called **chromatin.** Wrapping of DNA around histones and further organization of the histones themselves result in a final packaging ratio of approximately 1:10,000 for eukaryotic genomic DNA. As mentioned above, transcriptionally active regions are generally areas where the positive charge of histones is reduced by the addition of acetyl and methyl groups.

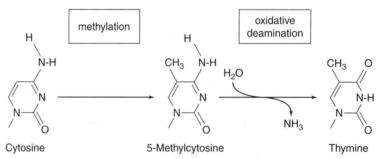

F I G U R E 6.9 *Methylation of cytosine by DNA methylase in eukaryotes. Methylases add methyl groups (—CH₃) to the nitrogenous base cytosine only when they occur as part of a CpG dinucleotide. A common type of chemical damage to DNA, oxidative deamination, converts methylcytosine to thymine and, as a result, makes CpGs hypermutable relative to all other possible dinucleotides.*

The resulting low affinity of those histones for negatively charged DNA causes the chromatin to be less tightly packed and more accessible to RNA polymerases. Such areas of open chromatin are known as **euchromatin** in contrast to transcriptionally inactive, densely packed **heterochromatin.** Information stored in heterochromatin is not lost but is much less likely to be used in gene expression, much like the way information in a textbook is much less likely to be accessed if the book is packed away in a box in an attic. The packaging of DNA differs significantly from one cell type to another, and genomic sequence information aside from CpG islands gives only hints as to what a region's chromatin structure will be. Among those hints is what can be gleaned from isochore compartmentalization, which is described next.

Isochores

The genomes of vertebrates and plants (and perhaps of all eukaryotes) display evidence of a level of organization called **isochores** that is intermediate between that of genes and chromosomes. The working definition of isochores, "long regions of homogeneous base composition," has two operative parts. First, the genomic sequences of isochores are in excess of 1 million base pairs in length. Second, the GC content of an isochore is relatively uniform throughout (i.e., a sliding window of 1,000 bp moving across an isochore's entire length would have a GC content that rarely differed from the isochore's overall GC content by more than 1%), although it differs significantly as the transition is made from one isochore to the next.

Experiments performed on human chromosomes suggest that our genome is a mosaic (Figure 6.10) of five different classes of isochores: two that are poor in G's and C's (called L1 and L2 with 39% and 42% GC content on average, respectively) and three that are comparatively rich in G's and C's (called H1, H2, and H3 with 46%, 49%, and 54% GC content on average, respectively). The H (high density on buoyant density gradients) isochores of humans and other eukaryotes are particularly rich in genes and an excellent place for genome sequencing efforts to start. The GC-richest isochore, H3, for instance has at least 20 times the density of genes found in the AT-richest isochore, L1 (the lowest density on buoyant density gradients).

Perhaps even more interesting is the fact that the types of genes found in GC-rich and GC-poor isochores is also very different. Even though the human H3 isochore represents a relatively small fraction of our total genome (between 3% and 5%), it contains within it approximately 80% of all of our housekeeping genes. In contrast, the L1 and L2 isochores (together comprising about 66% of the human genome) contain about 85% of our tissue-specific genes. Isochore compartmentalization is also known to be associated with several other important features of eukaryotic genomes including methylation patterns and chromatin structure (GC-rich isochores tend to have low levels of methylation of their CpGs and to be stored as transcriptionally active euchromatin); means of regulating gene expression (GC-rich regions tend to have promoter sequence elements closer to the transcriptional start site); intron and gene length (GC-rich

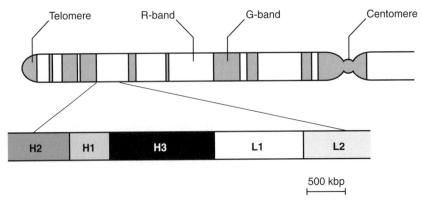

F I G U R E 6.10 *The isochore compartmentalization of the human genome. This schematic shows a portion of a metaphase human chromosome with a blowup showing the mosaic nature of its underlying isochores. Metaphase chromosomes are often treated with dyes like Giemsa to generate characteristic banding patterns such as the G-band (Giemsa staining) and R-band (reverse Giemsa staining) bands. The five putative isochores of the human genome (L1, L2, H1, H2, and H3) have each been assigned a different shade of gray according to their relative GC contents with the GC-poorest isochore (L1) being white and the GC-richest being black. Human chromosomes are essentially random assortments of long fragments from different isochores as shown. L1 regions from all chromosomes together comprise approximately half of all of the human genome.*

regions tend to have shorter introns and genes); the relative abundance of short and long repeated sequences described at the end of this chapter (SINEs tend to be found in GC-rich isochores while LINEs predominate in GC-poor isochores); and the relative frequency of amino acids used to make the proteins of different genes (genes in GC-rich isochores tend to use amino acids that correspond to triplet codons that are rich in G's and C's). All of these features and the correlations between them can provide important clues to gene recognition algorithms.

Codon Usage Bias

Every organism seems to prefer to use some equivalent triplet codons (i.e., they code for the same amino acid) over others. For example, across the entire yeast genome, the amino acid arginine is specified by the codon AGA 48% of the time even though the other five functionally equivalent codons for arginine (CGT, CGC, CGA, CGG, and AGG) are each used with lower, relatively equal frequencies (approximately 10% each). Fruit flies show a similar but distinctly different codon usage bias for arginine with the codon CGC (33%) being preferred to the five alternatives (occurring with a frequency of about 13% each). A complete set of codon usage biases determined from completed genome projects can be found on the web at http://www.kazusa.or.jp/codon/CUTG.html. Some of the biological basis for these preferences may be related to avoidance of codons that are similar to stop codons as well as a preference for codons that allow efficient translation because they correspond to particularly abundant tRNAs within the organism. Regardless of the reason for the preferences, codon usage bias can differ significantly between eukaryotic species, and real exons generally reflect those preferences whereas randomly chosen strings of triplets do not.

Gene Expression

Given all the uncertainties of gene recognition in eukaryotes, the true test of any gene prediction effort is still the laboratory-based demonstration that a living cell actually transcribes the region into an RNA molecule. In addition to providing final verification, **transcriptomes** (the complete set of an organism's RNA sequences) are also an extremely valuable tool for bioinformaticians interested in finding genes in the first place. Some useful DNA sequence features for eukaryotic gene recognition algorithms are as follows:

- Known promoter elements (i.e., TATA and CAAT boxes),
- CpG islands,
- Splicing signals associated with introns,
- Open reading frames with characteristic codon utilization, and
- Similarity to the sequences of ESTs or genes from other organisms.

Even when the nucleotide sequence of only some of an organism's RNA transcripts is known, that information can be used to greatly facilitate gene recognition efforts by simply employing a series of data searches and pairwise sequence alignments like those described in Chapter 2. However, it is important to not lose sight of the fact that an organism's ability to alter its pattern of gene expression in response to changes in its environment is central to the very idea of being alive. That alone justifies the substantial amount of effort that has been put into developing the methodologies described below that allow a determination of what portions of a genome are actually transcribed.

cDNAs and ESTs

cDNAs (short for complementary DNAs) represent convenient ways of isolating and manipulating those portions of a eukaryotic genome that are transcribed by RNA polymerase II. cDNAs are made from the RNA isolated from eukaryotic cells in the fairly simple process illustrated in Figure 6.11. The resulting double-stranded DNA copies of processed mRNAs can be cloned into vectors and maintained as a **cDNA library.** The mere fact that a region is transcribed makes it of special interest to molecular biologists, and even small fragments of sequence information from individual cDNAs are enough to provide useful **ESTs** (expressed sequence tags) that can be used in contig assembly (as in Figure 6.1) or for gene mapping and recognition. When cDNA sequences are complete they can also be

F I G U R E 6.11 *A commonly used method for preparing cDNAs from a diverse population of mRNAs. Twenty-nucleotide-long oligo(dT) primers specifically hybridize to the poly(A) tail of processed mRNAs and are used by an enzyme (reverse transcriptase) to synthesize a DNA copy. Ribonuclease H is then used to specifically degrade most of the RNA component of the resulting RNA–DNA hybrids. Some remaining portions of the original RNA are then used as primers for a DNA polymerase. The resulting double-stranded DNA molecules can then be cloned into a vector and maintained as a cDNA library.*

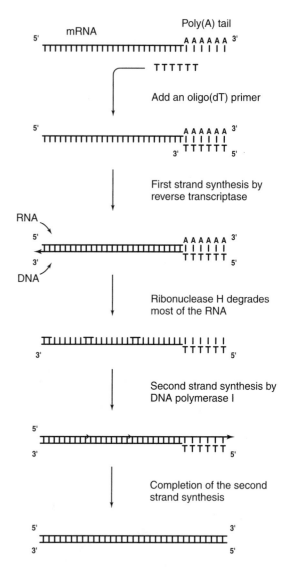

compared to genomic sequences to provide unambiguous evidence of exon–intron boundaries.

Because a cell's mRNAs are derived from protein-coding genes, cDNAs give invaluable insights into both the population of genes being expressed at any given time as well as the mRNA's relative abundance. One means of assaying the complexity of the mRNA pool within a cell involves reassociation kinetics much like the $C_0t_{1/2}$ analyses described in Chapter 1. In essence, an excess amount of RNA from a cell is allowed to hybridize with cDNA copies prepared from the same organism. The resulting $R_0t_{1/2}$ **values** (where R_0 is the starting concentration of RNA) typically indicate that, just like genomic DNA, RNA populations appear to have three components that differ in terms of their relative abundances. For instance, $R_0t_{1/2}$ analyses of chicken oviducts suggest that each cell contains roughly 100,000 copies of the ovalbumin mRNA (50% of all mRNA; $R_0t_{1/2}$ = 0.0015), 4,000 copies of 8 other mRNAs (15% of all mRNA; $R_0t_{1/2}$ = 0.04), and between 1 and 5 copies of 13,000 additional scarce mRNAs (35% of all mRNA; $R_0t_{1/2}$ = 30). In general, about 50% of the mRNA mass within a cell is found exclusively in that specific tissue (i.e., ovalbumin is expressed only in oviducts). Other, more sensitive methods such as those described below are needed to determine the extent of overlap of scarce mRNAs between different tissues.

Serial Analysis of Gene Expression

Determining the nucleotide sequence of every cDNA obtained from a single cell would certainly provide more detailed information about the expression patterns of eukaryotic genes. Sequencing several hundred thousand clones per cell (each with average lengths of over 1,000 bp) represents an impractical objective despite advances in high-throughput automated DNA sequencing. A sensitive alternative is **serial analysis of gene expression (SAGE).** In SAGE, cDNAs are made from a cell; the cDNAs are broken into small fragments (typically with restriction enzymes as described in Chapter 1) between 10 and 14 nucleotides long; and hundreds of those fragments are then randomly ligated (linked) into longer DNA molecules that are cloned and sequenced. Computers are then used to recognize the original small fragments in hundreds of clones by considering the recognition sequences of the restriction enzymes that were used as well as through comparisons to the sequences of known transcripts from the organism. The number of times that a tag from any particular transcript is observed should reflect the relative abundance of the corresponding transcript in the original cDNA pool.

Although computationally intensive, this approach has confirmed much of what was learned from the original $R_0t_{1/2}$ experiments. It has also provided important new details such as the fact that roughly 75% of the genes expressed in chicken liver and oviduct are the same. Specifically, approximately 12,000 genes are expressed in both liver and oviduct, about 5,000 additional genes are expressed only in liver, and a different set of 3,000 transcripts is found only in oviduct. Experiments using mammalian cells and tissues yield similar results and indicate that a set of roughly 10,000 housekeeping genes is constitutively expressed and codes for proteins whose functions are needed by every cell in an organism.

Microarrays

As mentioned in Chapter 1, a variant on the membrane-based Southern hybridization approach known as **microarrays** (Figure 6.12) is now routinely providing even more sensitive and detailed information about gene expression patterns than even the SAGE methodology allows. The small silica (glass) chips used in this approach are literally covered with thousands or tens of thousands of

(a)

Signal

(b)

①   PM   2091
     MM

②   PM   19383
     MM

③   PM   21719
     MM

F I G U R E 6.12 *"Gene chip" microarray analyses allow changes in gene expression to be sensitively measured for very large numbers of genes. (a) An Affymetrix U95Aver2 GeneChip containing 12,625 rat genes represented as sets of 16 probe pairs. Each "cell" or spot contains a 25-mer oligonucleotide. The intensity of signal in each probe cell is proportional to the amount of hybridized, biotin-labeled cDNA bound to it. (b) Expression levels of a single gene from three different U95Aver2 GeneChips. The relative expression of this gene is represented by the signal value that is calculated using the intensities of the 16 probe pairs. PM, probe cells containing oligonucleotides that are "perfect matches" to the gene; MM, probe cells containing oligonucleotides with mismatches in the central nucleotide of the 25-mer. Conditions 2 and 3 result in an elevation in this gene's expression relative to condition 1. (Images kindly provided by Dr. Steven Berberich, Wright State University.)*

relatively short nucleotides of known sequence. In the case of one set of commercially available high-density oligonucleotide arrays (HDAs), expression patterns associated with 6,181 ORFs in the yeast genome can be analyzed simultaneously.

Each microarray chip is fabricated by high-speed robotics and has 20 spots containing 25-nucleotide-long probes (at a density of as many as 500,000 spots per 1.25 cm² with some chips containing more than 1 million) that can perfectly base pair with complementary nucleotides in each of the 6,181 expected transcripts. Each HDA also includes 20 spots that contain 25-mers that differ from the perfectly matching oligonucleotide at just one position. Target sequences for each gene are duplicated many times at many different places in each gene as a method of detecting errors.

An advantage to using small targets of 25 nucleotides is the ability to be very sensitive to hybridization conditions such that a single nucleotide change results in failure of the probe to bind to the target. Alternative chips with much longer targets (i.e., 250 nucleotides) can hybridize with smaller amounts of probe but are less sensitive to mismatches (MMs). At the most superficial level, the expression level of any gene is determined by subtracting the average amount of fluorescently labeled cDNA bound to the mismatch oligos from the average amount bound to its perfect match (PM) partner. The results are typically displayed as a grid in which every square represents a particular gene and relative levels (or changes) in expression are indicated by a color or gray scales such as those shown in Figure 6.12.

Gene expression profiling (sometimes also referred to as transcriptional profiling) has been applied to a wide variety of important biological problems including mapping of metabolic pathways, tissue typing, environmental monitoring, and answering a wide range of questions pertaining to medical diagnosis of disease states. Extremely large amounts of gene expression data that allow comparisons of gene expression patterns in diseased and normal states as well as between tissue types are maintained at web sites such as http://www.ncbi.nlm.nih.gov/UniGene/ddd.cgi?ORG=Hs.

In one recent application, gene expression patterns were used to distinguish between two frequently misdiagnosed lymphomas (diffuse large B-cell versus follicular). Microarrays with probes for 6,817 different human genes indicated that significant differences in expression at 30 genes existed between the two types of tumors. Considered together, the expression patterns of these 30 genes allowed correct classification of 71 of 77 tumors (91%)—a substantial improvement over alternative cytological indicators. Such improvements in diagnosis can be vitally important especially when treatment regimens are significantly different (as they are for these lymphomas).

The medical applications of gene expression profiling do not necessarily end with diagnosis either. In the case of the 58 patients with large B-cell lymphomas in the previous study, changes in gene expression patterns in response to treatment were also evaluated. A supervised machine learning prediction method was applied to the resulting data and was able to categorize treated patients into two categories with very different 5-year overall survival rates (70% versus 12%) with a high degree of confidence ($p = 0.00004$). The implications should be clear: The sooner it can be determined that a patient has not responded to a treatment, the sooner a new treatment can be attempted and the greater the likelihood for a positive outcome. Analyses such as these suggest that there is great promise for the development of much more individualized treatments than those that are currently available. The relatively new field of **pharmacogenomics** hopes to maximize the efficacy (and minimize the unwanted side effects) of treatments in just such a way using information about individuals' genetic makeup as well as how their gene expression patterns change in response to different therapies.

Transposition

As mentioned earlier in this chapter, prokaryotic genomes are exceptionally streamlined in terms of their information content. Even still, DNA transposons that are often present in multiple copies and often quite dispensable to their host represent an important component of bacterial genome anatomy. A single *E. coli* genome, for example, may contain as many as 20 different **insertion sequences** (ISs). Most of the sequence of an IS is dedicated to one or two genes that code for a transposase enzyme that catalyzes its transposition from one part of the genome to another in a conservative (the number of copies of the repeat does not change) or replicative (the copy number increases) fashion. Other kinds of bacterial transposons include composite transposons (pairs of IS elements that facilitate the transposition and sometimes the horizontal transfer of genes), Tn3-type transposons (which always transpose replicatively), and transposable phages (viruses that transpose replicatively as part of their normal infection cycle). The DNA transposons of prokaryotes are often distributed randomly throughout the genome, and their presence (let alone their position) is usually sufficiently variable to allow reliable distinctions to be made between strains of the same species.

It should not be surprising that eukaryotic genomes, with their abundance of noncoding and apparently dispensable DNA, also have DNA transposons, although current estimates suggest that there are fewer than 1,000 DNA transposon sequences in the human genome. Well-studied examples of eukaryotic transposons include the *Ac/Ds* elements of maize made famous by B. McClintock in the 1950s. Another important eukaryotic transposon is the 1,250-bp-long *mariner*, which was originally found in fruit flies but has since been discovered in a variety of eukaryotes including humans (suggesting that it might be a promising vehicle for both natural and engineered horizontal gene transfers between eukaryotic organisms). Much more common in eukaryotes though are transposons that are propagated by RNA intermediates known as **retrotransposons,** which are described below.

Repetitive Elements

DNA transposons present in multiple copies within a prokaryotic or eukaryotic genome qualify as "repeated DNA" or repetitive sequence elements. While uncommon in prokaryotes, repetitive elements that do not propagate through the action of a transposase make up a very large fraction of the genomes of the most complex eukaryotes. Those repeated sequences are typically divided into two categories that differ in their mode of propagation: tandemly repeated DNA and repeats that are interspersed throughout a genome.

Tandemly repeated (head to tail repeats such as 5'-CACACACA-3' where the repeat unit 5'-CA-3' is repeated four times) DNA can itself be subdivided into two categories: (1) satellite DNA and (2) mini/microsatellites. **Satellite DNA** gets its name from the fact that its very simple sequences with skewed nucleotide compositions give rise to DNA fragments with unusual densities relative to other genomic DNA. Buoyant density gradients can be used to separate human genomic DNA into four bands with different densities: one main band with an overall GC content of about 40.3% G+C and three lower density "satellite" bands above it. The repeating DNA sequences that give rise to these bands range in length from 5 to 200 bp in different eukaryotes and are typically present in millions of copies. Although some satellite DNA is scattered throughout eukaryotic genomes, most is located in the centromeres. Their very simple sequences are no more capable of containing useful information than a string of 997 repetitions of the word "really" in a student's 1,000-word-long report that says a book was *really* good.

Minisatellites and **microsatellites** are typically not abundant or long enough to give rise to their own bands on buoyant density gradients. Minisatellites form clusters up to 20,000 bp in length and have many tandem copies of sequences not more than 25 bp in length. The term *microsatellite* is typically used to describe clusters of shorter repeated sequences (usually four or fewer nucleotides in a row) that usually span less than 150 bp overall. Although microsatellites are relatively short, there are usually many of them fairly evenly distributed across a complex eukaryote's genome. In humans, for example, microsatellites with a CA repeat such as 5'-CACACACACACA-3' occur approximately once every 10,000 bp and make up 0.5% of the whole genome (15 Mb in all). Single base pair repeats (i.e., 5'-AAAAAAAA-3') make up another 0.3% of the human genome. DNA polymerases apparently lose their place during replication of these simple sequences and give rise to longer and shorter versions quite frequently. The resulting high level of variability in the lengths of microsatellites from one individual to another has made them useful genetic markers to geneticists (as well as to forensic scientists and for paternity/maternity testing).

Many repeated sequences within eukaryotic genomes appear to be scattered fairly randomly across a genome rather than being tandemly clustered together as is the case for satellites and mini/microsatellites. This other kind of repeated sequence appears to be propagated by the synthesis of an RNA intermediate in a process called **retrotransposition.** The basic mechanism involves three steps: (1) An RNA copy of the transposon is transcribed by an RNA polymerase just like a normal gene, (2) the RNA copy is converted into a DNA molecule by a special enzyme called reverse transcriptase, and (3) the reverse transcriptase inserts the DNA copy of the transposon into another site elsewhere in the genome.

The reverse transcriptase required for this process does not seem to be part of the normal complement of genes in a eukaryotic genome but rather to be acquired from infecting (or stranded) retroviruses (viruses like the one responsible for AIDs in humans where the genome is stored as RNA rather than DNA). Very common kinds of **retroposons** within mammalian genomes are **LINEs** (long interspersed nuclear elements) and **SINEs** (short interspersed nuclear elements). LINEs are likely to be stranded retroviruses and contain a reverse transcriptase-like gene that is essential for the propagation of both themselves and SINEs. Human L1 repeats are a classic example of LINEs in that full-length repeats are 6,100 bp long and present in approximately 3,500 copies scattered throughout the human genome. Full-length L1 repeats as well as hundreds of thousands of truncated fragments comprise a total of approximately 5% of every mammalian genome.

Each mammalian order (i.e., primates, rodents, artiodactyls) has its own, independently derived SINE. The human genome's *Alu* repeat is a good example in that it is has an average length of 258 bp and is present in more than 1,000,000 copies scattered across the human genome. Even though SINEs comprise up to 10% of some mammalian genomes, they are often considered the epitome of "junk DNA" since they are generally not associated with functionally constrained sequences. The term "junk DNA" is one that must be used with caution, however, in that many sequences that have been relegated to that category have subsequently been found to simply have been playing previously unappreciated roles. Regardless, from a bioinformatics perspective, many genome analyzing algorithms (including database search programs) begin by "masking" known repeated sequences such as SINEs and LINEs because they are known to have little useful information content for gene recognition or typical comparisons between sequences.

Eukaryotic Gene Density

The C-value paradox described in Chapter 1 made clear that much of a eukaryote's genome is dispensable decades before molecular biologists began to seriously contemplate determining the nucleotide sequence of complete genomes. The human genome project alone has amply confirmed that observation. Of the 3,000 Mb in the human genome, not more than 90 Mb (3%) corresponds to coding sequences, and approximately 810 Mb (27%) are associated sequences such as introns, promoters, and pseudogenes. The remaining 2,100 Mb (70%) of the human genome can be divided into two different kinds of "junk" that is under little or no selective constraint: unique sequences (1,680 Mb or 56%) and repetitive DNA (420 Mb or 14%). In short, genes are definitely "far between" even in gene-rich regions such as the H3 isochores in the most complex eukaryotes where there seems to be little evolutionary pressure to rein in genome size. The average distance *between* human genes is in the range of 65,000 bp (given a genome size of 3 billion bp and a total of about 45,000 genes)—in the ballpark of 10% of the *total* genome size of a simple prokaryote like *M. genitalium*. To someone who is illiterate, only the pictures within an encyclopedia have useful information content. It is possible that all the sequences between the genes whose functions we recognize may one day take on a greater significance to us in much the same way that letters and punctuation between pictures becomes more important as one learns to read.

Mutational analyses (such as genetically engineered "knockout" organisms) are making it increasingly clear that many genes code for proteins that are responsible for multiple (often unsuspected) functions. Genomic sequence analyses are also suggesting that many genes are present in multiple, redundant copies of subtle variants—in humans, perhaps as many as an average of three to four genes for every function. Less complex eukaryotes tend to have higher densities of genes on their chromosomes than more complex organisms like vertebrates. The yeast genome, for instance, has an average ORF length of approximately 1,400 bp with an average separation of roughly 600 bp.

Chapter Summary

Gene recognition in prokaryotes is comparatively simple and can rely heavily on searches for statistically significant, long open reading frames. Prokaryotic genomes are characterized by a notably high density of information content and, as a rule, are fairly easy to analyze. Eukaryotic genomes with their very low density of information and prodigious sizes represent a striking contrast. Eukaryotic gene recognition software must consider a wide variety of different features when looking for genes. These features include adherence to codon usage biases within an ORF; the presence of an upstream CpG island complete with other promoter sequences; and splice junctions and internal branch sites that are good matches to the consensus sequences for introns. Unfortunately, the rules associated with all of these features are cluttered with common exceptions and often vary from one organism to another and even from one genomic or cell-type context to another. The best gene recognition algorithms to date take advantage of all of these features as well as others but are still plagued with high rates of both false positives and negatives. Recent increases in both the number and types of sequences used for training and evaluation coupled with additional data (i.e., knowing in advance the sequences of most if not all of an organism's mRNAs) should provide the basis for significant improvements in the years to come.

Readings for Greater Depth

Deciphering the evolutionary history of prokaryotic genes and genomes often requires an appreciation of their GC content such as that described in J. G. Lawrence and H. Ochman, 1998, Molecular archaeology of the *Escherichia coli* genome, *Proc. Nat. Acad. Sci. U.S.A.* **95**: 9413.

There has been much speculation regarding the minimum number of genes required for a free-living organism such as that presented in A. R. Mushegian and E. V. Koonin, 1996, A minimal gene set for cellular life derived by comparison of complete bacterial genomes, *Proc. Nat. Acad. Sci. U.S.A.* **93**: 10,268–10,273.

The process of initiation of transcription by RNA polymerase II in eukaryotes is described in careful detail in R. G. Roeder, 1996, The role of initiation factors in transcription by RNA polymerase II. *Trends Biochem. Sci.* **21**: 327–335. It is also reviewed in A. Ishihama, 2000, Functional modulation of *Escherichia coli* RNA polymerase, *Annu. Rev. Microbiol.* **54**: 499–518.

A comprehensive review of isochores and the many important features associated with them is provided by the founder of this field of research in G. Bernardi, 1995, The human genome: Organization and evolutionary history. *Ann. Rev. Genet.* **29:** 445–476.

A general review of the applications of computer-based studies in genome sequence analyses can be found in T. F. Smith, 1998, Functional genomics—Bioinformatics is ready for the challenge, *Trends Genet.* **14:** 291–293.

Determining the sequence of a genome is just the start of the process of understanding how an organism uses its information content. The first steps in the functional analysis of the yeast genome are described in S. G. Oliver, M. K. Winson, D. B. Kell, and F. Baganz, 1998, Systematic functional analysis of the yeast genome, *Trends Biotechnol.* **16:** 373–378.

Questions and Problems

* **6.1** Use Figure 6.3b to determine at how many sites within the –35 and –10 promoter regions of the Lac operon's promoter there are differences relative to the consensus sequence for σ^{70} promoters. How should those nucleotides be changed if you were interested in increasing the levels of expression of the operon within *E. coli*?

6.2 The promoter of a predicted *E. coli* gene is found to contain the following nucleotide sequence:

```
5'-ACTGGACCCTTGAAGGCGACGTCGGCCTACCCGATCTCCACTGTATGGATCCGGA-3'
```

What can you infer about the circumstances under which the gene is most likely to be expressed?

* **6.3** Suggest two different experimental strategies that might be used to generate the sequence data that would connect the two contigs illustrated in Figure 6.1 into a single, longer contig.

6.4 Find the longest stretch of nucleotides in the following single-stranded RNA sequence that would be able to form a hairpin loop such as the one shown in Figure 6.4.

```
5'-GGGCGCGAAUAUCCCGGAGUCCGUAUGACCCCAUGCGGACUACGGGAUAUUCA-3'
```

* **6.5** What three nucleotide substitutions to the nucleotide sequence in Question 6.4 would allow it to form a more stable secondary structure? Assume that G/C base pairs are more energetically stable than A/T base pairs and that the phosphodiester backbone of DNA requires at least four nucleotides to be in the "looped" portion of a hairpin loop. Explain your choices.

6.6 Assuming that all codons and nucleotides occur with the same frequency, what is the probability that a stretch of 316 codons does not contain a single stop codon simply by chance? How large does an ORF need to be to achieve a statistical significance of 1%?

* **6.7** In which prokaryotic RNA polymerase subunit would you expect to find mutations that confer resistance to antibiotic drugs that are structurally similar to nucleotides?

6.8 How do the RNA polymerases of prokaryotes and eukaryotes differ?

* **6.9** How many of the nucleotides in the following sequence of a human gene's promoter are likely to be methylated in a tissue where the gene is transcriptionally inactive? Active?

```
5'-GGGCGCGAATATCCCGGAGTCCGTATGACCTACATATTCATGATCGCTAGCC-3'
3'-CCCGCGCTTATAGGGCCTCAGGCATACTGGATGTATAAGTACTACGGATCGG-5'
```

6.10 Using the information in Table 6.5, what transcription factors are likely to bind to the promoter sequence given in Question 6.9? What can you conclude about the expression pattern of the associated gene?

* **6.11** The length of the primary transcript of the human dystrophin gene is roughly four times larger than the entire genome of some prokaryotes (i.e., *M. genitalium*). Compare the fraction of those two sequences that correspond to coding information that is actually used by ribosomes.

6.12 Into how many different mRNAs can an hnRNA be processed if it has three exons and if all its 5' splice junctions can be used with any downstream 3' splice junction? Diagram the information content of each mRNA.

* **6.13** Using the genetic code shown in Table 1.1, determine how many of the 20 amino acids could not be present at a position in a protein that corresponds to where an intron had been spliced out of an hnRNA.

6.14 Using Entrez on the NCBI home page (http://www.ncbi.nlm.nih.gov/Entrez/), find an entry that includes the sequence of one of the genes mentioned in this chapter. (*Note:* You should obtain the genomic sequence, not one that corresponds to an mRNA.) Print the corresponding GenBank file. Use the file's annotations to identify as many gene features as possible (i.e., transcriptional start site, polyadenylation signal, exons and introns) and mark those features on the sequence portion of the file. Make a scale diagram of the gene using the style shown in Figure 6.2 with open boxes being used to represent intron sequences and filled boxes to represent exons.

* **6.15** Given that *Arabidopsis thaliana* genes use the codon GUU three times more frequently than any of the three alternative codons for the amino acid valine, find the reading frame in the *A. thaliana* sequence below that is most likely to correspond to the one used by ribosomes during translation of the corresponding mRNA. Use ORF lengths and codon usage biases to explain your answer.

```
5'-GAGCGGAAGUGUUCGAUGUACUGUUCCAGUCAUGUGUUCACC-3'
```

Protein and RNA Structure Prediction

What a piece of work is man! How noble in reason! how infinite in faculties! in form and moving, how express and admirable!

Hamlet, Act II, scene ii

Amino Acids

Polypeptide Composition

Secondary Structure
Backbone flexibility, ϕ and ψ
Accuracy of predictions
The Chou-Fasman and GOR methods

Tertiary and Quaternary Structure
Hydrophobicity
Disulfide bonds
Active structures vs. most stable structures

Algorithms for Modeling Protein Folding
Lattice models
Off-lattice models
Energy functions and optimization

Structure Prediction
Comparative modeling
Threading: Reverse protein folding

Predicting RNA Secondary Structures

Proteins are the molecular machinery that regulates and executes nearly every biological function. Structural proteins, such as collagen, support and strengthen our connective tissues; mechanoenzymes, such as myosin in skeletal muscle, provide movement on both microscopic and macroscopic scales; other enzymes catalyze chemical reactions of all kinds, enabling and controlling digestion and metabolism, the immune system, reproduction, and a staggering array of other functions. Protein interactions with DNA and RNA enable the production of new proteins, and regulate their levels, responding as appropriate to internal and external environmental changes. One of the foremost tasks of molecular biology is to further the understanding of the relationships between the various genes in an organism's genome and the proteins they encode.

Proteins are synthesized as linear chains of amino acids, but they quickly fold into a compact, globular form *in vivo*. In his seminal work in the late 1960s, C. Anfinsen first demonstrated that unfolded, or **denatured,** proteins repeatedly assume the same conformation when allowed to refold. This **native structure** is essential for biological function. Only when folded into their native globular structure are most proteins fully biologically active. Understanding the forces that drive protein folding is perhaps the most significant unanswered question in biochemistry. No algorithm currently exists that will consistently predict the three-dimensional shape of a protein. The ramifications of such an algorithm would be so significant to molecular biology that the problem is considered a "grand challenge" problem—one of the most important problems to be addressed by contemporary computer science.

Amino Acids

Amino acids are the building blocks of proteins. Like DNA and RNA, proteins are synthesized as linear polymers (chains) composed of smaller molecules. Unlike DNA and RNA, in which there are four nucleotides from which to choose, proteins are constructed from 20 amino acids with a variety of sizes, shapes, and chemical properties.

Each amino acid has a **backbone** consisting of an amide ($—NH_2$) group, an **alpha carbon,** and a carboxylic acid, or carboxylate ($—COOH$) group. To the alpha carbon, a **side chain** (often denoted —R) is attached, as shown in Figure 7.1. The side chains vary with each amino acid, and these various side chains confer unique stereochemical properties on each amino acid.

The amino acids are often grouped into three categories. The **hydrophobic amino acids,** which have side chains composed mostly or entirely of carbon and hydrogen, are unlikely to form hydrogen bonds with water molecules. The **polar amino acids,** which often contain oxygen and/or nitrogen in their side chains, form hydrogen bonds with water much more readily. Finally, the **charged amino acids** carry a positive or negative charge at biological pH. Figure 7.2 shows the primary amino acid sequence of the prokaryotic protein superoxide dismutase.

FIGURE 7.1 *The structure of an amino acid. The side chain, represented as R, distinguishes the different amino acids. The backbone atoms are constant for all 20 amino acids.*

(a)

```
DEFINITION      P.leiognathi bacteriocuprein superoxide dismutase gene, complete cds.
ACCESSION       J02658
SOURCE          P.leiognathi (ATCC 25521) DNA, clone pPhB-2.
BASE COUNT         277 a      140 c       179 g       245 t
ORIGIN          256 bp upstream of BglII site.
        1 agtaaaaatt tagcaattaa gtagtgttga tgaaatggta agagtaaaaa gtacacacgc
       61 tatgggatta atcttcttag cgaatgtttg agatattatc gataactata atcgtaaata
      121 tcagctatac cttttgtta aaagcatgtt taatgcctgt ggaaaataaa aacaataagg
      181 ataaaatatg aacaaggcaa aaacgttact cttcaccgct ctagctttg gtttatctca
      241 ccaagcgtta gcacaagatc tcacggttaa aatgaccgat ctacaaacag gtaagcctgt
      301 tggtacgatt gaactaagcc aaaataaata cggagtagta tttacacctg aactggcaga
      361 tttaacaccg gggatgcatg gcttccatat tcatcaaaat ggtagctgtg cttcatcaga
      421 aaaagacggc aaagttgttt taggtggcgc tgctggtgga cattacgatc ctgagcacac
      481 aaataaacac ggtttcccat ggactgatga taatcataaa ggtgatctgc cagcactgtt
      541 tgtgagtgca aatggtttag caactaaccc tgtttagcg ccacgtttaa cgttgaaaga
      601 actaaaaggt cacgcaatta tgatccatgc tggtggtgat aatcactctg atatgccaaa
      661 agcattaggt ggcggcggcg cacgtgtggc gtgtggtgtg atccaataat ttagtgagaa
      721 ccagcagcga atttgtcgct gttggtttta ttttaatcag attaagtttt ttagaaacag
      781 ccagttaatt gtaaaatatg taaaaatgtg aaattcaggt gaatttgaaa tcttctctta
      841 a
```

(b)

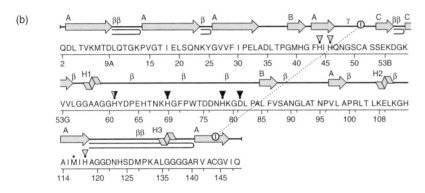

Active sites: ▽ CU   ▼ ZN   Residue interactions: • with metal

(c)

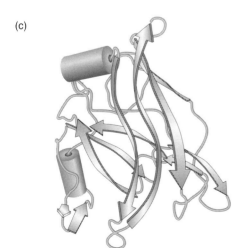

F I G U R E 7.2 *(a) Excerpts from the genbank entry for the Photobacterium leiognathi bacteriocuprein superoxide dismutase gene (accession #J02658). (b) The primary and secondary structure for the corresponding protein (arrows and coils represent the positions of beta strands and helical regions, respectively. (c) The tertiary structure of the protein (PDB entry 1BZO, rendered using VMD molecular graphics software [Humphrey, W. Dalke, A. and Schulten, K., "VMD—Visual Molecular Dynamics", J. Molec. Graphics 1996, 14(1), 33–38, www.ks.uiuc.edu/Research/vmd]).*

BOX 7.1	pH, pKa, and pI

A very important concept in chemistry and biology both is that of concentration: a measure of how much of a solute is dissolved in a solvent. At the heart of the idea of concentration is the ratio of molecules of solute to solvent. The molecular weight (essentially the sum total of all the protons and neutrons of a componound) of NaCl is 58. By definition, in 58 grams of NaCl there is 1 *mole* of NaCl. The actual number of molecules in a mole is 6.02×10^{23}. As a result, the number of molecules in 58 g of NaCl is the same as the number of molecules of NaOH in 40 g (because the molecular weight of NaOH is 40). A solution that has 1 mole suspended in 1 liter is said to be 1 *molar* (or *M*).

It is important to remember that water is a molecule whose atoms have notably different electronegativities. Occasionally, the oxygen atoms in water actually strip away one of the hydrogen's electrons and an ionic situation results. In other words, H_2O becomes H+ and OH–. About 1 molecule in 554 million water molecules has disassociated in this way in a bottle of pure water. What concentration does that correspond to? 1×10^{-7} molar (or

moles/liter of water). Although this dissociation is rare and is reversible, it is of great biological importance because the H+ and OH– are very reactive. As a result, the concentration of hydrogen ions has a special name and unit of measure: **pH,** where p stands for the negative of the log of the molar concentration. A solution of pure water where the concentration is 1×10^{-7} moles/liter is said to be pH 7 (or neutral).

Because living organisms are water-based systems, pH plays a role in nearly every biological reaction. Simply put, pH is a measure of the concentration of unassociated protons in a solution. When H+ ion concentrations are high, OH– concentrations are low because free OH– ions have more opportunities to reassociate with the abundant H+ ions. By the same token, when H+ ion concentrations are low, OH– concentrations are high because free OH– ions have fewer opportunities to reassociate with H+ ions. Acidic solutions, which contain relatively large concentrations of free protons, have lower pH values, while basic solutions, which contain few free protons, have higher pH. The value of pH typically ranges from 0 (very acidic) to 14 (very basic). The environ-

The order of the amino acids in a protein's primary sequence plays an important role in determining its secondary structure and, ultimately, its tertiary structure. It is worthwhile for the aspiring bioinformatician to study the structure and properties of each amino acid carefully, since the properties of these small molecules provide proteins with both their structure and their biological function.

Polypeptide Composition

A chain of several amino acids is referred to as a **peptide.** Longer chains are often called **polypeptides** or proteins. When two amino acids are covalently joined,

ment inside of a cell is generally close to neutral (pH = 7).

Just like water, many of the amino acid side chains have dissociable protons (essentially hydrogen atoms). For example, the carboxylic acid group of aspartic acid can exist in a protonated (OH) or deprotonated (O⁻) state, depending on the pH (i.e., the availability of free H⁺ ions) of its environment. The **pKa** of an amino acid is a measure of the relative ease with which it releases its dissociable protons. When the pH of the solution is equal to the pKa of an amino acid, approximately half of the residues will be protonated and half will dissociate (release their protons). At one pH unit lower than the pKa of an amino acid, that

amino acid will be approximately 90% protonated. At two pH units lower than the pKa of an amino acid, the amino acid will be approximately 99% protonated. For example, almost all aspartic acid (pKa = 4.3) amino acids within a polypeptide are deprotonated (negatively charged) at neutral pH (7.0) but only about half have a charge associated with them at the acidic pH of 4.3.

When the protons of an amino acid's side chain become dissociated, the amino acid becomes charged, having lost a proton, but no electrons. The more deprotonated a protein becomes, the more negative charge it accumulates. Likewise, as more residues become protonated, more positive charge is accumulated. The **isoelectric point (pI)** of a protein is the pH at which the net charge of the protein is neutral. Isoelectric points can reveal some valuable general information about the amino acid composition of a protein. For example, a protein with a greater amount of acidic amino acids than basic amino acids will have a pI of much less than 7. If the opposite is true, the pI will be much greater than 7. Human pepsin, a digestive enzyme, is very rich in glutamic and aspartic acids and has a pI of 1.2.

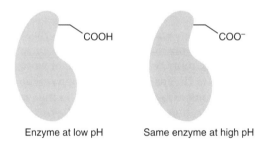

| Enzyme at low pH | Same enzyme at high pH |

Protonation of a carboxylate group.

one of the amino acids loses a hydrogen (H⁺) from its amine group, while the other loses an oxygen and a hydrogen (OH⁻) from its carboxylate group, forming a carbonyl (C=O) group (and water, H₂O). The result is a **dipeptide**—two amino acids joined by a **peptide bond**—and a single water molecule, as shown in Figure 7.3. In a polypeptide, the amino acids are sometimes referred to as amino acid **residues,** because some atoms of the original amino acid are lost as water in the formation of the peptide bonds.

Like DNA and RNA molecules, polypeptides have a specific directionality. The **amino terminus** (or N terminus) of the polypeptide has an unbonded amide group, while the **carboxy terminus** (or C terminus) ends in a carboxylic acid group instead of a carbonyl. Protein sequences are usually considered to start at the N terminus and progress toward the C terminus.

F I G U R E 7.3 *Two amino acids are joined by dehydration synthesis (meaning a water molecule is released) to form a dipeptide.*

The sequence of amino acids that comprise a protein completely determines its three-dimensional shape, its physical and chemical properties, and ultimately its biological function. This sequence is called the **primary structure** of the protein. It is worthwhile to learn the one-letter codes for each amino acid (see Figure 7.2), because these codes allow protein sequences to be expressed as a string of characters, much like nucleotide sequences.

Secondary Structure
Backbone Flexibility, ϕ and ψ

The non-side-chain atoms of the amino acids in a polypeptide chain form the **protein backbone.** As noted in Chapter 1, the bond lengths and planar bond angles of the covalent bonds in the backbone are more or less fixed. In other words, the peptide group is rigid and planar—the two bonds between the alpha carbon (C_α) and the other backbone atoms are the only two rotatable bonds in the protein backbone. All flexibility in the protein backbone is derived from the rotation of these two bonds. The angle of rotation about the bond between the amide nitrogen and the alpha carbon is referred to as ϕ (phi), while the angle of rotation about the bond between the alpha carbon and the carbonyl carbon is called ψ (psi).

The backbone conformation of an entire protein can be specified in terms of the phi and psi angles of each amino acid, as shown in Figure 7.4. Not all values of phi and psi are physically realizable. Some phi/psi combinations result in a **steric collision** (physical overlap of the space occupied by atoms) between the side-chain atoms of one residue and the backbone of the next. The Ramachandran plot (Figure 7.5 on page 162) illustrates the allowable values for phi and psi for nonglycine residues. Because of their lack of a side chain (other than hydrogen), glycine residues have a much greater range of allowable phi and psi angles than most other residues.

As described in Chapter 1, most protein backbones contain elements of secondary structure, including alpha helices ($\phi \approx \psi \approx -60°$), and beta strands ($\phi \approx -135°$ and $\psi \approx 135°$), which associate with other beta strands to form parallel or anti-parallel beta sheets. Given a protein sequence (or primary structure), the first step in predicting the three-dimensional shape of the protein is determining what regions of the backbone are likely to form helices, strands, and **beta turns**—the

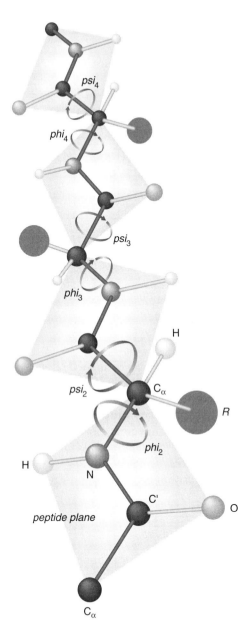

F I G U R E 7.4 *Rotation about the C_α bonds are the only degrees of conformational freedom available to the protein backbone. The structure of the peptide bond forces the rest of the backbone atoms into a rigid planar configuration.*

U-turn-like structures formed when a beta strand reverses direction in an anti-parallel beta sheet.

Accuracy of Predictions

Secondary structure prediction algorithms use a variety of computational techniques including neural networks, discrete-state models, hidden Markov models, nearest neighbor classification, and evolutionary computation. Most current

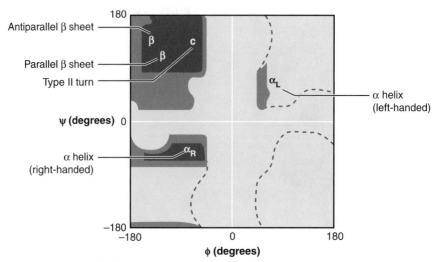

F I G U R E 7.5 *The Ramachandran plot shows the values of phi and psi that are physically realizable without causing steric clash (dark regions). Additional conformations can be achieved by glycine due to its small side chain (light regions).*

secondary structure prediction algorithms begin with a set of aligned sequences produced with algorithms such as BLAST, FASTA, and CLUSTALW. Using these aligned sequences, the degree of conservation of each of the amino acids in the target sequence (the sequence for which the secondary structure is being predicted) is calculated. With a protein sequence and the corresponding conservation levels as input, modern secondary structure prediction algorithms, such as PHD and Predator, can obtain accuracies in the range of 70% to 75%. Output from a secondary structure prediction algorithm is generally similar to the following:

```
APAFSVSPASGASDGQSVSVSVAAAGETYYIAQCAPVGGQDACNPAT
---------HHHHHHH-HHHhhh---EEEEEeee---EEEEee----
```

In this case, H and h represent predictions of helical conformation (with strong and weak confidence, respectively), while E and e represent predictions of extended (beta-strand) conformation.

The Chou-Fasman and GOR Methods

The Chou-Fasman method takes a straightforward statistical approach to predicting secondary structure. Each amino acid is assigned several **conformational parameters**, $P(a)$, $P(b)$, and P(turn). These parameters, representing the propensity of each amino acid to participate in alpha helices, beta sheets, and beta turns, respectively, were determined based on observed frequencies in a set of sample proteins of known structure. In addition, each amino acid is assigned four turn parameters, $f(i)$, $f(i+1)$, $f(i+2)$, and $f(i+3)$, corresponding to the frequency with which the amino acid was observed in the first, second, third, or fourth position of a hairpin turn. The resulting table of **Chou-Fasman parameters** is shown in Table 7.1.

Using the Chou-Fasman parameters, the algorithm for assigning secondary structure proceeds as follows:

1. Identify alpha helices as follows:
   a. Find all regions where four of six contiguous amino acid residues have $P(a) > 100$.
   b. For each region identified in part (a), extend the region in both directions until a set of four contiguous residues with $P(a) < 100$ is encountered.
   c. For each region extended in part (b), compute $\Sigma P(a)$, the sum of $P(a)$ values for each residue in the region, and $\Sigma P(b)$. If the region is >5 residues in length, and $\Sigma P(a) > \Sigma P(b)$, then the region is predicted to be an alpha helix.

2. Identify beta sheets using the same algorithm as in step 1, but search for regions where four of six residues have $P(b) > 100$. Once the regions are extended (part b), a region is declared a beta strand if the average $P(b)$ over all residues in the region is greater than 100, and $\Sigma P(b) > \Sigma P(a)$.

T A B L E 7.1 The Chou-Fasman parameters for the 20 common amino acids.

Amino acid	$P(a)$	$P(b)$	$P(turn)$	$f(i)$	$f(i+1)$	$f(i+2)$	$f(i+3)$
Alanine	142	83	66	0.06	0.076	0.035	0.058
Arginine	98	93	95	0.070	0.106	0.099	0.085
Asparagine	67	89	156	0.161	0.083	0.191	0.091
Aspartic acid	101	54	146	0.147	0.110	0.179	0.081
Cysteine	70	119	119	0.149	0.050	0.117	0.128
Glutamic acid	151	37	74	0.056	0.060	0.077	0.064
Glutamine	111	110	98	0.074	0.098	0.037	0.098
Glycine	57	75	156	0.102	0.085	0.190	0.152
Histidine	100	87	95	0.140	0.047	0.093	0.054
Isoleucine	108	160	47	0.043	0.034	0.013	0.056
Leucine	121	130	59	0.061	0.025	0.036	0.070
Lysine	114	74	101	0.055	0.115	0.072	0.095
Methionine	145	105	60	0.068	0.082	0.014	0.055
Phenylalanine	113	138	60	0.059	0.041	0.065	0.065
Proline	57	55	152	0.102	0.301	0.034	0.068
Serine	77	75	143	0.120	0.139	0.125	0.106
Threonine	83	119	96	0.086	0.108	0.065	0.079
Tryptophan	108	137	96	0.077	0.013	0.064	0.167
Tyrosine	69	147	114	0.082	0.065	0.114	0.125
Valine	106	170	50	0.062	0.048	0.028	0.053

3. If any of the helices assigned in step 1 overlap a beta strand assigned in step 2, then the overlapping region is predicted to be a helix if $\Sigma P(a) > \Sigma P(b)$, and a strand if $\Sigma P(b) > \Sigma P(a)$.

4. Finally, identify beta turns as follows:

   a. For each residue, i, calculate the turn propensity, $P(t)$, as follows: $P(t) =$ the $f(i)$ of the residue i + the $f(i+1)$ value of the following residue + the $f(i+2)$ value of the subsequent residue (position $i + 2$) + the $f(i+3)$ of the residue at position $i + 3$.

   b. Predict a hairpin turn starting at each position, i, that meets the following criteria:

      i. $P(t) > 0.000075$

      ii. The average $P(\text{turn})$ value for the four residues at positions i through $i + 3 > 100$

      iii. $\Sigma P(a) < \Sigma P(\text{turn}) > \Sigma P(b)$ over the four residues in positions i through $i + 3$.

Another statistical approach, the GOR (Garnier, Osguthorpe, and Robson) method, predicts secondary structure based on a window of 17 residues. For each residue in the sequence, 8 N-terminal and 8 C-terminal positions are considered along with the central residue. As with the Chou-Fasman method, a collection of sample proteins of known secondary structure was analyzed, and the frequencies with which each amino acid occupied each of the 17 window positions in helices, sheets, and turns was calculated, yielding a 17×20 scoring matrix. The values in this matrix are used to calculate the probability that each residue in a target sequence will be involved in a helix, sheet, or turn. The calculations used in the GOR method are based on information theory, and result in three-state prediction accuracies of around 65%.

Tertiary and Quaternary Structure

Predicting the secondary structure of a protein is only the first step in predicting the overall three-dimensional shape of a folded protein. The secondary structural elements of a protein pack together, along with less structured loop regions, to form a compact, globular native state. The overall three-dimensional shape of a folded polypeptide chain is referred to as its **tertiary structure.** Figure 7.6 illustrates some common tertiary structure motifs. For many proteins, the active form is a complex of two or more polypeptide units. **Quaternary structure** refers to the intermolecular interactions that occur when multiple polypeptides associate to form a functional protein, as well as the protein-to-protein contacts that can occur in multienzyme complexes.

The protein folding problem involves prediction of the secondary, tertiary, and quaternary structures of polypeptide chains based on their primary structure. Understanding the forces that drive a protein to fold is an active field of bio-

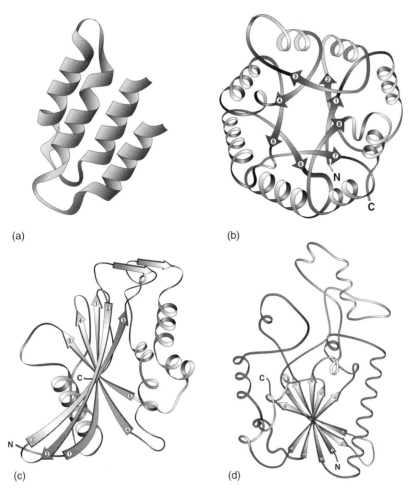

F I G U R E **7.6** *Several common tertiary structure motifs: (a) a four helical bundle, (b) an alpha-beta barrel, (c) and (d) open twisted beta sheets.*

chemical research. A diverse array of forces, including electrostatic forces, hydrogen bonds, and van der Waals forces, all play important roles in protein folding. The formation of covalent bonds between cysteine residues can also play a key role in determining protein conformation. The problem is made even more complex by the action of a special class of proteins called chaperonins, which act by altering protein structures in as yet unpredictable but important ways.

Hydrophobicity

The hydrophobic effect is generally accepted as one of the central forces involved in driving proteins to adopt a compact globular form. The native structure of most proteins includes a hydrophobic core, where buried hydrophobic residues are sequestered from solvent, and a solvent-exposed surface consisting mostly or entirely of polar and charged residues. The process of folding into a compact conformation that isolates hydrophobic residues from solvent is sometimes referred to as **hydrophobic collapse.** Membrane-integral proteins constitute a notable exception to this rule. These proteins contain one or more transmembrane regions, often primarily helical in structure, that are embedded in a membrane. Because membranes are generally composed largely of hydrophobic carbon and hydrogen atoms, these "surface" helices are actually protected from water molecules and are composed of mostly hydrophobic amino acids.

The importance of isolating hydrophobic residues from solvent is well illustrated by the molecular pathology of sickle-cell anemia. Human hemoglobin, the protein responsible for oxygen transport in our blood, is biologically active as a tetramer consisting of two alpha-globin and two beta-globin chains. The mutation of a single surface residue of the beta-globin protein from a charged glutamic acid residue to a hydrophobic valine residue causes a hydrophobic patch to be present on the solvent-exposed surface of the protein. The hydrophobic effect drives the valine residues to avoid contact with solvent and causes beta-globin molecules to stick to each other. Long chains of hemoglobin result and distort red blood cells from their normal donut-like shape to a characteristic sickle shape. The effect is particularly pronounced when oxygen levels are low (as they are in our extremities and during physical exertion), and the sickle cells become tangled with each other in narrow blood vessels. Pain, anemia, and, ultimately, gangrene result all because of a single amino acid difference.

The exact energetics of the hydrophobic effect and its contribution to protein folding are difficult to calculate. However, most protein folding algorithms that base their calculations on molecular forces include hydrophobic collapse as one of the central forces in driving protein folding.

Disulfide Bonds

When the sulfhydryl (—SH) groups of cysteine residues come into proximity they can become oxidized to form covalent **disulfide bonds,** cross-linking residues that may be far removed from one another in the primary structure of the protein (Figure 7.7). These reduced cysteine residues are sometimes referred to as cystine, and their stabilizing effect on a folded protein structure can be significant. When experimental methods require that a protein be denatured, reducing agents such as β-mercaptoethanol are often used to break any disulfide bonds. As mentioned previously, Anfinsen's seminal work demonstrated that protein structure is specified by sequence. In these experiments, ribonuclease was denatured and then allowed to form disulfide bonds in the presence of a high concentration (8 M) of urea. The urea reduced the effect of hydrophobicity on the protein conformation, allowing the formation of disulfide bonds differing from those found in the native conformation. The "scrambled" ribonuclease, with its incorrectly cross-linked cystine residues, had only 1% of the enzymatic activity of ribonuclease in its native conformation.

Active Structures vs. Most Stable Structures

Because of the huge number of degrees of freedom in protein folding, it has remained impossible to evaluate, in general, whether the native state of a protein is actually the most stable (energetically favorable) conformation. It is clear, however, that natural selection favors proteins that are both active and robust. Mutations in a protein's primary structure that reduce structural stability are likely to produce an evolutionary disadvantage, and thus be selected against.

In his prominent 1968 paper, C. Levinthal noted that the number of possible folds for even a modestly sized polypeptide chain is so vast that a random search of all possible conformations would take many years. This observation, which has come to be known as the **Levinthal paradox,** suggests that proteins fold by proceeding from the unfolded structure along a pathway of successively more stable intermediates, until the native state is reached. Whether or not this pathway ends in a conformation of globally minimum energy remains a matter of some debate.

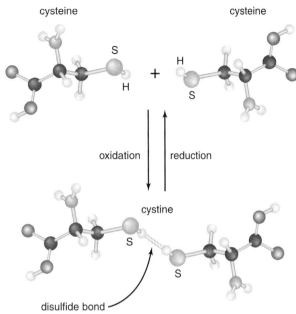

F I G U R E 7.7 *The sulfhydryl groups of two cysteine residues are oxidized to form a disulfide bond. Disulfide bonds are generally the only nonbackbone covalent cross-linkages within a protein.*

Algorithms for Modeling Protein Folding

To better understand how the amino acid sequence of a protein determines its unique native conformation, numerous algorithms have been developed to simulate the protein folding process at various levels of abstraction. No algorithm developed to date can determine the native structure of a protein with the same accuracy as experimental methods, such as X-ray crystallography (described in more detail in Chapter 8). Nevertheless, computational models of protein folding have provided novel insights into the forces that determine protein structure and the process by which proteins fold. The accuracy and power of computational protein folding algorithms continue to improve as new optimization and machine learning algorithms are applied to the problem, and as experimental biochemistry learns more about the various forces that contribute to the stability of a folded protein.

Lattice Models

Even the rapidly advancing computing power of modern microprocessors is insufficient to model all of the interactions involved in a folding polypeptide chain for more than a few femtoseconds (1 femtosecond = 10^{-15} seconds). As a result, most computational protein folding methods simplify various aspects of the protein in order to make the computations more tractable.

One such approach is to limit the degrees of conformational freedom available to the protein backbone. Instead of allowing all physically possible protein conformations, the alpha carbons are restricted to positions lying on a two- or three-dimensional grid (or lattice). This simplification considerably reduces the number of conformations a protein can adopt. As a result an exhaustive search of the conformational space can be performed for modest-sized polypeptides, revealing the global minimum energy conformation. For larger polypeptides, simplified lattice models allow nonexhaustive methods to sample a much greater proportion of all possible conformations, resulting in more accurate estimates of the global minimum energy conformation.

The best studied simple lattice model is the **H-P** (for **hydrophobic-polar**) **model.** The H-P model further simplifies the protein by representing each amino acid residue as a single atom of fixed radius. Each atom in the representation has one of two types: hydrophobic or polar. Figure 7.8 shows two- and three-dimensional H-P model representations for a short polypeptide. By convention, the N-terminal amino acid is placed at the origin of the coordinate system, and the following residue is placed at coordinates (1,0).

Scoring in the H-P model is based on hydrophobic contacts. To evaluate a particular conformation in the H-P model, the number of H-to-H contacts in the grid is counted. Each H-to-H contact is assumed to provide an energy contribution of –1, except for those involving two residues that are contiguous in the primary structure of the polypeptide. (Since these H-to-H contacts are present in every possible conformation, they are excluded for the sake of simplicity.) The optimal conformation is the one with the most H-to-H contacts. As it turns out, maximizing the number of H-to-H contacts is generally achieved by forming a hydrophobic core containing as many H residues as possible, relegating the P residues to the surface of the polypeptide. The score for both the 2D and 3D conformations shown in Figure 7.8 would be –3.

The assumption that hydrophobic collapse is the only significant factor in protein folding is obviously artificial, as are the conformational constraints imposed by a two- or three-dimensional lattice. Nevertheless, exhaustive searches of H-P models have provided some intriguing insights into the mechanisms of protein folding. For example, after examining optimal and near-optimal lattice structures for a variety of polypeptides, K. Dill suggested the **hydrophobic zipper** (Figure 7.9) as a possible mechanism for the formation of secondary structure.

(a)   (b)

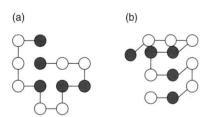

F I G U R E 7.8 *(a) Two-dimensional and (b) three-dimensional H-P model representations for a 12-residue polypeptide. Hydrophobic residues are shown in black and polar residues are white.*

As the size of a polypeptide chain grows, exhaustive searching of all possible conformations, even on a 90° lattice, becomes intractable. In this case, optimization (or search) algorithms must be used to find near-optimal conformations. Various advanced computational methods have been employed, including evolutionary computation, simulated annealing, Monte Carlo methods (described in Chapter 8), branch and bound search, and machine learning approaches.

A primary consideration in implementing a search algorithm for lattice-based protein folding models is how to represent a particular configuration. The simplest approach is to place the first residue on the lattice at position (0,0), and then represent the direction moved for each subsequent residue. Using this **absolute direction representation** for a 2D model, the choices at each position are up, right, left, and down (U, R, L, D), while the 3D model includes up, right, left, down, back (increasing Z-axis values), and forward (decreasing Z-axis values) or (U, R, L, D, B, F). For the two-dimensional configuration in Figure 7.8, the representation using this approach would be (R, R, D, L, D, L, U, L, U, U, R), whereas the 3D configuration would be represented as (R, B, U, F, L, U, R, B, L, L, F).

We can reduce the number of possible choices at each position by using a **relative direction representation,** which represents the turns taken by the main chain for each residue. In the case of a two-dimensional square lattice model, each residue after the second has three options, left, right, and forward (often represented as L, R, and F); in a three-dimensional square lattice, the options are left, right, forward, up, and down (L, R, F, U, D). For this approach, we must not only keep track of the current position, but also which direction the current residue is "facing." For the 2D model, the first residue is placed at grid position (0,0) facing to the right. That is, if the first move is F, then the second residue will be placed at position (1,0). Thus, the 2D configuration shown in Figure 7.8 would have the representation (F, F, R, R, L, R, R, L, R, F, R). For the 3D model, the first residue is placed at position (0,0,0), facing to the right. As we move, we must keep track of which direction the current residue is facing, and which way it currently considers to be "up." Using this representation, the 3D configuration in Figure 7.8 would be represented as (F, L, U, U, R, U, U, L, L, F, L).

A key difficulty that arises in using either of these direction-based representations is that some of the configurations generated will place two residues in the same position. For example, for the relative (turn-based) representation, any 2D configuration that begins with (L, L, L, L) will result in two residues placed at the origin (0,0), resulting in a **bump,** or steric collision. Several approaches have been

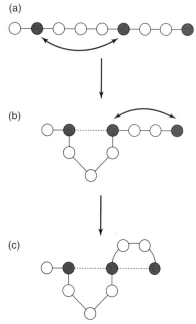

FIGURE 7.9 *The hydrophobic zipper mechanism. (a) Hydrophobic residues (shown as black filled circles) on the protein chain move together as a result of solvent interactions, causing intervening polar residues to form a loop as seen in (b). As the process is repeated (c), the basic structure of an anti-parallel beta sheet is formed.*

evaluated for dealing with bumps in conformational search. The simplest approach is to assign a very high energy to any configuration with bumps. Since the search algorithm is looking for low-energy configurations, configurations with bumps will be quickly eliminated from the search. Unfortunately, this draconian approach can hinder the search process by throwing away otherwise favorable conformations that might lead to a low-energy state if the bumps were resolved.

Alternate approaches include using local optimization strategies to resolve bumps before a configuration is scored, and using alternate representations that do not introduce configurations with bumps into the search. An example of such a representation is preference ordering. In this representation, each residue is assigned a permutation of all possible directions, rather than a single direction. For example, in a two-dimensional model, a single residue might be assigned the permutation {L, F, R}. This indicates that the most preferred direction is left; however, if a move to the left would result in a collision, forward is the next most preferred direction, followed by right. While this sort of representation can still introduce bumps (when a move in any direction results in a bump), they are introduced with much less frequency than in an absolute representation. Combinations of preference-ordered representations and local conformational search can be used to design representations that never introduce conformations containing bumps.

Off-Lattice Models

Moving off the lattice permits a protein model to adopt more realistic configurations. Using a complete backbone model and allowing phi and psi to adopt any values in the allowable regions of the Ramachandran plot, off-lattice folding models have produced configurations for small polypeptides that match experimentally observed configurations very closely. Error for off-lattice models is usually measured in terms of the C_α root mean squared deviation (RMSD) between the predicted and observed conformations. The C_α RMSD is simply the sum of the squared Euclidean distance between each C_α atom position in the predicted conformation and the observed conformation, when the two conformations are superimposed.

Improvements in the realism of protein models, however, come at the cost of added complexity. Off-lattice protein folding models may include alpha carbons only, all backbone atoms, or even all backbone and side-chain atoms. Backbone conformations are usually represented in terms of the phi and psi angles of each C_α atom. Side chains, if included, can be rigid, semiflexible, or fully flexible. For rigid side chains, the conformations of side chains in X-ray crystallographic structures are observed, and the most common conformation of each amino acid type is adopted as the only possible conformation for that type of amino acid.

For semiflexible side chains, a similar empirical method is used. Side-chain conformations in a set of X-ray structures are observed and the conformations are partitioned into similarly shaped groups. The average conformation of each group is called a **rotamer.** In a semiflexible model, each side chain is allowed to adopt any of its most commonly observed rotamers. This allows several possible conformations for each side chain, while reducing search complexity by disallowing conformations not commonly observed for a particular amino acid.

Energy Functions and Optimization

Off-lattice protein models, particularly less abstract models that include more backbone and side-chain atoms than the simple H-P model, require more sophisticated energy functions. In addition to hydrophobic contacts, energy functions for protein folding may consider hydrogen bonding, formation of disulfide bridges, electrostatic interactions, van der Waals forces, and solvent interactions. Since the relative contributions of each of these forces has remained difficult to calculate experimentally, the formulation of appropriate composite energy functions for protein folding remains an active field of study.

Two general approaches are used for formulating energy functions. The theoretical approach is based on the contributions of hydrogen bonds, electrostatic interactions, and other forces to the overall stability of a folded protein. The objective is to derive an approximated energy function, or force field, for which the crystallographically observed conformations of known proteins represent a minimum energy state. An example of such a force field might appear as follows:

$$\Delta G = \Delta G_{\text{van der Waals}} + \Delta G_{\text{H-bonds}} + \Delta G_{\text{solvent}} + \Delta G_{\text{Coulomb}}$$

The search for reliable energy functions is essentially a problem in molecular mechanics, and numerous competing functions have been devised.

While it makes sense to model proteins based on the physical forces and energies that actually drive their folding, these sorts of *ab initio* approaches have met with limited success for several reasons. First, the exact forces that drive the folding process and their various interactions are not yet well understood. In addition, these sorts of approaches, which attempt to model interactions among all atoms in a protein and the surrounding solvent, are often too computationally expensive to be feasible for realistic-sized polypeptides. An alternative to the *ab initio* approach is to devise an empirical pseudoenergy function based on the observed conformations of other proteins.

To formulate an empirical energy function, a set of X-ray crystallographic protein structures is selected (X-ray crystallography is discussed in detail in Chapter 8), and the three-dimensional neighbors of each amino acid are examined. A scoring matrix based on the relative positions of the various amino acids is thus formulated. For example, the number of times a serine residue and a threonine residue occur within 3.6 Å might be noted in the scoring matrix. To evaluate the empirical "energy" of a putative protein conformation, the neighbors of each residue in the protein are examined. Those local conformations that were found to be common in the example database receive low-energy scores. Uncommon local conformations receive higher, less favorable energy values. For example, if a particular serine residue is found to have three neighboring residues within 6 Å, an aspartate, a histidine, and a glutamate, and the scoring matrix indicated that Asp, His, and Glu were commonly found in proximity to Ser in the database of example protein structures, then the serine residue would receive a low-energy score. If, however, it was found that

Ser and Glu rarely occur in proximity, then the Ser residue might receive a higher empirical energy value. The local values are then summed over the entire protein to compute the global empirical energy. In effect, empirical energy functions favor conformations similar to the observed conformations of known proteins, while penalizing novel or unusual conformations.

In summary, formulation of an algorithm for protein folding consists of numerous steps. First, a protein model must be selected. Abstract models allow fast calculation and exhaustive searches, but cannot approximate actual protein conformations well. More exact models are realistic, but require expensive energy calculations to evaluate. Once a model is selected, a representation must be devised to represent each possible conformation. For lattice models, simple representations that encode which direction to move next are sufficient. For more exact models, the phi and psi angles of each C_α atom are often used. Next, a scoring function must be chosen to evaluate the favorability of a given conformation. Finally, an optimization method must be selected to search through all possible conformations for the structure that represents a global minimum for the energy function used.

An innovative approach to dealing with the computational complexity of *ab initio* methods has been devised by V. Pande. The Folding@Home program, which acts as a screensaver, uses idle CPU cycles to perform protein folding calculations. The calculations required to model a particular protein are divided into parts and distributed via the Internet to machines running the Folding@Home code. The results from each machine are sent back to the server, where they are combined and analyzed. By using the distributed computing power of the Internet, the Folding@Home algorithm can perform *ab initio* modeling of large polypeptides, a task that would be otherwise intractable for all but the largest supercomputers and networks. To participate in the Folding@Home project, you must be running a Windows, Linux, or Mac OS and be connected to the Internet. More information can be found at http://foldingathome.stanford.edu.

Structure Prediction

While protein folding models have helped molecular biologists and biochemists to understand the process of protein folding and the forces involved, no current *ab initio* protein folding algorithm is able to obtain very high accuracy (<3.0-Å backbone RMSD from the experimental structure) for large protein structures. For applications such as drug lead discovery and ligand design (discussed further in Chapter 8), a very accurate picture of the active site of a protein is required. Proteins often bind their ligands with such specificity that a deviation of less than an angstrom in the position of a key main-chain atom can result in a significant reduction in binding affinity. When the tertiary structure of one or more proteins similar in primary structure to a target protein is known, the target protein can be modeled, often with a high degree of accuracy, using comparative techniques.

Comparative Modeling

Comparative modeling, sometimes called homology modeling, seeks to predict the structure of a target protein via comparison with the structures of related proteins. The method relies on the robustness of the folding code. That is, small changes to the amino acid sequence of a protein usually result in minimal change to the tertiary structure of the protein. Numerous sequence changes must generally accumulate before a radical change in native conformation results. A generalized process for comparative modeling of a target protein proceeds as follows:

1. **Identify a set of protein structures related to the target protein.** Since the three-dimensional structure of the target protein is unknown, similarity is based on sequence. Sequence database search tools such as BLAST and FASTA are used to identify the related structures. Since these structures will serve as a template for the model, they are referred to as template structures.

2. **Align the sequence of the target with the sequences of the template proteins.** A multiple alignment tool, such as CLUSTALW, is used to generate the alignment. The multiple alignment allows us to identify regions of the target that are highly conserved across all template structures and those that are less conserved. When the sequence identity between the target and templates is less than ~30%, automated multiple alignment methods may not provide high-quality alignments. In this case, the alignments must be adjusted manually. For example, it is preferable to move gaps out of secondary structure elements and into surface loops, where they are less likely to disrupt the model structure.

3. **Construct the model.** Several methods may be employed to build the model structure. One of the most common is to superimpose the template structures and find the structurally conserved regions. The backbone of the template structure is then aligned to these conserved fragments of structure, forming a core for the model. When the structures of the template proteins diverge, methods such as secondary structure prediction for the target protein, sequence similarity, and manual evaluation must be used to select the correct structure for the model. Since the structures of the templates are far more likely to diverge in loop regions than in regions of secondary structure, loops are generally modeled separately after the core.

4. **Model the loops.** A number of computational methods are available for modeling loops. The two most common methods are (1) select the best loop from a database of known loop conformations, and (2) perform conformational search and evaluation. The second method is similar to a limited protein folding approach. While there are numerous methods to choose from in modeling loops, it is difficult to obtain an accurate conformation for loops longer than six residues.

5. **Model the side chains.** Once the backbone model has been constructed, the positions of the side-chain atoms must be determined. Again, a variety of

methods are commonly employed, ranging from rotamer library search to limited molecular dynamics approaches.

6. **Evaluate the model.** Various software packages are available to evaluate the quality of a protein structure. Examples include PROCHECK, WHAT CHECK, Verify-3D, and others. Validation algorithms usually check for anomalies such as phi/psi combinations that are not in the allowable regions of the Ramachandran plot, steric collisions, and unfavorable bond lengths and angles. Once structural anomalies are identified, the model is usually adjusted by hand, if possible, to correct the problems reported.

While comparative modeling involves numerous computational methods, it is nevertheless a manual process, involving expert intervention and decision making at each step. Automated methods are currently under development, but the need to produce very high-quality models for ligand design, active site analysis, and so on, suggests that the process will require a significant manual component for the near future. Nevertheless, comparative modeling remains the best available method for the construction of high-quality models for proteins of unknown structure.

Threading: Reverse Protein Folding

An approximate model of a protein's tertiary structure can be constructed quickly by finding another protein that assumes roughly the same conformation. If we assume a particular conformation, then we can use the same evaluation methods used in protein folding algorithms to determine whether the conformation is favorable. The process of assuming a particular conformation and evaluating its favorability is called **protein threading.** Threading is sometimes compared to protein folding in reverse, since you start by assuming a particular fold, and then evaluate the quality of the resulting structure.

A common application of threading algorithms is to determine which fold family a particular sequence is likely to belong to. Several hierarchical databases have been developed that identify groups of similarly folded proteins (e.g., CATH, SCOP, LPFC, Pclass, FSSP, and others) at various levels of abstraction. These databases group proteins of similar structure into categories such as fold families, superfamilies, and classes. To identify which fold family or superfamily a protein belongs to, you can take an average structure representing all of the structures in a family and evaluate the quality of the resulting structure if the target protein were to assume this conformation.

The evaluation is repeated for each fold family, and the conformation with the most favorable score is selected as the likely fold family for the target sequence. Assignment of a protein sequence to a particular fold family not only gives a rough approximation of the native structure of the protein, but also provides information about possible functions of the protein and its relationship to other proteins and biological pathways.

Predicting RNA Secondary Structures

Unlike DNA, which most frequently assumes its well-known double-helical conformation, the three-dimensional structure of single stranded RNA is determined by the sequence of nucleotides in much the same way the protein structure is determined by sequence. RNA structure, however, is less complex than protein structure and can be well characterized by identifying the locations of commonly occurring secondary structural elements.

For RNA, the elements of secondary structure are quite different than those for proteins. Like DNA, complementary base pairs of RNA will form hydrogen bonds, inducing a helical structure. However, in single stranded RNA, the base pairing occurs within a single RNA molecule, forming base-paired **stem** regions. Where the RNA chain reverses directions to allow this base pairing, a **hairpin turn** is formed. When a small number of bases along the RNA chain are not complementary, a small bulge or a larger loop region may form. Figure 7.10 illustrates the types of secondary structure that can be formed by an RNA molecule. The most difficult type of RNA structure to predict is the **pseudoknot**, where bases involved in a loop pair with other bases outside the loop. Because of the difficulty in pseudoknot prediction, many of the early algorithms for prediction of RNA secondary structure ignored them entirely, predicting the rest of the secondary structure elements as if no pseudoknot regions were present.

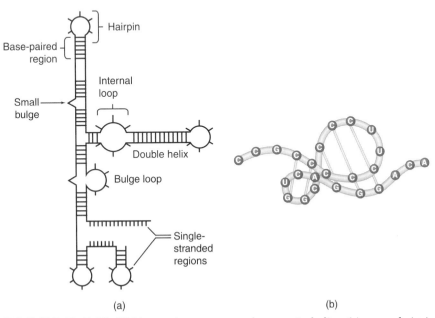

F I G U R E 7.10 *RNA secondary structure elements, including (a) stems, hairpin turns, bulges/loops, and (b) pseudoknots.*

F I G U R E 7.11 *Nearest neighbor energy rules: All of the nucleotides in the region labeled Loop can potentially interact, so all pairs within the loop must be considered when calculating the energy of this structure. The nucleotides in the region labeled Exterior, however, cannot pair with any of the nucleotides in the loop region without forming a pseudoknot. Thus, pairwise interactions between these bases and those in the loop are ignored by nearest neighbor energy rules.*

```
            C   U
        G           G
    A                   G
    C                       A     ⎤ Loop
    G                   G         ⎦
         A – U
         C – G
         A – U
             G                    ⎤
             U                    ⎦ Exterior
             A
```

Various approaches have been devised for predicting the secondary structure of RNA molecules. Many of these methods attempt to minimize the free energy of the folded macromolecule, thus searching for the most stable structure. One of the most popular packages, Zuker's Mfold program, uses a set of **nearest neighbor energy rules** to calculate the energy of the structure. The rules are called "nearest neighbor" rules because the RNA structure being evaluated is broken into interacting regions and energy calculations are performed only on "neighbors"—base pairs that can potentially interact with one another. Thus, pairwise interactions that cross base-paired stem regions do not have to be considered (see Figure 7.11), speeding up the calculations considerably.

Because RNA is the intermediary language between DNA and proteins, accurate prediction of RNA secondary structure is important for understanding gene regulation and expression of protein products. Furthermore, many RNAs have been found to bear catalytic properties of their own. These RNAs, now referred to as **ribozymes,** have been implicated in the splicing of tRNA molecules, the activity of ribosomes, the processing of eukaryotic hnRNAs, and many other functions. While they usually occur in the context of a protein–RNA complex, it has been demonstrated that ribozymes can exhibit catalytic activity even without their protein partners under some circumstances. Often RNA acts as the structural scaffolding for DNA, RNA, and polypeptide processing reactions. In addition, since some viruses (such as HIV) are encoded in RNA, understanding the secondary structure of RNA can help in the process of discovering and testing pharmaceutical agents against these pathogens.

Chapter Summary

Proteins are complex macromolecules that display a diverse range of three-dimensional structures. Scientists are just beginning to understand how it is that the sequence of amino acids that makes up a protein chain encodes a unique three-dimensional structure. The secondary structure of a protein can be predicted with reasonably high accuracy (>75%) using neural networks, hidden Markov models, and other advanced computational techniques. Tertiary and quaternary structures are far more difficult to predict, and a variety of algorithms have been devised to solve the problem of protein fold prediction at various levels of abstraction. Protein folding algorithms, comparative modeling methods, and threading are advancing our knowledge and understanding of the process of protein folding, while producing increasingly accurate structural predictions. No less important is the prediction of RNA secondary structure, which, like protein secondary structure prediction, can be achieved with good accuracy using neural networks, hidden Markov models, and other computational methods.

Readings for Greater Depth

Numerous methods are available for prediction of protein secondary structure, including PhD, Jpred, GOR, NNSP, Predator, DSC, MULPRED, and many others. The web page for Jpred provides a brief summary and link to these algorithms and others: http://jura.ebi.ac.uk:8888/refs.html.

Chou and Fasman's well-known technique for the prediction of secondary structure is described in P. Prevelige, Jr., and G. D. Fasman, 1989, Prediction of secondary structure, in G. Fasman (ed.), *Prediction of Protein Structure and the Principles of Protein Conformation*, pp. 1–91, Plenum Press, New York.

The GOR method for secondary structure prediction is described in J. Garnier, D. J. Osguthorpe, and B. Robson, 1978, *J. Mol. Biol.* **120:** 97–120, as well as in J. Garnier and B. Robson, 1989, The GOR method for predicting secondary structures in proteins, in G. Fasman (ed.), *Prediction of Protein Structure and the Principles of Protein Conformation*, pp. 417–465, Plenum Press, New York.

The famous Levinthal paradox was first described in C. Levinthal, 1968, Are there pathways for protein folding?, *J. Chem. Phys.* **65:** 44–45; which can be obtained online at http://brian.ch.cam.ac.uk/~mark/levinthal/levinthal.html.

Anfinsen's experiments on protein renaturation are described in C. B. Anfinsen, 1973, Principles that govern the folding of protein chains, *Science* **181:** 223–230.

John Moult provides a detailed comparison of the two basic methods for formulating energy functions for protein folding in J. Moult, 1997, Comparison of database potentials and molecular mechanics force fields, *Curr. Opin. Structural Biol.* **7:** 194–199.

Worthwhile summaries of secondary structure prediction methods can be found at http://cubic.bioc.columbia.edu/predictprotein and http://genamics.com/expression/strucpred.htm.

A step-by-step summary of the process of comparative structure prediction is provided at http://guitar.rockefeller.edu/~andras/watanabe.

Details of Zuker's Mfold algorithm can be found in M. Zuker, D. H. Mathews, and D. H. Turner, 1999, Algorithms and thermodynamics for RNA secondary structure prediction: A practical guide, in J. Barciszewski and B. F. C. Clark (eds.), *RNA Biochemistry and Biotechnology*, NATO ASI Series, Kluwer Academic Publishers, Boston, and at http://bioinfo.math.rpi.edu/~zukerm/seqanal.

Questions and Problems

* **7.1** The charges associated with proteins often play important roles in their biochemical separation from other proteins also found in cells. Consider a polypeptide that is found to bind tightly to a column packed with a cation-exchange resin at pH 3.5. Explain why it might be possible to wash this protein off the column by passing a buffer of pH 8 through the column.

7.2 Using the Chou-Fasman algorithm and the parameters in Table 7.1, predict the regions of alpha helices and beta strands for the following sequence:

    CAENKLDHVADCCILFMTWYNDGPCIFIYDNGP

* **7.3** For the sequence in Question 7.2, use the Chou-Fasman method to predict the hairpin turns.

7.4 Assuming an energy contribution of –1 for each nonbackbone hydrophobic contact, determine the energy score for the following 2D H-P model configuration:

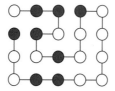

* **7.5** Draw a 2D H-P configuration for a peptide with an energy score of –7.

7.6 Assuming a relative direction representation using L = left, R = right, and F = forward, what is the representation for the 2D configuration in Question 7.4?

* **7.7** A preference ordering representation using L = left, R = right, and F = forward is used along with a 2D H-P model. Draw the conformation corresponding to the following representation (assume all residues are polar): (FLR), (RFL), (LFR), (LRF), (LFR), (LFR), (LFR), (LRF), (LFR), (LRF), (LFR).

Proteomics

> If a little knowledge is dangerous, where is a man who has so much as to be out of danger?
>
> *Thomas Henry Huxley*
> *(1825–1895)*

From Genomes to Proteomes

Protein Classification
Enzyme nomenclature
Families and superfamilies
Folds

Experimental Techniques
2D electrophoresis
Mass spectrometry
Protein microarrays

Inhibitors and Drug Design

Ligand Screening
Ligand docking
Database screening

X-Ray Crystal Structures

NMR Structures

Empirical Methods and Prediction Techniques

Post-Translational Modification Prediction
Protein sorting
Proteolytic cleavage
Glycosylation
Phosphorylation

While a genome is the sum total of an organism's genetic material, a **proteome** is the sum total of its proteins. The very nature of genes (their simple chemical makeup and their ability to serve as templates for exact copies of themselves) has made them comparatively easy to study and amenable to automated analysis. The nature of proteins (with their 20 building blocks, complex chemical modifications, and barriers to duplication) is very different. Many detractors of the numerous completed and ongoing genome projects have questioned the wisdom of investing so much in those DNA-level efforts when they actually give us very little knowledge about how an organism actually works. Proteins are what get things done for cells, and now that biology is beginning to enter into what many are already calling the "post-genome era" the larger task of characterizing proteomes looms on the horizon.

The previous chapter described the still imprecise process of inferring a protein's three-dimensional structure from just the nucleotide sequence of the gene that codes for it. This chapter highlights the difficult task of simply cataloging a cell's set of proteins as well as the problems of determining their relative abundance, modes of interaction, and roles that they play. Some laboratory and computational tools do exist, but much still needs to be learned before proteomes can be reverse engineered back to the level of genomes and the bioinformatics story is made complete.

From Genomes to Proteomes

Despite their exquisite sensitivity and capacity to generate staggering amounts of data, state-of-the-art gene expression analyses such as those described in Chapter 6 give disappointingly little information about what proteins are present in cells, let alone what those proteins do and how they function. First, the longevity of an mRNA and the protein it codes for within a cell are usually very different—the correlation between the relative abundance of an mRNA and the relative abundance of its corresponding protein within any given cell is routinely less than 0.5. Second, many proteins are extensively modified after translation in a wide variety of ways including proteolytic cleavage, glycosylation, and phosphorylation (as described later in this chapter). These modifications almost invariably alter the activity of proteins and clearly happen differently in different tissues and circumstances, yet the amino acid sequence of a protein explains only some of the molecular features that are scrutinized prior to modification. Third, many proteins are not functionally relevant until they are assembled into larger complexes or delivered to an appropriate location either inside or outside of a cell. Amino acid sequences alone only hint at what those interactions and final destinations might be.

These difficulties in inferring the population of proteins in a cell and the roles that those proteins play are compounded by the fact that proteins themselves are much less amenable to direct analysis than are nucleic acids. Proteins require much more careful handling than DNA because their functionally important tertiary structures can be easily altered when they come in contact with an inappropriate surface or environment. Also, as described in Chapter 1, the ability of nucleic acids to specifically base pair with other strings of nucleotides makes DNA identification a fairly simple task. Protein identification is much more difficult and requires complicated mass spectrometric analyses in conjunction with sophisticated software (described in more detail below) or the generation of specific antibodies. Finally, most analyses of both nucleic acids and proteins rely on the ability to manipulate large numbers (typically billions) of identical molecules at some point in the process. Generating large numbers of copies of any given gene is fairly easy due to their ability to serve as a template for their own amplification (usually PCR in an efficient, controlled, and cell-free environment). Obtaining large numbers of protein molecules for analysis almost always requires inefficient and laborious chemical isolation from large numbers of living cells.

In the final analysis, it is fair to say that "genes were easy" when considering the challenges facing proteomics researchers. None of the obstacles to proteome analysis are insurmountable and workable solutions are already in place for many. The power that should come from the knowledge of an organism's proteome promises to make the remaining challenges worth facing. Proteomic insights have already played important roles in understanding the molecular basis of diseases such as cystic fibrosis, converting cells to molecular factories, improving the efficiency of genetically engineered organisms, and designing new drugs. The real work of bioinformatics has just begun.

Protein Classification

Indexing and cataloging proteomic data are challenging tasks due to the wide variety of different proteins cells need to manipulate their internal environments. Several alternative methods of classifying proteins have been suggested to help with that process and to facilitate comparisons between different organisms and cell types. The oldest systematic method, that of the International Enzyme Commission, is based on protein function and assigns proteins to one of six different categories. Alternative means of classification include ones based on evolutionary history (dividing all proteins into 1 of about 1,000 different homologous families) and structural similarity.

Enzyme Nomenclature

Rapid growth in the number of known enzymes during the 1950s made it necessary for a set of widely accepted naming conventions to be put in place. Prior to the formation of the International Enzyme Commission in 1955 it was not uncommon for a single enzyme to be known by several different names, while in other instances the same name was given to distinctly different enzymes. Further, many of the names conveyed little or no idea of the nature of the reactions catalyzed. By 1965 a systematic approach to naming enzymes was suggested that

T A B L E 8.1 The main enzyme classes according to the International Enzyme Commission.

Main Class	Type of Reaction Catalyzed
1. Oxidoreductases	Oxidation-reduction reactions of all types
2. Transferases	Transferring an intact group of atoms from a donor to an acceptor molecule
3. Hydrolases	Cleaving bonds hydrolytically
4. Lyases	Cleaving bonds by means other than hydrolysis or oxidation
5. Isomerases	Interconversion of various isomers
6. Ligases	Bond formation due to the condensation of two different substances with energy provided by ATP

divided all enzymes into six main classes on the basis of the general type of reaction they catalyze (Table 8.1).

By using a numbering system throughout the scheme, each enzyme (i.e., chitinase) can be assigned a numerical code, such as 3.2.1.14, where the first number specifies the main class, the second and third numbers correspond to specific subclasses, and the final number represents the serial listing of the enzyme in its subclass. For example, the enzyme traditionally known as alcohol dehydrogenase is identified as 1.1.1.1 (main class: oxidoreductase; class: acting on the CH—OH group of donors; subclass: with NAD or NADP as an acceptor; alcohol dehydrogenase: the first of 269 enzymes entries in this category). By the same token, DNA-directed RNA polymerases are identified as 2.7.7.6 (main class: transferases; class: transferring phosphorus-containing groups; subclass: nucleotidyl-transferases; DNA-directed RNA polymerases: the sixth of 60 entries in this category). New enzymes are constantly being added to the list of thousands assigned these identifiers, and updates are routinely available at the International Enzyme Commission's web site (http://www.chem.qmw.ac.uk/iubmb/enzyme).

Families and Superfamilies

Sequence similarities among the many thousands of proteins for which an amino acid sequence is available suggest that all modern-day proteins may be derived from as few as 1,000 original proteins. It is unclear if this fairly small number is dictated more by the physical restraints on the folding of polypeptide chains into three-dimensional structures (Chapter 7), by the fact that these different proteins provided sufficiently varied structural and chemical properties such that no others have been needed during the course of evolution, or by some combination of these two possible explanations. One of the strongest arguments for an evolutionary explanation came in a study published in 1991 by Dorit, Schoenbach, and Gilbert (see the suggested readings at the end of this chapter). They suggested that exons themselves correspond closely to the functional domains of proteins and that all proteins are actually derived from various arrangements of as few as

1,000 to 7,000 exons. Regardless of the basis for the similarities, though, sequence alignments and database similarity searches such as those described in Chapter 2 are often employed to discover familial relationships between different proteins. These relationships have subsequently been extremely helpful in attempts to predict protein structures since the shapes of proteins seem to be under tighter evolutionary constraint than their specific amino acid sequences.

By definition, proteins that are more than 50% identical in amino acid sequence across their entire length are said to be members of a single **family.** By the same token, **superfamilies** are groups of protein families that are related by lower but still detectable levels of sequence similarity (and therefore have a common but more ancient evolutionary origin). All proteins can be further categorized on the basis of their predominant secondary structural features as shown in Table 8.2. Features include membrane/cell surface proteins; mainly alpha; mainly beta; and both alternating alpha/beta structures and alpha+beta structures.

Several databases that group proteins in this way have been assembled with varying combinations of manual inspection and automated methods. They include SCOP (Structural Classification of Proteins; http://pdb.wehi.edu.au/scop), CATH (Class, Architecture, Topology and Homologous superfamily; http://www.biochem.ucl.ac.uk/bsm/cath_new/index.html), and FSSP (Fold classification based on Structure-Structure alignment of Proteins; http://www.hgmp.mrc.ac.uk/Databases/fssp). All intend to provide a detailed and comprehensive description of the structural and evolutionary relationships between all proteins whose structures are known through X-ray crystal analysis (described later).

Folds

Whereas protein families have clear evolutionary relationships, and protein superfamilies have probable evolutionary relationships, proteins are said to have a common **fold** if they have the same major secondary structures in the same arrangement and with the same topological connections. Different proteins with

T A B L E 8.2 Structural classification of proteins.

Class	Folds	Superfamilies	Families
All alpha proteins	144	231	363
All beta proteins	104	190	303
Alpha and beta proteins (α/β)	107	180	409
Alpha and beta proteins ($\alpha+\beta$)	194	276	428
Multidomain proteins	32	32	45
Membrane and cell surface proteins	11	17	28
Small proteins	56	81	123
Total	648	1,007	1,699

Note: According to the October 2001 release of the SCOP Database (v. 1.57). A total of 14,729 protein database entries (http://www.rcsb.org/pdb) were analyzed and divided into 35,685 domains.

the same fold often have peripheral elements of secondary structure and turn regions that differ in size and conformation. In many respects, the term *fold* is used synonymously with *structural motif* but generally refers to larger combinations of secondary structures—in some cases, a fold comprises half of a protein's total structure.

Proteins placed together in the same fold category may not have a common evolutionary origin though they may be the result of **exon shuffling,** in which proteins with new functions are created by the process of recombining exons corresponding to functional domains of existing genes at the level of DNA. Alternatively, the structural similarities could arise just from the physics and chemistry of proteins favoring certain packing arrangements and chain topologies.

Experimental Techniques

As was the case with genome analysis, much of proteome analysis is limited by the experimental techniques that are currently available. Unfortunately, from the perspective of proteomics, the nature of proteins makes laboratory analysis especially difficult and much less precise than what is available for genome analysis. Since it plays such an important role in the field's progress, it is especially important that bioinformaticians appreciate the few strengths and significant weaknesses of proteomic methods.

2D Electrophoresis

The workhorse laboratory technique of proteomics is two-dimensional (2D) gel electrophoresis. As the name implies, the approach involves two different gel electrophoretic separations that give rise to a pattern of protein dots with distinctive x and y coordinates such as those shown in Figure 8.1. The first separation involves **isoelectric focusing** (IF) of proteins. This step exploits differences in the pI value of proteins (the pH at which the net molecular charge is zero; see Chapter 7) and is capable of separating proteins with extremely small differences in pI (as little as 0.0025 pH units). The relatively recent availability of immobilized pH gradient (IPG) strips has significantly standardized the first dimension of separation, which had been fraught with artifacts and variability when the gradients had been made by hand for each 2D gel. After the first dimension is run, the strips are laid on a sodium dodecyl sulfate (SDS) polyacrylamide gel to separate the molecules by molecular weight in much the same way that nucleic acids can be size fractionated (see Chapter 1). The SDS in the gel is actually a detergent that binds uniformly to all proteins in the gel and confers on them a negative charge that allows the electric current to pull them through the gel's molecular sieve.

The combined resolution of this IF-SDS procedure is outstanding and routinely yields autoradiograms like the ones shown in Figure 8.1. Clear differences in the protein populations of different cell types such as human kidney

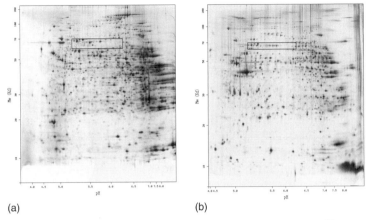

F I G U R E 8.1 *2D gels of proteins in two different types of human cells. Each spot corresponds to a single different protein present in cell extracts from each type of tissue. (a) A 2D gel generated from human liver cells and (b) 2D gel generated from human kidney cells.*

(Figure 8.1a) and human liver (Figure 8.1b) are readily apparent, and relative amounts of each protein can be determined by quantitating the intensity of each spot. Those differences can be readily correlated with a variety of disease states as well as different stages of development, and a large collection of heavily analyzed 2D gels is available for perusal on the Internet (http://us.expasy.org/ch2d/). Differential labeling of proteins (i.e., radioactively labeling one preparation with ^{15}N and another with ^{14}C) can even allow direct comparisons to be made on a single 2D gel. Several companies have risen to the challenge of generating sophisticated software packages that automate the process of aligning spots between gels and integrating the intensities of each spot. They include Amersham Pharmacia Biotech's ImageMaster and Compugen's Z3.

At first glance 2D electrophoresis might appear to be a method perfectly suited for annotating and tracking the proteome. Literally thousands of proteins can be reproducibly separated in a single experiment. However, the method has several important limitations including the fact that the human genome codes for many tens of thousands of proteins, underrepresentation of membrane-bound proteins due to poor solubility in sample preparations and gels, and relatively insensitive detection methods. The single greatest difficulty associated with 2D gel electrophoresis of proteomes, however, is that of determining exactly which protein is represented by each spot. Those determinations are typically only made after extensive computational analysis of mass spectra data as described below.

Mass Spectrometry

The ability of mass spectrometry to uniquely identify the proteins associated with each spot in a 2D gel has been the driving force behind most recent progress in proteomics. After proteins have been separated on 2D gels, identification usually requires spot excision, enzymatic digestion into peptide fragments with a protease such as trypsin, and then deposition on a substrate for matrix assisted laser desorption ionization (**MALDI**) for subsequent mass spectrometric analysis. An alternative to MALDI is electrospray ionization (**ESI**), and both are capable of identifying and quantifying a wide variety of large biological molecules.

Mass spectrometry itself is a technique that is commonly used by analytical chemists. For proteomic applications, protein fragments are made into positively charged ions by either MALDI or ESI and then accelerated through a charged array into an analyzing tube. The paths of the protein fragments are bent by magnetic fields such that those with low masses are deflected the most and collide with the walls of the analyzer. High-momentum ions pass through the analyzer more quickly. Collision of the positively charged ions with a collector at the end of the analyzer generates an electric current that can be amplified and detected as a series of signal peaks corresponding to a **peptide mass fingerprint**.

Identification of proteins with mass spectrometry requires a marriage between instrumentation and computation, in which a peptide mass fingerprint must be matched up with the theoretical mass spectrum of any of a large number of proteins derived from a genomic database. The problem gets even more complicated when trying to identify a protein from an organism whose genome sequence is not yet complete. Innovative approaches to these complex search problems have been essential, and examples of mass spectrum analysis software include ProFound (http://prowl.rockefeller.edu/cgi-bin/ProFound), which correctly identified the protein in a 2D gel spot after the MALDI mass spectrometric analysis shown in Figure 8.2.

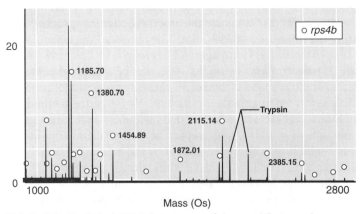

FIGURE 8.2 *MALDI spectrum of the proteolytic products from a tryptic digest of a 30-kDa 2D gel protein spot. Open circles indicate peaks that match with masses of the theoretical tryptic fragments of rps4b. Trypsin (the proteolytic enzyme that was used to digest the original spot) self-digestion products are labeled "Trypsin." (Derived from Figure 2 in Zhang and Chait, 2000.)*

Protein Microarrays

Protein microarrays are beginning to get widespread attention because they have the potential to allow large-scale analyses of proteins in much the same way that gene chips have revolutionized transcriptome analyses (see Chapter 6). The concept behind protein chips is very similar to the one that underlies gene chips: Tiny amounts of individual probes are covalently attached to the surface of silica (glass) chips in high-density arrays. Protein extracts from cells are then fluorescently labeled and washed over these chips. Just as with gene chips, amounts of material (now proteins) bound to the probes are determined by laser excitation of the fluorescent labels. In addition to arrays of proteins for detecting protein–protein interactions, protein–compound interactions, and so on, researchers may use arrays of capture probes (i.e., antibodies) that bind proteins in a sample such that their relative expression levels can be detected.

Several hurdles still need to be overcome before these protein chips have the same impact brought about by gene chips. First, unlike DNA sequences with their unique binding characteristics determined exclusively by base pairing rules, it is reasonable to expect that single proteins will interact with multiple, different probes. Also, the binding kinetics (see Appendix 2) of each probe are likely to be subtly different, and differences in signal intensity might be due to differences in binding affinities. Finally, proteins are notoriously sensitive to the chemistry of their environment and the surfaces they encounter, and both the cell extracts and the probes themselves may behave differently than expected when exposed to the testing procedure.

These problems and others should be solvable through the application of computer analyses of the resulting data. In the meantime, researchers are likely to use gene chip arrays first to help them home in on proteins of interest. Once they have narrowed the field, proteomic analyses of small subsets of proteins will be analyzed on custom-made protein chips. In one study, researchers developed methods to array more than 10,000 proteins on a single glass microscope slide and then showed that their arrays could be used to study the enzymatic activity of proteins (*Science*, 2000; **289**: 1760–1763). Notably, they were able to detect the binding of small, drug-like molecules to particular proteins on microarrays.

Inhibitors and Drug Design

One of the most important applications of bioinformatics is the search for effective pharmaceutical agents to prevent and cure human disease. The development and testing of a new drug is a costly and time-consuming undertaking, often spanning as many as 15 years, at a cost of up to $700 million. Functional genomics, structural bioinformatics, and proteomics promise to reduce the labor associated with this process, allowing drugs to be developed faster and at a lower cost.

While the exact steps in the development of a drug vary, the overall process can be broken into two major components: discovery and testing. The testing process, which involves preclinical and clinical trials, is generally not subject to significant enhancement using computational methods. The discovery process, however, is labor intensive and expensive and has provided a fertile ground for bioinformatics research. The discovery process itself can be broken into several components, including target identification, lead discovery and optimization, toxicology, and pharmacokinetics.

The objective of **target identification** is to identify a biological molecule that is essential for the survival or proliferation of a particular disease-causing agent, or **pathogen.** Once a target is identified, the objective of drug design is to develop a molecule that will bind to and inhibit the drug target. Since the function of the target is essential to the life processes of the pathogen, inhibition of the target either stops the proliferation of the pathogen or destroys it. An understanding of the structure and function of proteins is an important component of drug development because proteins are the most common drug targets. For example, HIV protease is a protein produced by the human immunodeficiency virus (HIV)—the pathogen that causes AIDS—in the context of a human host cell. HIV protease is essential to the proliferation of the virus. If this protein can be effectively inhibited, then the virus cannot infect any additional cells, and the advance of the disease is stopped.

How might a molecule act to inhibit an enzyme like HIV protease? Proteases are proteins that digest other proteins, much like restriction enzymes are used to specifically cut DNA molecules (Chapter 1). Many of the proteins that HIV needs to survive and proliferate in a human host are produced as a single, large polypeptide chain. This polypeptide must then be cut into the functional component proteins by HIV protease. Like many enzymes, HIV protease has an **active site** where it binds to and operates on other molecules. A drug design objective in this case, then, might be to discover and refine a molecule that will bind in the active site of HIV protease in a way that prevents it from functioning normally.

Ligand Screening

The first step in the discovery of an inhibitor for a particular protein is usually to identify one or more **lead compounds** that might bind to the active site of the target protein. Traditionally, the search for lead compounds has been a trial-and-error process in which numerous compounds are tested using various biochemical assays until a sufficient number of compounds with some inhibitory effect is found. Recently, high-throughput screening (HTS) methods have made the procedure much more efficient, but the underlying process remains essentially an exhaustive search of as many potential leads as possible. Ligand docking and screening algorithms strive to streamline the lead discovery process by moving as much of the *in vitro* experimentation as possible into the realm of computation. Since lead discovery is an expensive and time-consuming process, some of the most dramatic contributions of computational methods to drug development will likely involve reducing the human effort and time associated with finding lead compounds.

Ligand Docking

In many cases, the three-dimensional structure of a protein and its ligand are known (see X-Ray Crystal Structures section below), but the structure of the complex they form is unknown. The objective of computational docking is to determine how two molecules of known structure will interact. In the case of drug design, molecular docking is most often employed to aid in determining how a particular drug lead will bind to the target, or how two proteins will interact to form a binding pocket.

Molecular docking algorithms share a great deal in common with algorithms for protein folding. Both problems involve identifying the energy of a particular molecular conformation, and then searching for the conformation that minimizes the free energy of the system. As with protein folding, there are far too many degrees of freedom to exhaustively search all possible binding modes or conformations, so **heuristics**—general rules that tend to lead to good solutions, but cannot be guaranteed to lead to optimal solutions—and search algorithms must be used to find suboptimal solutions that approach the global energy minimum.

As in protein folding, there are two primary considerations in designing a molecular docking algorithm. First, an energy function must be formulated to evaluate the quality of a particular complex, and then a search algorithm must be employed to explore the space of all possible binding modes and conformations in search of a minimal energy structure. Another important consideration in the design of a docking algorithm is how to deal with flexibility in both the protein and the putative ligand. **Lock and key approaches** to docking assume a rigid protein structure, to which a flexible ligand structure is docked. This approach is attractive because it is far less computationally expensive than **induced fit docking,** which allows for flexibility in both the protein and the ligand. Induced fit approaches vary in the amount of flexibility afforded to proteins. A common compromise is to assume a rigid protein backbone, while allowing for flexibility in the side chains near the ligand binding site.

AutoDock (http://www.scripps.edu/pub/olson-web/doc/autodock), a well-known method for docking of rigid or flexible ligands, uses a grid-based force field for evaluating a particular complex. The force field is used to score a complex based on formation of favorable electrostatic interactions, the number of hydrogen bonds formed, van der Waals interactions, and several other factors.

To find a docking that minimizes the free-energy function, the original version of AutoDock employed a Monte Carlo/simulated annealing approach. The **Monte Carlo algorithm** is a commonly used method of energy minimization that essentially makes random changes to the current position and conformation of the ligand, keeping those that result in a lower energy (that is, a more stable configuration) than the current configuration. When a move results in a higher energy, it is usually not accepted. However, in order to allow the algorithm to find low-energy states that may have an energy barrier (Figure 8.3), moves that result

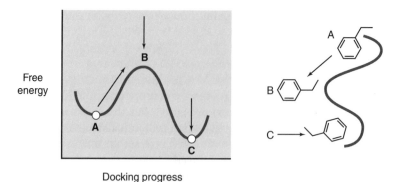

F I G U R E 8.3 *Sometimes a docking algorithm must accept a move that results in an unfavorable energy state in order to find a global minimum.*

in higher energies are sometimes accepted. The frequency with which higher energy states are accepted is set relatively high at the beginning of the algorithm, and then slowly decreased as the algorithm iterates. This probability is often thought of as a temperature factor, and the gradual reduction of the temperature factor during a run is thought of as a cooling process. Thus the analogy with the process of annealing metals and the name *simulated annealing*. More recent versions of AutoDock use variations of genetic algorithms—optimization programs that emulate the dynamics of natural selection on a population of competing solutions—to accomplish the search for a minimal energy configuration.

AutoDock is, of course, only one example of the numerous algorithms for docking biological molecules. FTDock (http://www.bmm.icnet.uk/docking) is often used for protein–protein docking. Binding modes determined by FTDock can be further refined by its companion program, MultiDock. The HEX algorithm is specialized for docking proteins to other proteins and does so with surprising speed. Other algorithms, including DOCK, Hammerhead, GOLD, FLEXX (http://cartan.gmd.de/flexx), and many more, use a variety of protein representations, force fields, and search algorithms.

Database Screening

A primary consideration in designing ligand docking algorithms is the balance between the need for a complete and accurate search of the possible ligand conformations and binding modes, and the necessity of designing an algorithm with a reasonable computational complexity. A docking algorithm that always produces perfect results is not useful if it takes years to complete. For screening of databases containing possible drugs, algorithms need to essentially dock thousands of ligands to a protein active site and, therefore, need even greater efficiency.

A common approach for screening ligand databases is to use a fast docking algorithm, such as Hammerhead, FLEXX, or HEX, to dock a variety of ligands to the target protein, using the energy score from the docking algorithm as a predictor of binding affinity. For large databases containing hundreds of thousands of lead compounds, however, such an approach is impractical, requiring hundreds of days to screen a database for a single drug target.

Methods that are designed specifically for database screening, such as the SLIDE algorithm, often reduce the number of compounds that must be docked using database indexing techniques to rule out lead compounds that are highly unlikely to bind to the target active site prior to docking. SLIDE characterizes the target active site according to the positions of potential hydrogen bond donors and acceptors, and hydrophobic interaction points, forming a template. Each potential ligand in the database is characterized in a similar manner, and a set of indices is constructed. These indices allow SLIDE to quickly rule out ligands that are, for example, too large or too small to fit the template (Figure 8.4 on page 192). By reducing the number of ligands that undergo the computationally expensive docking procedure, SLIDE and similar algorithms can screen large databases of potential ligands in days (and sometimes even hours) rather than months.

X-Ray Crystal Structures

Many of the bioinformatics techniques that we have discussed in this and the previous chapter, including computational docking, ligand database screening, and the formulation of empirical energy functions for protein folding, depend on experimentally observed three-dimensional protein structures. While even the most powerful microscopy techniques are insufficient to determine the molecular coordinates of each atom in a protein, the discovery of X-rays by W. C. Roentgen in 1895 has led to the development of a powerful tool for analyzing protein structure: X-ray crystallography. In 1912, M. von Laue discovered that **crystals,** solid structures formed by a regular array of molecules, diffract X-rays in regular and predictable patterns. In the early 1950s, pioneering scientists such as D. Hodgkin were able to crystallize complex organic molecules and determine their structure by looking at how they diffracted a beam of X-rays. Today, X-ray crystallography has been employed to determine ~15,000 protein structures at very high levels of resolution.

The first step in crystallographic determination of a protein's structure is to grow a crystal of the protein. While this can often be a sensitive and demanding process, the basic idea is simple. Just as sugar crystals can be grown by slow evaporation of a solution of sugar and water, protein crystals are often grown by evaporation of a pure protein solution. Protein crystals, however, are generally very small (~0.3 to 1.5 mm in each dimension), and consist of as much as 70% water, having a consistency more like gelatin than sugar crystals (Figure 8.5 on page 193). Growing protein crystals generally requires carefully controlled conditions and a great deal of time; it sometimes takes months or even years of experimentation to find the appropriate crystallization conditions for a single protein.

**For all possible anchor fragments defined by all triplets of
interaction centers in each of the screened molecules**

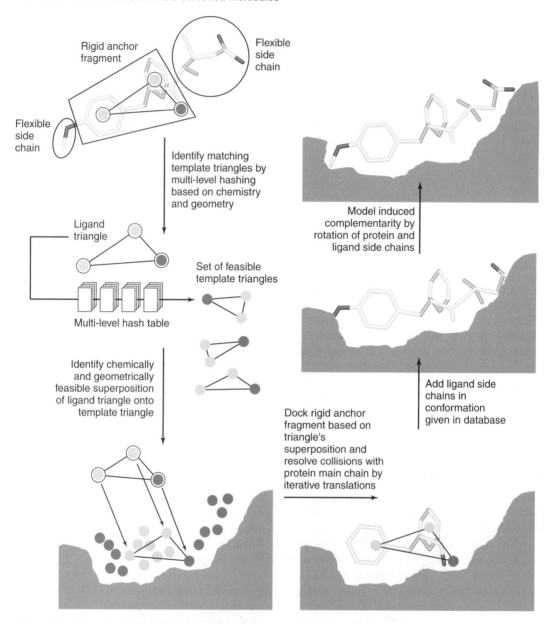

F I G U R E 8.4 *The steps involved in finding potential ligands in SLIDE.
Ligands are characterized by hydrogen bond donor and acceptor positions and by
hydrophobic interaction points. Each triangle composed of three such points is indexed
in a set of hash tables according to the length of the longest side, the perimeter
distance, and other features. The hash tables allow ligands that will not fit into the
active site to be eliminated before the computationally expensive docking steps begin.*

F I G U R E 8.5 *A protein crystal.*

Once protein crystals are obtained, they are loaded into a capillary tube and exposed to a beam of X-ray radiation, which is then diffracted by the protein crystal (Figure 8.6 on page 194). In early crystallography, the diffraction pattern was captured on X-ray film. Modern crystallography equipment uses X-ray detectors that transfer the diffraction pattern directly to a computer for analysis. Figure 8.7 on page 194 shows an example of an X-ray diffraction pattern.

Once the diffraction data are obtained, a crystallographer uses a very complex mix of reverse Fourier transformations, crystallographic software tools, and protein modeling skills to determine the three-dimensional structure of the protein. The Protein Data Bank (PDB) at http://www.rcsb.org serves as the primary repository for protein structures derived from X-ray crystallography. PDB also serves as a repository for protein structures derived from nuclear magnetic resonance (**NMR**), another technique for resolving protein structures. The structures stored in the PDB are kept in two distinct formats. The original PDB format is text based and remains the most commonly used method for storing and processing crystallographic structures. The format of text-based PDB files is convenient for parsing and analysis using string processing languages such as Perl. For each atom in the protein, a line in the PDB file contains the X, Y, and Z coordinates in angstroms (0.1 nm or 10^{-10} m), along with a few other pieces of information relevant to that atom. Example number 8 in Appendix 3 demonstrates how to read and parse the molecular coordinates in a text-based PDB file.

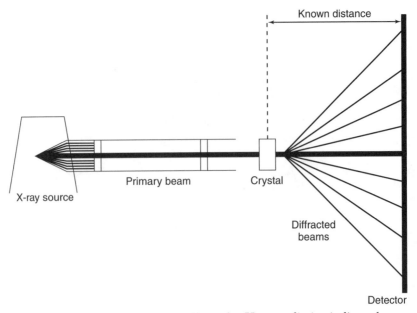

F I G U R E 8.6 *In X-ray crystallography, X-ray radiation is directed at a protein crystal. The electrons in the protein diffract the X-rays, producing a diffraction pattern that is captured by the detector.*

F I G U R E 8.7 *An X-ray diffraction pattern.*

Each structure in the PDB is assigned a four-character PDB code. For example, the PDB entry 2APR contains the molecular coordinates of rhizopuspepsin, an aspartic protease. PDB formatted text files are generally named either XXXX.pdb, or pdbXXXX.ent, where XXXX is the four-letter PDB code for the structure.

In 1990 the International Union of Crystallographers (IUCr) formalized a new standard, the mmCIF (macromolecular crystallographic information file) format. This format is designed to provide additional flexibility and richness over the original PDB file format. However, PDB text files currently remain the most common format for distribution of protein structural data. Further details on the PDB and mmCIF formats can be found at http://www.rcsb.org.

The Protein Information Resource (PIR) is another rich source of protein sequence and structure data. The PIR web site (http://pir.georgetown.edu) is the home of the PIR-PSD, a richly annotated protein sequence database, the *i*ProClass protein classification database, various sequence search and prediction algorithms, and numerous other tools and data sources related to protein structure and function. Additionally, a number of proteomics tools and databases can be found at the ExPASy server (http://www.expasy.ch), including the SwissProt database, a richly annotated protein sequence database; the Prosite database of protein families and domains; and numerous proteomics tools, including software tools for some of the techniques mentioned earlier in this chapter, such as peptide mass fingerprinting.

While the three-dimensional coordinates found in a PDB entry are not particularly well suited for human viewing, numerous molecular graphics tools are available for visualizing protein structures from X-ray coordinates. RasMol, along with the Microsoft Windows® version, RasWin (http://www.bernstein-plus-sons. com/software/rasmol), is among the easiest to install and learn, and provides various views of a protein that can be rotated and manipulated on even a modestly powered Windows, Mac, or UNIX-based system.

Other useful and easy to learn visualization tools include the Swiss PDB viewer (http://www.expasy.ch/spdbv), VMD (http://www.ks.uiuc.edu/Research/ vmd), Spock (http://quorum.tamu.edu/jon/spock), and Protein explorer (http:// www.umass.edu/microbio/chime/explorer). Protein explorer provides numerous molecular graphics and protein analysis tools and runs within the Netscape web browser. Protein explorer can download PDB coordinates directly from the PDB site, obviating the need to download PDB files to your own hard disk. One of the most useful tools in Protein explorer is the comparator, which visualizes two structures side by side, allowing simultaneous manipulation and comparison of both structures. DINO (http://www.bioz.unibas.ch/~xray/dino) provides a wide array of visualization methods, at the expense of a slightly steeper learning curve.

Numerous other molecular graphics packages are available, representing a wide range of capabilities and complexity. Many of them are listed in the Links section of the PDB web site: http://www.rcsb.org/pdb/software-list.html#Graphics. Figure 8.8 shows some of the protein representations that can be generated by some of the molecular graphics tools mentioned above.

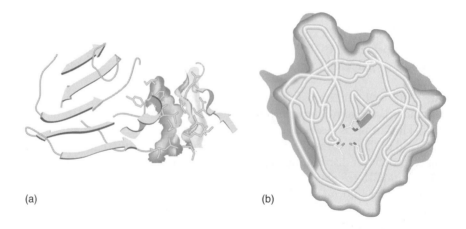

(a)   (b)

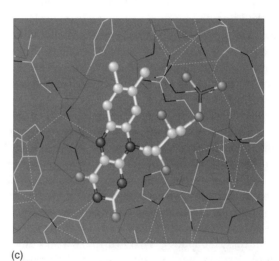

(c)

F I G U R E 8.8 *Several molecular graphics representations of proteins. (a) The cartoon method highlights regions of secondary structure. (b) Molecular surface representations reveal the overall shape of the protein. (c) The wireframe and ball-and-stick representations illustrate specific molecular interactions.*

Finally, note that crystallographic structures are essentially averaged over the many copies of the protein in a single crystal and also over the time that the crystal is exposed to the X-ray. Proteins in a crystal are not completely rigid, and the mobility of specific atoms in a protein will "blur" the crystallographic signal. The positions of water molecules in the crystal, which are often included in a PDB entry, are particularly difficult to resolve and subject to noise. Nevertheless, protein crystallography remains the primary method for obtaining a glimpse of the structure of a protein at an atomic resolution.

NMR Structures

Nuclear magnetic resonance spectroscopy provides an alternative method for determining macromolecular structures. At the heart of the NMR technique is the fact that the nuclei of the atoms of some elements (such as hydrogen and radioactive isotopes of carbon and nitrogen) vibrate or resonate when the molecules they are a part of are placed in a static magnetic field and exposed to a second oscillating magnetic field. The magnetic fields of these atomic nuclei vibrate as they try to become aligned with the external magnetic fields, and those resonances can be detected by external sensors as NMR spectra. The behavior of any atom is influenced by neighboring atoms in adjacent residues such that closely spaced residues are more perturbed than distant residues. Interpretation typically requires extensive and complex reverse Fourier transformations, much like X-ray crystallography. The complexity of the data analysis alone usually limits the utility of the approach for any proteins or domains larger than 200 amino acids.

A key advantage of NMR methods is that they do not require crystallization of the protein. Because not all proteins can be effectively crystallized (many membrane integral proteins, in particular, have proven resistant to crystallization), NMR is an important source of 3D structural information. The result of an NMR experiment is a set of constraints on the interatomic distances in a macromolecular structure. These constraints can then be used, along with a protein's known sequence, to provide a model of the protein's structure. It is, however, generally the case that more than one model can effectively satisfy the constraints obtained by NMR, so NMR structures usually contain several models of a protein (that is, several sets of coordinates), while crystallographic structures usually contain only a single model.

Empirical Methods and Prediction Techniques

The wealth of protein structural data provided by crystallography has opened up the way for numerous empirical studies of protein structure and function. Computational techniques from statistics, data mining, computer vision and pattern recognition, evolutionary computation, and many other fields have all been applied to glean a deeper understanding of how protein molecules behave and interact with other biological molecules. While far too many studies of this kind exist to provide a comprehensive treatment of the subject here, many empirical algorithms follow a pattern recognition approach in their general design. Thus, a simple example can be employed to demonstrate some of the features common to many empirical methods.

Suppose we are given the task of designing an algorithm that, given the three-dimensional structure of a protein, predicts which residues in the protein are likely to be involved in protein–protein contacts. Since many proteins are only active when associated with other proteins in multienzyme complexes, this might be an interesting question to pursue. How would one go about designing an algorithm to make such predictions about specific residues, given only the three-dimensional coordinates of a protein? For an empirical algorithm, the answer is "by observing the properties of residues that are known to be involved in protein–protein contacts (we'll call them *interfacial* residues) and those that are not."

From the structures in the PDB, we might begin by selecting a set of example structures that show two or more proteins complexed together. In each of these structures, there will be some interfacial residues involved in the contact surface between two proteins, and some noninterfacial residues that are not near the protein–protein interface. For each residue, we can select a set of features to measure. For example, we might choose to measure the number of other residues within a certain radius of each residue; this would give us an idea of how crowded the area around the residue is. Other features we choose to measure might include the net charge of the residue and surrounding residues, the level of hydrophobicity of the residue, the hydrogen bonding potential of the residue, and any other feature we think might be relevant to whether or not the residue is part of a protein–protein interface.

Once the features are measured, each residue in our database is represented as a **labeled feature vector.** The label represents whether the residue is an interfacial residue or not, and the feature vector is just the list of feature values for that residue. These labeled feature vectors serve as the training data for a prediction algorithm, as illustrated in Figure 8.9. The prediction algorithm can be a statistical method, a neural network, an evolutionary algorithm, or one of any number of other computational techniques for learning from example data. The goal of the prediction algorithm is to learn, by observing the labeled training data, which feature values are associated with interfacial residues and which values indicate noninterface residues. Ideally, once the predictor is trained, we can give the algorithm a new residue without the label and it will predict whether the new residue is an interface or noninterface residue.

This general method has been applied to develop algorithms that predict a diverse array of protein properties, including secondary and tertiary structure; binding to ligands, other proteins, and water molecules; active site location; and even general biological function.

Post-Translational Modification Prediction

The wide variety of protein structure and functions is due, in part, to the fact that proteins undergo a wide variety of modifications after being transcribed. These modifications may remove segments of a protein; covalently attach sugars, phosphates, or sulfate groups to surface residues; or cross-link residues within a pro-

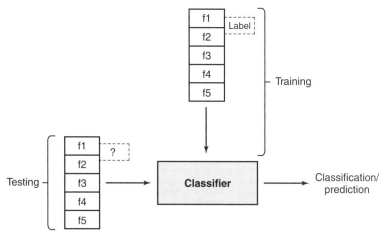

F I G U R E 8.9 *During training, labeled feature vectors are provided to the classification algorithm. After it has learned the feature values that distinguish each class, the algorithm is presented with an unlabeled feature vector to classify.*

tein (disulfide bond formation). Many of these modifications are themselves performed by other proteins that must recognize specific surface residues as appropriate for modification. The question of what signals a protein-modifying enzyme to operate on a particular residue is an important question to understanding protein function, regulation, and localization.

Protein Sorting

The presence of internal, membrane-bound compartments is one of the single most distinguishing features of eukaryotic cells. The chemical environment within those different compartments can differ dramatically as can the population of proteins found within them. It is both functionally and energetically imperative that eukaryotes deliver proteins to the appropriate compartment. For example, histones (DNA binding proteins associated with chromatin; see Chapter 6) are only functionally useful within a eukaryotic cell's nucleus where its chromosomes are sequestered. Other proteins such as the proteases found within peroxisomes are quite dangerous to a cell anywhere but within their proper compartment. Eukaryotic cells appear to consider proteins as belonging to one of only two distinctly different classes with regard to their localization (Figure 8.10 on page 200): those that are not associated with membranes, and those that are associated with membranes.

The first set of proteins is translated exclusively by ribosomes that remain suspended (sometimes called "free-floating") within the cytoplasm. mRNAs translated by free-floating ribosomes can ultimately be delivered to some of the following important destinations: the cytoplasm itself, the nucleus, the mitochondria, chloroplasts, and peroxisomes. Residence within the cytoplasm seems to be the default state for proteins. In contrast, delivery to the nucleus, mitochondria,

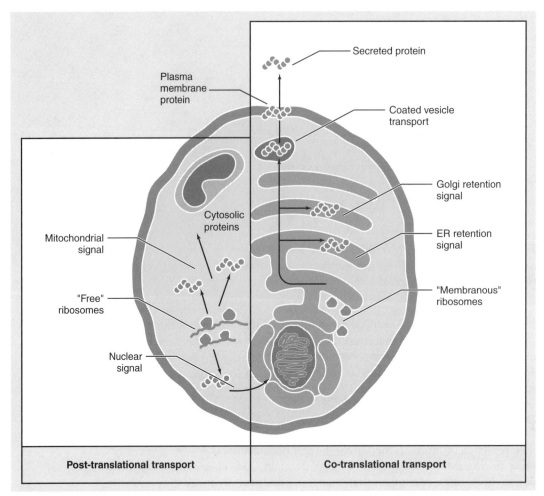

F I G U R E 8.10 *Proteins released into the cytosol by free ribosomes may depend on various protein sorting signals to determine their cellular destination, or they may remain in the cytoplasm. Proteins synthesized by membrane-bound ribosomes in the ER move to the Golgi apparatus and then through the plasma membrane unless they contain specific localization signals to determine their final destination.*

chloroplasts, or peroxisomes requires the presence and recognition of specific localization signals (Table 8.3).

Nuclear proteins (such as histones and transcription factors) are targeted to the nucleus by their possessing a **nuclear localization sequence:** a stretch of 7 to 41 amino acids that is rich in lysine and/or arginine. Mitochondrial proteins all possess an amphipathic helix 12 to 30 amino acids long at their N terminus. This **mitochondrial signal sequence** is ultimately recognized by a receptor on the surface of mitochondria and then often removed to activate the protein as it is transported into the mitochondria. Chloroplast proteins encoded by nuclear

T A B L E 8.3 Several protein localization signals used by all eukaryotic cells.

Organelle	Signal location	Type	Signal length
Mitochondria	N terminus	Amphipathic helix	12–30
Chloroplasts	N terminus	Charged	Roughly 25
Nucleus	Internal	Basic	7–41
Peroxisome	C terminus	SKL	3

genes all possess a **chloroplast transit sequence** (a string of roughly 25 charged amino acids at their N terminus) that is similarly recognized by receptor proteins on the surface of chloroplasts. By the same token, proteins destined for peroxisomes all have one of two **peroxisomal targeting signals** that are recognized by receptors that ensure their delivery to the correct destination.

The second set of proteins is translated by membrane-bound ribosomes that are associated with the **endoplasmic reticulum (ER).** The endoplasmic reticulum itself is a web-like network of membranes that is intimately associated with the Golgi apparatus in which a great deal of additional protein processing (such as glycosylation and acetylation) also takes place, as described below. All proteins translated by ER ribosomes actually begin to be translated by free-floating ribosomes in the cytoplasm. When the first 15 to 30 amino acids to be translated correspond to a special **signal sequence,** a signal recognition particle binds to it and stops further translation until the ribosome and its mRNA are delivered to the ER. While no particular consensus sequence for the signal sequence is evident, a hydrophobic stretch of 10 to 15 residues, ending with one or more positively charged residues, is found in almost all of these targeting motifs. When translation resumes, the new polypeptide is extruded through a pore in the membrane of the ER into the ER's lumen (inner space). Once a protein is transported across the ER membrane, a **signal peptidase** cleaves the N-terminal targeting sequence from the protein unless it is to be retained permanently as a membrane-bound protein itself.

Various computational methods have been employed for the identification of targeting signals and predicting protein localization. PSORT (http://psort.nibb.ac.jp) uses a **nearest neighbor classifier.** The nearest neighbor classifier is a statistical method that classifies according to similarity. A database of examples of signal peptides and nonsignal peptides is consulted. To predict if a particular sequence is a signal peptide, it is compared with the sequences in the database. The sequences that are very similar to the sequence being predicted are identified and tallied. If the majority of these "near-neighbor" sequences are signal peptides for a particular cellular location, then the sequence in question is also predicted to be a signal peptide for that location. Another localization signaling prediction tool, SignalP (http://www.cbs.dtu.dk/services/SignalP), uses artificial neural networks, a computational method that has been successfully employed in the analysis of a wide range of bioinformatics problems and data sets as described previously in the context of gene recognition (Chapter 6).

Proteolytic Cleavage

Both prokaryotic and eukaryotic organisms have numerous enzymes responsible for the cleavage and degradation of proteins and peptides. Examples of proteolytic cleavage are abundant, ranging from the removal of the initial methionine residue present at the start of every polypeptide (because start codons also code for methionine; see Chapter 1), to the removal of the signal peptides discussed in the previous section. Many of these enzymes recognize specific sequence motifs as indicators of cleavage sites. Sometimes, the cleavage signal can be as short as a single residue. Examples include chymotrypsin, which cleaves polypeptides on the C-terminal side of bulky and **aromatic** (ring-containing) residues such as phenylalanine; trypsin, which cleaves the peptide bond on the carboxyl side of arginine and lysine residues; and elastase, which cleaves the peptide bond on the C-terminal side of small residues such as glycine and alanine. In many cases, however, the sequence motif is larger and more ambiguous, much like the localization motifs previously discussed. Protein cleavage by **proteasomes** (multienzyme structures involved in protein degradation and immune response) can be predicted with high levels of accuracy (>98%) using a neural network (http://www.paproc.de).

Glycosylation

Glycosylation is the process of covalently linking an **oligosaccharide** (a short chain of sugars) to the side chain of a protein surface residue. The presence of glycosylated residues can have a significant effect on protein folding, localization, biological activity, and interactions with other proteins. There are several types of glycosylation in eukaryotes, the most important of which are N-linked and O-linked glycosylation.

N-linked glycosylation is the addition of an oligosaccharide to asparagine residues during protein translation. The primary signal that an asparagine (Asn) residue should be glycosylated is the local amino acid sequence. The consensus sequence Asn-X-Ser or Asn-X-Thr, where X is any residue other than proline, is nearly always found at glycosylated Asn residues. However, the sequence alone is insufficient to determine glycosylation, because some Asn-X-Ser/Thr triplets have nonglycosylated asparagine residues. The most common computational technique for identifying glycosylation sites involves the use of neural networks trained to identify glycosylated Asn residues using a procedure much like that described in the previous section on empirical methods and prediction techniques. Modern neural network-based approaches obtain accuracies around 75% for predicting N-linked glycosylation sites.

O-linked glycosylation is a post-translational process in which the enzyme *N*-acetylglucosaminyl transferase attaches an oligosaccharide to the oxygen atom of a serine or threonine residue. Unlike N-linked glycosylation, there is no known sequence motif that signals an O-glycosylation site, other than the presence of proline and valine residues in the vicinity of the Ser or Thr to be glycosylated. Again, a common method for identification of these sites is to use prediction algorithms based on neural networks, trained using local sequence context and surface accessibility as features. The resulting algorithms have >85% accuracy in predicting glycosylated residues.

Phosphorylation

Phosphorylation (attachment of a phosphate group) of surface residues is probably the most common post-translational modification in animal proteins. **Kinases,** the enzymes responsible for phosphorylation, are involved in a wide variety of signaling and regulatory pathways. Since phosphorylation frequently serves as an activation signal for an enzyme, it is often an ephemeral condition. **Phosphatases** are the enzymes responsible for removing phosphate groups from phosphorylated residues.

Often, kinases themselves are activated by phosphorylation, so that activation of a particular kinase can result in a cascade of successive phosphorylation events. One of the most well studied of these **signal cascades** is the cyclic AMP (cAMP) cascade, which controls glycogen synthesis and breakdown. Glycogen is a glucose polymer that serves as an energy-storage molecule. The synthesis and breakdown of glycogen are controlled by a number of hormones including glucagon, insulin, and epinephrine. When epinephrine is released by the adrenal medulla it leads to an increase in the cytosolic level of cAMP, which activates protein kinase A. Protein kinase A (PKA) then phosphorylates and activates phosphorylase kinase, which, in turn, phosphorylates and activates phosphorylase, the enzyme responsible for glycogen breakdown. PKA simultaneously phosphorylates and *deactivates* glycogen synthase, the enzyme responsible for glycogen synthesis. The multiple phosphorylation events in this cascade facilitate a very rapid response to epinephrine release.

Because phosphorylation of key tyrosine, serine, and threonine residues serves as a regulation mechanism for a wide variety of molecular processes, the various types of kinases involved in each process must have high specificity in recognizing particular enzymes. As a result, no single consensus sequence identifies a residue as a phosphorylation target. However, some patterns do exist, allowing computational prediction of phosphorylation sites. Neural network-based approaches, such as NetPhos, have obtained sensitivity greater than 70% in predicting phosphorylation targets based on sequence and structural information.

Chapter Summary

While genomics is rapidly becoming a mature research area, proteomics techniques are only now beginning to identify the proteins encoded within the genome and their various interactions. Characterization of an organism's proteome promises to bridge the gap between our understanding of the genome and the physiological and morphological effects of the genes therein. Various taxonomies have been developed to classify and organize proteins according to enzymatic function, sequence similarity, and three-dimensional shape. Armed with these databases of protein families, superfamilies, and folds, along with experimental techniques such as 2D electrophoresis, peptide mass fingerprints, and mass spectrometry, investigators can separate, purify, and identify the various proteins expressed by a cell at a particular time. One important application of proteomic information is in pharmaceutical drug design. Advances in knowledge of protein structure and X-ray crystallography have allowed computational methods for protein ligand screening and docking to contribute to the process of drug discovery. While the three-dimensional structure of a protein is the keystone for understanding a protein's function and interactions with other proteins, some important information can be obtained from sequence alone. Protein localization and various post-translational modifications are signaled by sequence motifs in the protein's primary structure.

Readings for Greater Depth

A summary of the means by which proteins can be grouped into families and superfamilies on the basis of their evolutionary history can be found in C. Chothia, 1992, Proteins, one thousand families for the molecular biologist, *Nature* **357**: 543–544.

The idea of exons being regions that code for portions of proteins with distinct functionalities is well described in R. L. Dorit, L. Schoenback, and W. Gilbert, 1991, How big is the universe of exons? *Science*, **253**: 677–680.

The integration of fast database searching techniques and Bayesian statistics for protein identification from mass spectra data is spelled out in W. Zhang and B. T. Chait, 2000, ProFound—An expert system for protein identification using mass spectrometric peptide mapping information, *Analyt. Chem.* **72**: 2482–2489.

The AutoDock algorithm, one of the first methods for completely automated molecular docking, was first described in D. S. Goodsell and A. J. Olson, 1990, Automated docking of substrates to proteins by simulated annealing, *Proteins: Structure, Function, and Genetics*, **8**: 195–202. The most recent version of AutoDock, version 3.0, is described in G. M. Morris, D. S. Goodsell, R. S. Halliday, R. Huey, W. E. Hart, R. K. Belew, and A. J. Olson, 1998, Automated docking using a lamarckian genetic algorithm and an empirical binding free energy function, *J. Computational Chem.* **19**: 1639–1662.

The Fourier transform-based methods of FTDock are described in E. Katchalski-Katzir, I. Shariv, M. Eisenstein, A. A. Friesem, C. Aflalo, and I. A. Vakser, 1992. Molecular surface recognition: Determination of geometric fit between proteins and their ligands by correlation techniques, *Proc. Nat. Acad. Sci. U.S.A.* **89**: 2195–2199.

The speedy HEX docking program is detailed in D. W Ritchie and G. J. L. Kemp, 2000, Protein docking using spherical polar Fourier correlations, *Proteins: Structure, Function, and Genetics*, **39**: 178–194.

SLIDE, an algorithm for screening large databases for protein ligands, is described in V. Schnecke and L. A. Kuhn, 1999, Database screening for HIV protease ligands: The influence of binding-site conformation and representation on ligand selectivity, *Proc. Seventh Int. Conf. Intelligent Systems for Molecular Biology*, pp. 242–251.

NetPHOS, a neural network-based method for predicting phosphorylation sites, is discussed in N. Blom, S. Gammeltoft, and Sùren Brunak, 1999, Sequence and structure-based prediction of eukaryotic protein phosphorylation sites, *J. Molecular Biol.* **94**: 1351–1362.

More information on neural networks, nearest neighbor classification, and other computational pattern recognition methods can be found in R. Duda and P. Hart, 1973, *Pattern Classification and Scene Analysis*, John Wiley & Sons, New York.

Many of the computational prediction algorithms referenced in this chapter can be found at the Center for Biological Sequence Analysis, Technical University of Denmark's web page: http://www.cbs.dtu.dk, and at the ExPASy tools page: http://www.expasy.ch/tools.

Questions and Problems

* **8.1** Briefly describe how the cAMP cascade allows a rapid response to the release of epinephrine.

8.2 Modify the Perl code in Example 8 of Appendix 3 to find the centroid of a protein by finding the average X, Y, and Z values of all the ATOM records in a PDB file.

* **8.3** Starting with your solution for Question 8.2, add some Perl code to find and print the atoms closest to and furthest from the centroid.

8.4 Briefly describe the key difference between ligand docking and ligand screening algorithms. What trade-offs must be considered when designing a ligand screening algorithm?

* **8.5** Describe in detail how one might go about designing an empirical algorithm to predict whether or not a particular cysteine residue will form a disulfide bond, based on crystallographic structures from the PDB.

8.6 Given that glycosylation typically takes place within the Golgi apparatus, how likely is it that nuclear proteins like histones and transcription factors will be normally glycosylated within eukaryotic cells? Why?

* **8.7** Assuming that all amino acids are utilized with the same frequency and that there are a total of approximately 1,000 unique destinations for a protein within a eukaryotic cell, what is the minimum length that a signal sequence must be to ensure that its associated protein will be delivered appropriately?

A Gentle Introduction to Computer Programming and Data Structures

Creating and Executing Computer Programs

Variables and Values
Data typing
Basic operations

Program Control
Statements and blocks
Conditional execution
Loops

Readability
Structured programming
Comments
Descriptive variable names

Data Structures
Arrays
Hashes
Working with strings

Subroutines and Functions

Input and Output

Regular Expressions

Where to Go from Here

Anyone who uses a computer regularly will quickly learn to appreciate the advantages of knowing how to write programs. Nowhere is this more true than in the field of bioinformatics, where new algorithms and techniques are constantly being developed, and the standards for file and data formats are diverse and rapidly evolving. Learning the basics of computer programming will allow you to read, reformat, and write data files; perform basic calculations on your data; and even make additions and refinements to the bioinformatics tools that you use in your research, since the source code for many bioinformatics algorithms is freely available on the World Wide Web.

The objective of this chapter is to teach the basic skills and concepts involved in writing and debugging computer programs. We have chosen Perl as an example language because it is commonly used in bioinformatics software, and because it is a simple enough language to be examined in the scope of this appendix. Once you have learned the programming concepts presented here, you will find that you can not only write simple programs in Perl, but also quickly learn and use other programming languages. Most commonly used languages are based on the underlying concepts discussed in this chapter. Once you understand the basics of programming in Perl, you will find it much easier to learn to use other languages including C, C++, Java, Python, and many more.

This chapter is not intended to be a complete Perl language reference, but rather an introduction to the fundamental concepts of computer programming, using Perl as an example language. For a more detailed discussion of the Perl programming language, refer to the additional resources listed at the end of the chapter.

Creating and Executing Computer Programs

A computer program is actually nothing more than a text file (or, more often, a collection of text files) that contains instructions for accomplishing a certain task. Writing a computer program is a lot like writing a recipe or a laboratory protocol—the first step is to outline exactly what needs to be done. The main difference between writing a computer program and writing a recipe is that the author of a computer program is limited to a specific list of legal instructions. While there may be many ways to tell a cook to include a dash of salt in the soup, there is generally only one instruction that accomplishes a specific task in a computer programming language.

Many programming languages exist, but computers actually speak only one language, **machine language.** Most programs are not written in machine language directly because machine language is not very easy for humans to read and write. Instead, we use a **compiler** to translate a list of instructions (i.e., a computer program) from a programming language (such as C++) into machine language. The resulting program is then ready to run on your computer. In the Windows operating system, programs that have been compiled and are ready to run have file names that end in ".exe" for "executable." Perl, however, is a special type of programming language that does not require a compiler. To write a Perl program, we simply create a text file containing a list of Perl commands. This text file is called a **Perl script,** or sometimes a Perl program. To run the program, we must start the **Perl interpreter,** and tell it to run our newly written Perl script. The way in which we start the Perl interpreter depends on what type of computer we are using. On UNIX and most Windows systems, we can usually type **perl** ***scriptname*** where *scriptname* is replaced with the name of our Perl script. Perl programmers often use file names ending in ".pl" for their scripts. On properly configured Mac and Windows systems, a Perl script can be executed by double-clicking on the script file.

In summary, writing a computer program in Perl includes the following steps:

- First, we write the program as a text file. As a general rule, we give the file a name ending in ".pl", such as "myscript.pl".

- Next, we run the interpreter, which executes the script. The way in which we start the interpreter depends on the type of computer we are using.

Variables and Values

One of the most important concepts in computer programming is the idea of a variable. In general, variables in computer programs work in much the same way as variables in algebra. If we have the following two algebraic equations:

$$x = 7$$
$$y = x + 5$$

we can conclude that $y = 12$. Each variable acts as a named storage location where a value is stored. In algebra, variables are usually named using single letters, such as x and y in the above example. In computer programs, longer names are often used to make the program easier to read. The legal names for variables depend on the language you are using. In Perl, most combinations of letters, numbers, and a few other characters including the hyphen (-) and underscore (_) characters, are legal variable names. For now, all of our variable names must begin with the character $. In Perl, a dollar sign indicates that a variable is a **scalar variable,** or a variable that can hold only one value. We will discuss scalar and other types of variables in more detail shortly. The value stored in a variable can be retrieved or changed at any time, and we can perform operations on it. The Perl language includes most of the basic arithmetic operations. Consider the following bit of Perl code:

```
$var1 = 9;
$var2 = 7;
$product = $var1 * $var2;
$sum = $var1 + $var2;
$remainder = $var1 % $var2;
```

In this example, `$product` is a variable containing the value 63, and `$sum` is a variable containing the value 16. In Perl, the symbol % is used to compute the remainder when the first operand is divided by the second, so in the above example the variable `$remainder` contains the value 2.

Data Typing

Unlike algebra, the variables in our computer programs can contain more than just numbers. In Perl, a variable might contain an integer number, such as 7, a real number such as 3.1417, or a character string such as "hello world," among other things. In many languages, you must declare what kinds of values a variable can contain before using it. In C and C++, for example, if you decide that a certain variable can contain integers, then that variable cannot contain text, real numbers, or any other kind of data. In Perl, however, a variable can contain any kind of data at any time. The only decision we must make when creating a variable in Perl is whether the variable will hold only one value or many values. A variable that can hold only a single value is called a scalar variable, as described previously, and begins with the character $. Two other types of variables, arrays and hashes, can hold many values. Arrays and hashes will be discussed in more detail in the Data Structures section.

In most languages, you must list all of the variables you wish to use at the start of your program. This is called **declaring** the variables. In Perl, declaring variables is not necessary. Variables are created the first time you refer to them. The following Perl script uses a single variable to store several types of data:

```perl
$my_variable = 7;
print("my variable contains the value: $my_variable \n");
$my_variable = 7.3217;
print("my variable contains the value: $my_variable \n");
$my_variable ="apple";
print("my variable contains the value: $my_variable \n");
```

If you type the lines above into a text file and execute it in Perl, you will see the following output:

```
my variable contains the value: 7
my variable contains the value: 7.3217
my variable contains the value: apple
```

In this short script, the variable `$my_variable` contained first an integer value, then a real value, and finally a text string. This flexibility in handling variables makes Perl one of the easiest programming languages to learn and to write short programs in quickly.

Before we go on, a few features of the preceding Perl script merit further discussion. First, note that each line of Perl code ends in a semicolon. The reason for this is discussed further in the Program Control section. Also note that text strings are enclosed in double quotes. To store the word *apple* in the variable `$my_variable`, we enclose it in double quotes. Text strings can consist of more than one word, so the following instruction would also be legal in Perl:

```
$my_variable ="a ripe red apple";
```

Finally, note that we can use the `print` instruction to send output to the computer's display. The "\n" at the end of each print instruction is a special code to move to the next line of the display screen. Without the "\n" in each print instruction, all the output would have printed on the same line of the display screen, which would have been difficult to read. Text strings and special characters, such as \n, will be discussed further in the Data Structures section.

Basic Operations

As mentioned previously, Perl contains symbols for most of the basic algebraic and math operations. As a convenience for programmers, Perl also contains some shortcuts for common combinations of operations. For example, it is often necessary to add or subtract a number from a variable, as in the following example:

```
$var2 = $var2 + 12;
```

Perl provides the += operator to make this operation easier. The following line of Perl code produces exactly the same results as the previous line:

```
$var2 += 12;
```

Table A1.1 shows some common operators used in Perl and their effects.

Program Control

At this point we have discussed enough of the Perl language to do simple numeric calculations, but we haven't yet seen anything that could not be done faster and more easily on a pocket calculator. The real power of a computer lies largely in its ability to make decisions. To achieve this ability, all programming languages

T A B L E A1.1 A few commonly used Perl operators.

Operator	Effect
*, /, +, –	Algebraic multiplication, division, addition, and subtraction, respectively
%	Modulus (remainder)
++, – –	Increment or decrement (`$var++` adds 1 to the numeric value in $var, `$var--` subtracts 1 from $var)
+=, -=, *=, /=	Shortcuts for algebraic operations (`$var1 += 12` is the same as `$var1 = $var1 + 12`)
**	Exponentiation: `$var**3` is $var cubed
.	String concatenation: If `$var1` = "hi" and `$var2` = "there", `$var1 . $var2` = "hithere"
×	String repetition: `$string = "hi" × 3` sets the value of $string to "hihihi"

provide some facility for **program control.** That is, there must be a way to tell the computer to execute one set of instructions if a certain condition is true, and another set of instructions otherwise. In Perl, program control is mostly realized by **conditional** or **if statements,** and by loops. Before we can discuss these two structures, however, it is necessary to have an idea of the basic units of structured code in Perl: the statement and the block.

Statements and Blocks

The basic unit of execution in Perl is the statement. A **statement** represents one instruction, and is generally terminated with a semicolon. In each of the previous examples there is a semicolon at the end of each statement. Sometimes a statement needs to be longer than a single line of code. Because each Perl statement ends in a semicolon, there is no difficulty in determining where a statement ends, even when it spans multiple lines, as in the following example:

```
$total_annual_sales = $first_quarter_total +
    $second_quarter_total + $third_quarter_total +
    $fourth_quarter_total;
```

The second and third lines of the statement are indented to make the line more readable. The indentation, however, is only used to help human readers see where the statement ends, and it is optional. The Perl interpreter knows where the statement ends by looking for the semicolon.

A **block** is a set of statements enclosed in curly braces. We will discuss code blocks further shortly. For now, simply remember that each block of code starts with an opening curly brace ({) and ends with a closing curly brace (}).

Conditional Execution

As you begin to write Perl programs, you will find that you often want to include some statements that are only executed under certain conditions. If these conditions are not met, then the code is skipped. In Perl, we can easily write this sort of code using the `if` statement. The `if` statement in Perl is the most commonly used mechanism for **conditional execution.** In the following example, we wish to take the absolute value of the variable `$x` and place it in the variable `$abs_x`. The actions we need to take depend on whether the value of `x` is positive or negative:

```
$abs_x = $x;
if ($abs_x < 0)
{
    $abs_x *= -1;
}
print("The absolute value of x is $abs_x \n");
```

Let's examine how this code will execute in detail. When the first line is executed, the value of `$x` is copied into `$abs_x`. Next, the `if` statement tests whether the value of $abs_x is less than zero. If so, the block of code following the if statement is executed. If not, the block of code is skipped and the program continues with the print statement, which will print the value of $abs_x. For example, if $x = -7, then the print statement above will print the following line to the computer screen:

```
The absolute value of x is: 7
```

There are several important things to note about this seemingly simple piece of code. First, notice that after the if statement we include a test inside a pair of parentheses. If the result of this test is true, then the block of code following the if statement is executed, otherwise it is skipped. This is the one of the most important uses of blocks in Perl: After an if statement, the next block of code is the **conditional code**—the code that will only be executed if the test is true. Any code that follows the closing brace of the block, such as the print statement in the above example, will be executed regardless of whether the test in the if statement is true or false.

Sometimes, when the test condition is not true, you may wish to execute an alternate block of code, rather than simply skipping the conditional block. For this purpose most languages that provide the if statement also provide the capability for an else block, which is executed when the test in the if statement is false. In Perl, the use of an else block looks like this:

```perl
if ($x > 0)
{
  print("$x is positive\n");
}
else
{
  print("$x is either zero or negative\n");
}
```

In fact, Perl and many other languages take the concept a step further: By using the elsif statement, we can include additional conditions, as in the following example:

```perl
if ($x > 1000)
{
  print("x is large and positive\n");
}
elsif ($x > 0)
{
  print("x is small and positive\n");
}
elsif ($x > -1000)
{
  print("x is negative\n");
}
```

```
else
{
  print("x is VERY negative\n");
}
print("done!\n");
```

In this example, the first line will test whether the value stored in $x is greater than 1,000; if so, the first conditional block is executed, printing "x is large and positive", then the program will jump to the end of the else block, and the last print will be executed, printing "done!". If, however, $x is not greater than 1,000, then the first elsif test will be performed: If $x is greater than 100, then the conditional block following this test will be executed, printing "x is small and positive", and as before we will jump to the end of the if/else code and execute the last print statement. If $x is not greater than 100, we move on to the next elsif, and so on until we find one for which the test is true. If we reach the final else statement, and none of the elsif tests have passed, then we execute the final conditional block and print out "x is VERY negative".

This if/else construct ensures that one, and only one, of the conditional blocks will be executed, depending on the value of $x. Regardless of which conditional block is executed, the program will always move on to the final print statement and print "done!" afterward.

Most languages provide some sort of conditional execution mechanism, and most of them look very similar to the if, elsif, and else statements provided by Perl. In all of these examples, we are using the simple relational operator '>' to test if the value of a variable is greater than a certain number. Perl includes numerous other tests that we can include inside the parentheses of a conditional statement. Table A1.2 shows some of the operators that we can use to test conditions for if statements and other program control statements.

T A B L E A1.2 Common relational and logical operators in Perl.

Operator	Description
<, >, <=, >=	Numerical comparisons. ($x < $y) returns TRUE when the value of $x is less than $y. <= and >= are "less than or equal to" and "greater than or equal to," respectively.
lt, gt, le, ge	String comparisons. ($x lt $y) returns TRUE when the string $x would come before $y if the two strings were sorted alphabetically.
= =, !=	Numerical equality. = = returns TRUE when the two arguments are numerically equal. != returns TRUE when the arguments are not equal.
eq, ne	String equality. Similar to = = and !=, but for string comparisons.
&&, ||	Combination operators. (test) && (test) returns TRUE only if both of the tests in parentheses return TRUE. (test) || (test) returns TRUE if either of the tests in parentheses returns TRUE.
!	Logical "not" operator. !(test) returns TRUE when the test in parentheses returns FALSE.

Note that each of the comparison and equality operators has both a numerical (<, >, <=, etc.) and a string version (lt, gt, le, etc.). The difference between these operators is most clearly illustrated by a simple example. Suppose we assign values to a pair of variables as follows:

```
$var1 ="0012.0";
$var2 ="12";
```

Numerically, the two strings have equal values (12), so the test (`$var1 == $var2`) would return TRUE. The two strings, however, are not the same, so the test (`$var1 eq $var2`) would return FALSE.

It is important to note that the numerical comparison operator uses two equals signs. A common mistake for beginning programmers is to write code similar to the following:

```
if ($var1 = $var2) {
  print("the two variables are equal\n");
}
```

The test in this `if` statement should be (`$var1 == $var2`), the numerical test for equality. Instead, the `if` statement contains the assignment `$var1 = $var2`. This will copy the value of $var2 into $var1, and will also return TRUE (indicating that the value was copied successfully). Not only will the value of $var1 be unexpectedly changed, but the conditional code will always be executed. This sort of error can be very difficult to find, so it is important to exercise care to always use two equals signs when testing for numerical equality.

We can use the operators `&&` and `||` to combine conditions. When `&&` is used, the conditional block is only executed if both conditions are true. When `||` is used, the conditional block is executed if either one of the conditions is true. Parentheses placed around each of the conditions helps to keep the meaning clear. In the following example, the conditional code would be executed only if both of the conditions, `$x > 5` and `$y <= 10`, are true:

```
if (($x > 5) && ($y <= 10)) {
  conditional code;
}
```

Another useful operator is `!`, which tests for the opposite of a condition. The `!` operator is sometimes read as "not." For example, if I wish to execute some code only if the value of `$x` is not 3, I can either use the `!=` operator, as follows:

```
if ($x != 3)
{
  do something . . .
}
```

or I can use the `!` operator to test for the opposite of the condition (`$x == 3`), as shown below:

```
if (!($x == 3))
{
  do something . . .
}
```

Loops

Another common need in programming is the ability to repeat a block of code either a fixed number of times or until a certain condition is met. For that purpose, most languages provide **loop statements.** Two of the most commonly used loop statements in Perl, as well as many other languages, are the `while` loop and the `for` loop.

A `while` statement is structured very similar to an `if` statement:

```
$x=0;
while ($x < 5) {
  print("The value of x is $x\n");
  $x++;
}
```

Unlike an `if` statement, however, the block of code following the `while` statement is repeatedly executed for as long as the condition between the parentheses following the keyword `while` is true. In the example above, the block following the `while` statement will be executed five times (recall that the last line of code in the conditional block is shorthand for the statement $x = $x + 1;). Execution of this code will produce the following output on the screen:

```
The value of x is: 0
The value of x is: 1
The value of x is: 2
The value of x is: 3
The value of x is: 4
```

Note that the condition in the `while` statement is tested before executing the following block of code, so it is possible that the conditional block will not be executed at all. In the previous example, if the first line had read $x = 7; then the block of code following the `while` statement would not have been executed at all.

Another common loop structure is the `for` loop. A `for` loop is very similar to a `while` loop, but is slightly more limited in use. A `for` loop is used when we wish to execute a block of code a fixed number of times. The previous example can be rewritten using a `for` loop as follows:

```
for($x = 0; $x < 5; $x++)
{
  print("The value of x is: $x\n");
}
```

Note that the expression in parentheses in the `for` statement consists of three parts, separated by semicolons. The execution of a `for` loop proceeds as follows:

1. The first part of the `for` statement ($x = 0) is executed immediately when the `for` statement is reached.

2. Next, the second part of the `for` statement ($x < 5) is tested; if the condition is not met, then the rest of the `for` statement is skipped and we proceed with the code following the conditional block.

3. If the condition in the second part of the `for` statement is true, then the conditional code is executed.

4. The last part of the `for` statement (`$x++`) is executed.

5. Go to step 2 and continue. As long as the test in the second part of the `for` statement remains true, the conditional block and the last part of the `for` statement will continue to be executed. As soon as the test becomes false, the rest of the `for` statement is skipped and execution continues with the line following the conditional code.

You might have noticed at this point that using `for` loops in Perl is not strictly necessary—anything that can be done using a `for` loop can also be done with a `while` loop and a few more lines of code. The `for` loop is provided as a convenience to make it easier to write and read code for the very common situation in which we wish to have a block of code executed a fixed number of times. Examine the example shown earlier until you are convinced that it will produce the same results as the previous example using a `while` loop.

A final type of loop provided by Perl is the `foreach` loop. This loop is very similar in function to a `for` loop, but it executes the code in the loop once for each value in a list of values. The concept is best illustrated by an example:

```
foreach $value (7, 3, -3, 5, 2)
{
  print("The value is: $value\n");
}
```

This loop will execute five times, once for each value in the list in parentheses. For each iteration, the next value in the list will be assigned to the variable `$value`.

Readability
Structured Programming

As you begin to write longer and more complex programs, it becomes increasingly important to write code that is easy to read and understand. Although the examples we have looked at so far have only been a few lines long, real-world programs can range from a few to tens of thousands of lines of code. For such large and complex programs, it is essential to write well-organized and readable code. Furthermore, it is not uncommon for one programmer to pass along code to another to be modified for use on a slightly different problem. When sharing code with other programmers, writing clear and readable programs becomes even more important.

There are several habits that you can develop that will help you to produce easily readable code. The first is to use a **structured programming** style such as the one demonstrated in the previous examples. The basic elements of a well-structured program include appropriate use of new lines and consistent indenting of code blocks. The following example shows a well-structured program fragment. Note how each **nested block** of code is indented further than the previous block. It an easy matter to identify which opening and closing braces are paired because they are indented to the same level. Using correct program structure not only makes your programs easier to read, but also helps you to avoid mismatched parentheses and braces.

```
if ($x < 0)
{
  print("$x is negative, counting up . . . \n");
  while ($x < 0)
  {
    print("the value of x is $x\n");
    $x++;
  }
}
else
{
  print("x is positive, counting down . . . \n");
  while ($x > 0)
  {
    print("the value of x is $x\n");
    $x--;
  }
}
```

Comments

As your programs become longer and more complex, they will become more difficult for others to read and understand. Even when looking at your own code, it can be difficult to recall the function of a particular loop or block of code. Fortunately, Perl and most other commonly used programming languages provide a mechanism for jotting down notes, or **comments,** in your code that can help yourself and others to understand what the code does. You should employ comments liberally in your code to describe the function of complex blocks of code, variables, and so on. In Perl, comments are initiated using the # character. Any text following a # character is considered a comment. The following example shows a complete Perl script, with appropriate comments:

```
##############################################
# Factorial program                          #
#     John C. Programmer; July 2001           #
# This program prints the integers from      #
# 1 to 10 and the factorial of each to the   #
# screen.                                     #
##############################################
```

```
# For each number from 1 to 10 . . .
for ($number = 1; $number <= 10; $number++)
{
  # Print the number to the screen:
  print("Number: $number\t");

  # Initialize factorial to 1
  $factorial = 1;

  # Compute the factorial by multiplying the
  # current value by 2, 3, 4, . . . $number
  for ($i = 2, $i <= number, $i++)
  {
    $factorial *= $i;
  }

  # Now the factorial is computed; print it
  # and go on to the next number:
  print("Factorial: $factorial\n");
}
```

The control character \t, used in the first print statement, prints a tab character to the screen. Using the \t instead of \n in the first print statement allows each number and its factorial to be printed on the same line. You should examine this code until you are convinced that it will print the factorial of every integer from 1 to 10. Note how the consistent indentation makes it easier to see where the two nested `for` loops in this program start and end. There is no doubt that the final closing brace in this script matches the opening brace from the first `for` loop, because they are vertically aligned. Likewise, the indention of the second `for` loop makes it clear where this inner loop starts and ends. The liberal use of comments in the code clarifies the function of each block of code and makes the entire script easier to read and understand.

Descriptive Variable Names

Note the variable names in the previous example. Using descriptive variable names, like `$number` and `$factorial`, instead of nondescriptive names such as `$x` and `$y` helps to make your code easier to understand. One exception to this rule is simple loop counters, like `$i` in the example above, which are often reused several times and are quite often named using single letters. In general, the more descriptive the variable names, the better. Don't be afraid of using long variable names such as `$velocity_squared`—you will thank yourself later when you don't have to keep track of your variables on a piece of scratch paper while you are programming.

Data Structures

So far we have dealt only with simple scalar variables. Each scalar variable can hold only a single value. Sometimes, however, it is necessary to store and manipulate very large amounts of data. Data structures are variables that can store more than one value. Correct use of data structures is a key element of writing efficient and readable code.

Arrays

Suppose you are asked to write a program that stores 1,000 numbers entered by the user, and then sorts them by value and prints them to the screen. Using only the simple variable types we have discussed so far, it would be necessary to use 1,000 variables to store all of the numbers until they are sorted. Such a cumbersome solution is not necessary, however, because Perl provides us with **arrays**—variables that can store multiple values. Using an array, we can use a single variable to store all 1,000 numbers. An array variable in Perl begins with the @ character. For our array of 1,000 numbers, we might use an array named `@numbers`. However, we will only need to use the name `@numbers` when we wish to refer to the entire array at once, which will not occur very often. Instead, we will reference individual elements of the array, which are accessed using square braces as follows:

```
$numbers[20] = 20;
$numbers[21] = 15;
```

Note that each element of an array is an ordinary scalar value, so it starts with a $ character. It is not necessary to include any special code in our Perl script to create the array `@numbers`. The first time we access an element of the array (e.g., `@numbers[3] = 5;`) the array `@numbers` will be created. It is important to distinguish between the different types of variables that might have similar names:

- `$numbers`—a scalar variable containing one value,
- `@numbers`—an array variable containing many values, and
- `$numbers[3]`—an element of the array `@numbers`.

In Perl, the elements of an array are usually numbered starting at 0. So the 1,000 elements of our `@numbers` array are named `$numbers[0]` through `$numbers[999]`. The number of a particular array element (in square brackets) is called the **index.** Once we have declared our array, we can even use another variable to identify which element to access. So the code to print 1,000 values stored in our `@numbers` array can be as simple as this:

```
for ($i = 0; $i < 1000; $i++)
{
  print("The next number is $numbers[$i]\n");
}
```

Note that this `for` loop will result in values of `$i` ranging from 0 to 999. The following example program computes the average of 10 numbers entered by the user. The `<STDIN>` operation, used in this example to get a number typed by the user, will be discussed in detail in the Input and Output section. Note in this example how an array is used to store the numbers entered by the user and how a `for` loop is used to step through the array and sum the values.

```
###################################################
# Averaging program; John C. Programmer, 2001     #
#                                                  #
# This program prompts the user for 10 numbers     #
# and then prints their average.                   #
###################################################

# prompt the user for all 10 numbers and store
# them in the array 'numbers'
for($i = 0; $i < 10; $i++)
{
  print("Enter another number\n");
  $numbers[$i] = <STDIN>;
}

# Sum up all the values in the array 'numbers' */
$sum = 0;
for($i = 0; $i < 10; $i++)
{
  $sum += $numbers[$i];
}

# Divide sum by 10 to get the average
$average = $sum / 10.0;

# Print the average
print("The average of all 10 numbers is $average\n");
```

Hashes

One of the most useful data structures provided by Perl, particularly for bioinformatics applications, is the **hash.** A hash is similar to an array, but its indexes are not limited to integers. Instead, a hash can use any numeric or string value to select or index its elements. For example, suppose we wish to store the number of heavy (nonhydrogen) atoms in the side chain of each of the 20 amino acids. Using an array, we would have to number the amino acids from 0 to 19, and then store the counts as follows:

```
$atom_count[0] = 1; # Alanine (A) is amino acid 0
$atom_count[1] = 2; # Cysteine (C) is amino acid 1
$atom_count[2] = 4; # Aspartate (D) is amino acid 2
. . .
```

The primary difficulty with this method is that we have to remember the number for each amino acid. Using a hash instead, we can use a string, such as the one- or three-letter abbreviation for the amino acid, as the index for the hash entries, as in the following example. Note that the index for a hash is enclosed by braces, rather than the square brackets used for array indices.

```
$atom_count{"ALA"} = 1;
$atom_count{"CYS"} = 2;
$atom_count{"ASP"} = 4;

 . . .
```

Just as with arrays, the individual elements of a hash are ordinary scalar variables, and so we refer to them using a dollar sign. To refer to the entire hash at once, the hash name is prefixed with a % sign. The hash created in the previous example would be named %atom_count. We will examine some examples where we need to refer to an entire array or an entire hash at one time in the Functions section.

Working with Strings

Because Perl uses scalar variables to hold strings, and because Perl makes it very easy to create and work with strings, it may seem that strings are not really much of a data structure at all. However, note that in many languages string variables are more tedious to create and manipulate. One of the great strengths of Perl for bioinformatics is the ease with which it allows us to read, write, and manipulate strings of text. Nevertheless, there are a few important things to keep in mind when dealing with scalar variables that contain text strings. One of the most important concepts in working with strings is knowing when variables will be **evaluated,** or replaced with their contents, and when they will not. Most of our examples so far have contained statements similar to the following:

```
print("The value of x is $x\n");
```

Assuming that the variable $x contains the value 5, this will print the sentence "The value of x is 5" to the screen. When the string is printed, the variable $x is replaced with the value 5. Any time we create a string using double quotes, any variables inside the string are replaced with their contents. Consider the following example:

```
$first_name = "John";
$middle_initial = "Q.";
$last_name = "Programmer";

$full_name = "$first_name $middle_initial $last_name";
```

After this code is executed, the variable $full_name will contain the string "John Q. Programmer". When we use double quotes to create the string in the last line, the variables $first_name, $middle_initial, and $last_name are replaced with their values.

What if we want to create a string in which the variables are not evaluated (replaced with their values)? We can do this in Perl by enclosing the string in single quotes. If the last line of the previous example appeared as follows:

```
$full_name = '$first_name $middle_initial $last_name';
```

Then the value of the variable `$full_name` would be the string "`$first_name $middle_initial $last_name`". No variable evaluation would occur.

Occasionally, when working with variables and strings, it is not clear where a variable name should end. For example, suppose I wish to append the letter "y" to a string variable. If I use the following code:

```
$name = "Mike";
$nickname = "$name y";
```

I would get the string "Mike y" in `$nickname`, not "Mikey". However, if I do this:

```
$name = "Mike";
$nickname = "$namey";
```

then Perl will look for the variable `$namey`, which doesn't exist. The solution is to use curly braces around the variable name. In Perl, we can use braces after a dollar sign to surround the name of the variable. So `${name}` is the same as `$name`, but the former method makes it clear where the name of the variable starts and ends. Now we can create our nickname variable as follows:

```
$name = "Mike";
$nickname = "${name}y";
```

As we hoped, the variable `$nickname` now contains the string "Mikey".

Another difficulty in dealing with strings occurs when we wish to include a double or single quote within a string. For example, what if we wish to print the following string to the screen, exactly as it appears below?

```
His name is Mike, but people call him "Mikey".
```

How can we include the double quotes in the string above, without prematurely ending our string? The answer is to use **escape sequences,** special character sequences that, in Perl, are initiated with a backslash. We already know two escape sequences: \n, which moves the cursor to the beginning of the next line on the screen, and \t, which moves the cursor right to the next tab stop position (on most screens, the tab stop positions occur every eight characters). The escape sequences \" and \' allow us to insert a double or single quote into a string, without ending the string earlier than we intend. To print the string from the previous example, we can use the following code:

```
print("His name is Mike, but people call him \"Mikey\".");
```

To place an ordinary backslash character into a string, we can use the escape sequence \\.

Subroutines and Functions

As you write more programs in Perl, you will often find that you need to perform the same calculations repeatedly in the same program. For example, if you are writing a program that deals with protein atom coordinates, you might find that you need to compute the Euclidean distance between two atoms several times in one program. One way to deal with this would be to write some code to compute the distance, and then cut and paste this code into each spot where you need it. This approach, however, has several drawbacks. First, you will end up with a very long program consisting largely of repeated code. Even worse, if you should discover an error in your Euclidean distance calculation, you have to find every place in your program where you have pasted your code and fix the error in every one of them. Finally, your program won't be particularly efficient. That is, it will use more computer memory than it really needs because each copy of your distance calculation code takes up some space in memory.

Fortunately, most programming languages provide a way to avoid repeated code by writing a single block of code that can be used repeatedly in your program without cutting and pasting. In Perl, a reusable block of code is called a **subroutine.** The following simple example shows a subroutine that prints the coordinates of an atom:

```perl
####################################################
# Program to print the coordinates of two atoms #
####################################################

# Create atom 1, use an array with three elements
# for the three dimensions
$atom1[0] = 3.12;    # X-Coordinate
$atom1[1] = 22.5;    # Y-Coordinate
$atom1[2] = 112.34;  # Z-Coordinate
# Call the subroutine to print the coordinates
print("Atom 1:\n");
print_coords($atom1[0], $atom1[1], $atom1[2]);

# Create another atom
$atom2[0] = 121.1;    # X-Coordinate
$atom2[1] = 62.25;    # Y-Coordinate
$atom2[2] = 23.12;    # Z-Coordinate

# Call the subroutine to print the coordinates
print("Atom 2:\n");
print_coords($atom2[0], $atom2[1], $atom2[2]);
print("\n");

# Exit the program
exit;
```

```
##########################################################
# print_coords -- print three-dimensional coordinates to
#                 the screen
#
# Inputs: Three coordinates: x, y, and z.
#
# Outputs: None
#
# This subroutine expects three arguments, which are
# printed to the screen.
##########################################################
sub print_coords
{
  # Copy the three arguments to the subroutine into
  # $x, $y, and $z
  my $x = $_[0];
  my $y = $_[1];
  my $z = $_[2];

  print("X Coordinate: $x\n");
  print("Y Coordinate: $y\n");
  print("Z Coordinate: $z\n");
}
```

This program would produce the output:

```
Atom1:
X Coordinate: 3.12
Y Coordinate: 22.5
Z Coordinate: 112.34

Atom2:
X Coordinate: 121.1
Y Coordinate: 62.25
Z Coordinate: 23.12
```

The main program in this example simply declares two arrays named `atom1` and `atom2`, each of which contain three elements: the `x, y,` and `z` coordinates of the atom. After the array is created, the three elements are passed to the subroutine `print_coords`, which prints them to the screen. The line `print_coords($atom1[0], $atom1[1], $atom1[2]);` calls the subroutine, and passes it three values, the `x, y,` and `z` coordinates of `atom1`. To call a subroutine, we simply use the subroutine name, followed by any **parameters** to the subroutine, enclosed in parentheses. Parameters are the values on which we want the subroutine to operate. The benefit of using a subroutine is that we can call it many times with different parameters. Sometimes the parameters to a subroutine are also referred to as its **arguments.**

The definition of the subroutine begins with the line `sub print_coords`. This defines the name of the subroutine to be `print_coords`. Everything enclosed in the pair of braces following this line is part of the subroutine. The first few lines of the subroutine define some **local variables.** These are variables that exist only inside this subroutine, and are declared using the keyword `my`. If there is a variable called `$x` in our main program, or in another subroutine, it is different from the `$x` used in `print_coords`, because we declared `$x`, `$y`, and `$z` preceded by the keyword `my`. To put it another way, changes to `$x` in `print_coords` will not change the values of any other variables named `$x` elsewhere in this program. If we don't use `my` when creating variables in subroutines, then they are **global variables,** meaning they are visible elsewhere in the program, and any changes we make will affect any other variables elsewhere that have the same name. Using local variables inside your subroutines is a good programming practice to follow, because it eliminates the need to check the variable names in all the other subroutines in a program to make sure they aren't the same as the variables in the current subroutine.

In addition to declaring `$x`, `$y`, and `$z` as local variables, the first few lines of the subroutine copy the three parameters to the subroutine into these variables. In Perl, the parameters to a subroutine are stored in a special array whose name is simply the underscore (_) character. This array has as many elements as there were parameters passed to the subroutine when it was called. Since we called `print_coords` with three arguments, this array has three elements in the subroutine. Because array numbering in Perl starts at 0, the elements are named `$_[0]`, `$_[1]`, `$_[2]`. The rest of the subroutine is fairly straightforward; it simply prints the values of the three arguments to the subroutine using the now-familiar `print` statement.

When an entire array is passed as an argument, Perl passes all of the elements of the array as if they were typed out in the parentheses following the subroutine name. So, instead of listing all three elements of the array `atom1`, we could have called the `print_coords` subroutine as follows, with the same results:

```
print_coords(@atom1);
```

Note that we use the @ character to refer to the entire array `atom1` at once.

This example subroutine captures the first three variables in the `@_` array into `$x`, `$y`, and `$z`. If we call the subroutine with more than three parameters, the extras are simply ignored. Sometimes it is useful to write a subroutine that can accept any number of parameters. Using the `foreach` control structure, this is very easy to do in Perl, as in the following example:

```
####################################################
# Example program using foreach
####################################################

# Declare array1 with 5 elements
@array1 = (7, 5, 9, 12, -3);

# Call the print_array subroutine
print_array(@array1);
```

```
Declare array2 with 7 elements
@array2 = (3, 5, 9, 12, 3, -3, 5);

# Call the print_array subroutine
print_array(@array2);

####################################################
# print_array -- print the contents of an array
####################################################
sub print_array
{
  $count = $#_+1;
  print("The array contains $count elements.\n");
  print("The elements of the array are:\n");
  foreach $element (@_) {
    print("$element\n");
  }
}
```

Note that this example introduces a new way to create an array. Rather than having to tediously create an array element by element ($array1[0] = 7; $array[1] = 5; etc.), we can create an array all at once using a list of values enclosed in parentheses. Secondly, note that the variable $#arrayname contains the index of the last element in the array @arrayname. Since array numbering starts at zero, the number of parameters passed to the subroutine will equal $#_+1. By using an array in place of the usual list of values in a foreach statement, the loop iterates with each value of the array assigned to the variable $element. This sort of loop is very convenient for creating subroutines that act on each input parameter, no matter how many parameters are passed to the subroutine.

It is often useful to create a subroutine that performs some computation on the parameter values and returns the result to the main routine. A subroutine that returns a value is often referred to as a **function.** In Perl, there is not much difference between a function and a subroutine, except that functions use the return statement to return a value to the calling program. When you call a function, you can assign the returned value to a variable. For example, if I wrote a function called average that returned the mean of the input parameters, I would assign the result to a variable as follows:

```
@values = (23, 17, 83, 21, 54, 23, 87);
$mean = average(@values);
```

The following example program demonstrates the use of a function to compute the Euclidean distance between two points.

```
############################################################
# This program example computes the Euclidean distance
# between two atoms.
############################################################

# Store the coordinates for atom1 in the array @atom1
@atom1 = (1.212, 19.215, 102.23);
```

```
# Store the coordinates for atom2 in the array @atom2
@atom2 = (32.202, 220.21, 23.022);

# Compute the distance between the two atoms
$distance = euclid_dist(@atom1, @atom2);
print("The distance from atom1 to atom2 is $distance\n");

#######################################################
# euclid_dist - compute the Euclidian distance        #
#                  between two points                 #
#                                                     #
# Inputs: Two points in 3D space, specified by        #
#          their x, y, and z coordinates. Each        #
#          point's coordinates are stored in a        #
#          hash with elements x, y, and z.            #
#                                                     #
# Returns: The distance between the two points        #
#######################################################
sub euclid_dist
{
  # Call the input parameters point1 and point2
  my @point1 = ($_[0], $_[1], $_[2]);
  my @point2 = ($_[3], $_[4], $_[5]);

  # compute the distance along each dimension
  my $xdist = $point1[0]-$point2[0];
  my $ydist = $point1[1]-$point2[1];
  my $zdist = $point1[2]-$point2[2];

  # compute the sum of the squared distances
  my $edist = $xdist * $xdist;
  $edist += $ydist * $ydist;
  $edist += $zdist * $zdist;

  # take the square root for euclidean distance
  $edist = sqrt($edist);

  return($edist);
}
```

When the two arrays are passed to the subroutine euclid_dist, the arrays are expanded as though all elements of each array were parameters to the subroutine, as previously discussed. Thus, the line

```
$distance = euclid_dist(@atom1, @atom2);
```

is equivalent to

```
$distance = euclid_dist($atom1[0], $atom1[1], $atom1[2],
   $atom2[0], $atom2[1], $atom2[2]);
```

The subroutine assigns the first three parameters to the array `@point1` and the second three to the array `@point2`. It then computes the distance in each dimension, squares them, and adds them to `$edist`. Finally, the square root of this sum of squared distances in `$edist` is computed and returned to the calling program.

Input and Output

One of the reasons why Perl is a popular language for bioinformatics applications is the ease with which it allows manipulation of text files. Many bioinformatics tools read text files containing sequences, sequence alignments, or protein structures as their input, and produce text files of various formats as output. As you develop your Perl programming skills, you will find that Perl is a powerful tool that you can use to convert data between formats, summarize your results, and even perform sophisticated analyses of sequence and structural data. To do all of these things, it is necessary to know how to read and write information to and from text files in Perl.

Before a file can be read from or written to in Perl, it must first be *opened*. When you open a file, you create a special variable associated with the file. Once the file is opened, we use the variable to refer to the file whenever we want to perform a read or a write operation. The Perl function **open** is used to open a file, as follows:

```
# This program will echo the contents of the file
# poem.txt to the screen

open(POEM, "<poem.txt");

while(<POEM>) {
  $line = $_;
  print($line);
}
```

This fairly short script, which prints the contents of the file "poem.txt" to the screen, presents a number of new concepts. First, take a look at the **open** function. The first argument to the function is the special variable to be associated with the file we are about to open. This variable is called the **file pointer,** and it is neither a scalar variable, a hash, nor an array, so it doesn't start with any of the special characters ($, %, @) we usually associate with Perl variables. To make it easier to remember that this is a file pointer variable, it is common Perl programming practice to use a name consisting of all capital letters (in this case, POEM). The second argument to **open** is the name of the file to open. In this example, we want to open the file "poem.txt". By placing the character '<' before the file name, we have indicated that we wish to open the file only for reading. Perl looks at the first character of the file name in an open statement to determine whether the file should be opened for reading, writing, or both. For our file "poem.txt" some of the file names we might use include:

- "<poem.txt"—open poem.txt for reading only.
- ">poem.txt"—open poem.txt for writing only. Erase the current contents of the file, and start writing at the beginning.
- ">>poem.txt"—open poem.txt for append. Leave the current contents intact and begin writing/appending at the end of the file.
- "+>poem.txt"—open the file for both reading and writing.

To read a line from a file that has been opened for reading, we use the operator <> with the file pointer variable. In the example code, the command <POEM> reads the next line of the file. The file pointer variable POEM keeps track of the last line read, so each time we execute <POEM> we get the next line of the file. As the line is read, it is placed in the special variable $_. The first statement inside the while loop copies the line into the variable $line, and the statement prints the line to the screen.

In this example, the <POEM> command is also used as a test. Each time the command executes, it reads the next line of the file poem.txt and places the line into the variable $_. If this process succeeds (that is, there was another line in the file to read), then <POEM> also returns the value TRUE, just like the test ($x < 3) returns TRUE when the value of $x is less than 3. When there are no more lines to read in poem.txt, <POEM> returns FALSE. Thus, we can use it as a test in the while loop. Thus, the while loop in this example proceeds as follows:

```
while (there are more lines to read in poem.txt) {
  get the next line into the variable $_;
  copy the line into $line;
  print($line);
}
```

You may notice that copying the value into the variable $line is not strictly necessary. In the example, this was done only to clarify the operation of the <POEM> operation. We could just as well rewrite the loop as follows:

```
while(<POEM>) {
  print($_);
}
```

Believe it or not, we can shorten the loop even a bit further. When the print function is called with no arguments, it prints the special variable $_ by default. So we could actually write the while loop as:

```
while(<POEM>) {
  print;
}
```

Perl has a number of shortcuts, similar to this one, that can make your programs more concise. However, these shortcuts generally come at the cost of making your program less readable as well. Given the choice between the original `while` loop given in the example and the loop above, the former provides the same function while being easy to read, even for a nonexpert in Perl.

Regular Expressions

One of the most powerful components of Perl is the regular expression, but unfortunately it is also among the easiest ways to write short, cryptic sections of code. There is nothing that a regular expression does that cannot also be performed by a larger amount of code, but depending on the regular expression, this code could turn out to be rather large and difficult to write. This section is intended to provide an introduction to regular expressions so that you will understand what you're seeing if you encounter them in Perl code written by someone else, but it is not intended to be a comprehensive guide.

In short, a regular expression is a shorthand method for matching portions of strings, by stating a template against which the string is compared. Two of the most common uses of regular expressions are in `if` statements and transliteration, or `tr` statements, which are covered later in this section.

Now that the generalities have confused you, let's look at an example that will hopefully make things clearer. Suppose we wanted to look at a string and see if it contained the word *alpha* somewhere within it. Assuming that the string we want to compare is contained within the variable `$string`:

```
if ( $string =~ /alpha/)
{
  printf( "Match!\n");
}
else
{
  printf( "No match.\n");
}
```

Several new elements are introduced here, so let's consider each one separately. First off, there's the shorthand notation `/alpha/`—this is the string that we wish to match. To show that matching is what we want to do, we use the `=~` or **binding operator,** which in this context you can think of as being the same as `==`, but for regular expressions.

Suppose we want to match not just a particular string, but several variations of that string, such as CAU or CAC, representing histidine. We could do an `if` containing an or clause, but there is an easier way using regular expressions. We can use a matching string that contains a **character class,** as `/CA[CU]/`. This says that the string must match CA, followed by either C or U. Although not appropriate to this example, we can also use the hyphen character to indicate a sequence of characters; instead of saying `[ABCDEFabcdef]`, we can say `[A-Fa-f]`.

After specifying a character class, suppose that we want to indicate that it can appear multiple times. This requires the special **quantifiers** * and +. The * quantifier means that the class can appear 0 or more times, while + means that it can appear 1 or more times but must occur at least once. For instance, if we want to indicate that a number must occur, we might say something like [0-9]+, or if we want to say that it cannot start with a zero, [1-9][0-9]*.

There is also a special wildcard character, indicated by a period. For instance, if we wanted to indicate that we're looking for the words *alpha* and *helix*, with anything at all in between them (or nothing at all), we would use the regular expression /alpha.*helix/. If we wanted to indicate that something had to occur between them, we would simply change the * to a +.

You can anchor an expression by using the special characters ^ or $ in the regular expression. These mean that the given pattern must occur at either the beginning or end of the string, respectively. For instance, /^alpha/ would only match if the word *alpha* occurs at the beginning of the string, while /helix$/ only matches if the word *helix* occurs at the end.

As mentioned previously, besides matching, regular expressions can also be used to perform **transliteration.** This means that the matching characters are changed, or transliterated, into other characters. The operator used to do this is tr and, as a simple example, suppose that we wanted to take an RNA sequence and convert it to DNA, changing all the U's to T's. Using tr, we can do this simply as:

```
$sequence ="GCUACGUUCGAAGCU";
$sequence =~ tr/U/T/;
printf("sequence is $sequence\n");
```

This would result in the output: sequence is GCTACGTTCGAAGCT. Note that the tr operator can be destructive—the contents of $sequence have been changed.

Additionally, the output of the tr operator is a count of the number of characters transliterated. This can be used to our advantage, allowing us to not only count the number of changes, but to count changes without actually making any! We do this by simply not stating what the matching characters should be changed to. For example, if we want to count the number of U's in a sequence without changing them:

```
$sequence ="GCUACGUUCGAAGCU";
$Ucount = ( $sequence =~ tr/U//);
printf( "There are $Ucount uracil in the sequence\n");
```

Where to Go from Here

The tools you have learned about in this chapter will allow you to write simple Perl scripts to perform a variety of tasks. Many of the concepts presented are common to other languages including C, C++, Java, and Python, so you should now have the tools you need to learn and use most of the programming languages commonly employed for bioinformatics applications. For all but the most demanding or specialized bioinformatics programs, Perl is more than powerful enough to get the job done. However, this appendix has only scratched the surface of the many functions, operators, and other facilities available in Perl. For bioinformatics applications, the string parsing and pattern matching features of Perl, in particular, are indispensable. Other aspects of Perl that are of interest for bioinformatics programming include:

- Regular expressions and string substitution operators,
- Command-line arguments: @ARGV,
- Perl modules and the Perl module library,
- References, typeglobs, and parameter passing, and
- Lists of lists and multidimensional arrays in Perl.

Numerous references are available to help you learn to use these operators. With what you now know about programming in general, and Perl in particular, these references should be accessible and useful for creating powerful bioinformatics applications in Perl.

Readings for Greater Depth

Numerous introductory materials are available on the World Wide Web for learning basic and advanced Perl programming. Since these resources change at a rapid pace, the best strategy is to use a web search engine with keywords such as "Perl tutorial" and "Perl introduction" to find the most recent material.

Several books from O'Reilly are available that present various aspects of the Perl language, including *Learning Perl, Learning Perl on Win32 Systems, Perl in a Nutshell, Perl Cookbook,* and *Advanced Perl Programming.*

A good next step for bioinformaticians wishing to learn additional programming skills in Perl is J. Tisdall, 2001, *Beginning Perl for Bioinformatics,* O'Reilly & Associates, Sebastopol, CA.

For further exploration of fundamental concepts in programming, a college-level textbook on data structures and algorithms is recommended, such as T. H Corman, C. E. Leiserson, and R. L. Rivest, 2001, *Introduction to Algorithms,* 2nd edition McGraw Hill, New York, NY.

If you are using Perl on a UNIX system, *man* pages are generally available that can serve as useful references and reminders of the format for the various Perl functions and operators. From a UNIX command prompt, type `man perl` for more information. Two of the most useful are the page on Perl operators (`man perlop`) and the page describing Perl functions (`man perlfunc`).

Questions and Problems

* **A1.1** Write a short Perl script to print the integers from 1 to 100 to the screen.

A1.2 Write a Perl script to print the integers from 1 to 100 that are divisible by 7 to the screen. Use the modulus function (%) to determine if a number is divisible by 7.

* **A1.3** Write a Perl script to read a file named "values.txt" containing real numbers, one number per line, into an array. Once all of the numbers have been stored in the array, print the average (mean) of the numbers to the screen.

A1.4 Rewrite the script in Question A1.3 using a function to compute the mean. Pass the array as an argument to the function.

* **A1.5** Create a text file containing the following triplets of X, Y, and Z coordinates:

45.010	48.193	104.291
60.160	55.939	117.081
39.849	48.051	135.613
46.676	46.998	66.327
31.434	85.158	97.469
32.996	37.720	111.954
47.852	44.686	100.663
29.227	37.351	103.290
54.642	90.459	126.119

Assuming that each line represents the X, Y, and Z coordinates of an atom, in angstroms, write a Perl script to count the number of atoms within 20 angstroms of the point 45.0, 45.0, 100.0. [*Hint:* You can use the `split()` function to split a line into several variables. For example, assuming you have read the first line of the file into `$line`, you can use `($x, $y, $z) = split(", $line)`, which will set `$x = 45.010`, `$y = 48.193`, and `$z = 104.291`. There is a single space between the two single quotes, which tells `split` to split the line wherever there are spaces between characters.]

A1.6 Write a subroutine that checks a string of characters and returns "true" if it is a DNA sequence. Write another that checks to see if it is a protein sequence written in the one-letter code for amino acids.

Enzyme Kinetics

Enzymes as Biological Catalysts

The Henri–Michaelis–Menten Equation

V_{max} and K_m
Direct plot
Lineweaver–Burk reciprocal plot
Eadie–Hofstee plot

Simple Inhibition Systems

Competitive inhibition
Noncompetitive inhibition
Irreversible inhibition
Effects of pH and temperature

An important emerging area of bioinformatics, systems biology, strives to model biological systems (including biochemical pathways, genetic regulation and even interactions between cells, tissues, and whole organisms). The remarkable integration and interdependency of metabolic processes pose daunting challenges to systems biologists. Learning which molecules are in a particular metabolic pathway is a good starting point, but knowing how each protein functions and interacts with other molecules is essential for useful understanding. Despite the underlying complexity of protein structure and almost unique catalytic strategy of every enzyme, much of enzyme kinetics can be reduced to a few fairly simple equations and essential parameters. Determination of an enzyme's V_{max} and K_m, although considered to be "old-fashioned biochemistry" by some, gives remarkably clear insight into the normal physiology of an organism and is a fundamentally important starting point for any attempts at higher order modeling.

Enzymes as Biological Catalysts

From an energetics perspective, chemical reactions are substantially more than the conversion of reactants to products (Figure A2.1). **Transition state theory** states that products are formed only after reactants have (1) collided in an appropriate spatial orientation and (2) acquired enough **activation energy (E_{act})** to reach a transition state. Transition states represent something of a halfway point in a chemical reaction when the chemical bonds of the reactant(s) are distorted in a way that allows conversion to product(s). The lower a reaction's E_{act}, the more easily the transition state will be reached and faster the reaction will occur. Catalysts, including enzymes, increase rates of chemical reactions by selectively lowering E_{act}. This property of enzymes can have extremely dramatic effects. For instance, carbonic anhydrase is an enzyme within mammalian blood that converts carbon dioxide (CO_2) and water (H_2O) to carbonic acid (H_2CO_3). Even when no catalyst is present, the reaction takes place at a rate of about one product being produced every 2 minutes at normal concentrations and temperature in blood. A single molecule of carbonic anhydrase in the same circumstances increases the reaction rate by over one million fold—100,000 molecules of CO_2 are converted to carbonic acid every second. A surprisingly small reduction in activation energy (2×10^4 calories/mole versus 1×10^4 calories/mole in the presence of carbonic anhydrase) is responsible for this dramatic effect. While some enzymes enhance reaction rates by a factor of up to 10^{15}, most enzymes cause specific chemical reactions to proceed 1,000 to 10,000 times faster than they would have occurred in their absence and have fairly small effects on activation energies.

Notice in Figure A2.1 that the chemical reaction proceeds from a state in which the reactants have a high energy to a product that has a lower amount of energy associated with it. The energy associated with a closed system is determined solely by the energy stored in its chemical bonds (H, usually described in terms of joules/mole); its temperature (T, described in terms of degrees Kelvin, K); and the extent to which it is disordered (S, also usually described in terms of

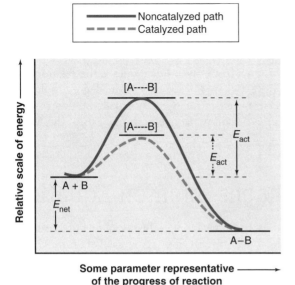

F I G U R E A2.1 *Energy profile diagrams of a chemical reaction with and without a catalyst. In the hypothetical reaction $A + B \rightarrow B - A$, the transition state energy (E_{act}) is greater than either the energy levels of the reactants or the product. In the presence of a catalyst for this reaction (dashed line), E_{act} is lower than in its absence (solid line) and the reaction proceeds more quickly. The total amount of energy released during the course of the reaction (E_{net}) remains the same both with and without a catalyst.*

joules/K/mole). The total energy of a system is usually described in terms of its *Gibbs free energy* (G), and changes in G (ΔG) can also be described in terms of chemical energy, temperature, and disorder ($\Delta G = \Delta H - T\Delta S$). Chemical reactions that release energy are **exergonic** and have negative Gibbs free energies ($-\Delta G$; $G_0 > G_1$). The energy released in reactions like these can be used to do work if it is not lost as heat. In contrast, reactions that require a net input of energy to convert reactants to products are **endergonic** and have positive ΔG's ($G_0 < G_1$). Many of the chemical reactions that are necessary for life are very endergonic and can only occur when they are coupled by enzymes to other chemical reactions that are even more exergonic. The large negative values for the ΔG of the exergonic reactions offset the positive ΔG of the desired reaction. While chemical reactions with large negative values for their ΔG are more **thermodynamically favorable** than those with positive or smaller negative values for their ΔG, they do not necessarily take place any more quickly. Reaction rates are determined entirely by the amount of energy that must be acquired to reach the reaction's transition state (and not necessarily the energy difference between reactants and products).

Appreciate also that chemical reactions are usually **reversible,** meaning that products can be converted back to reactants. In Figure A2.1 the activation energy for the forward reaction ($A + B \rightarrow A - B$) is lower than that of the reverse reaction ($A - B \rightarrow A + B$). That difference means that if reactants and products are present at the same concentrations the rate k_1, at which the forward reaction occurs, will be greater than the rate k_{-1}, at which the reverse reaction occurs. In time, though, more product ($A - B$) will be available for conversion to reactants ($A + B$), and the net number of conversions between the two states will be the same. The point at which the relative concentration of products and reactants no longer changes occurs when an **equilibrium constant, K_{eq},** is reached. If the forward reaction occurs 100 times more rapidly than the reverse reaction, then $K_{eq} = k_1/k_{-1} = 100$ and there will be 100 times more product than reactants when the reaction is in equilibrium. For any given reaction, enzymes always enhance both k_1 and k_{-1} to the same degree—as a result, they have no effect on K_{eq}.

Among the most powerful insights from thermodynamics is the relationship between K_{eq} and ΔG: $\Delta G = -RT\ln K_{eq}$ (where $R = 2.0 \times 10^{-3}$ kcal/degree/mole and T = temperature in degrees Kelvin). Values for K_{eq} can usually be determined easily in the laboratory and, as a result, allow ready determinations of the ΔG of reactions as well.

The Henri–Michaelis–Menten Equation

In the late 1800s studies of enzymes had revealed that the initial rate of a reaction was directly proportional to the concentration of enzyme used (Figure A2.2a). However, reaction rates were also observed to increase in a nonlinear manner and to approach a limiting maximum rate as reactant concentration was increased (Figure A2.2b). By 1903, V. Henri was able to use those observations to theoretically derive a general mathematical equation that related v_0 (the rate at which an enzyme catalyzed a reaction when substrate concentrations were low, as in the left-hand part of the curve in Figure A2.2b) to [E] (enzyme concentration) and to [S] (a specific concentration of reactants, or substrates).

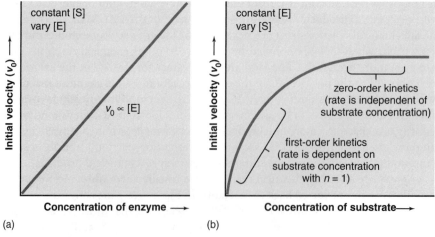

F I G U R E A2.2 *Kinetic features of an enzyme-catalyzed reaction. (a) Reaction rate is linearly related to enzyme concentration. (b) Reaction rate and substrate concentration have a hyperbolic relationship. When substrate concentrations are low, the reaction rate increases in a way that is directly proportional to substrate concentration. However, when substrate concentrations are high, reaction rates change very little and asymptotically approach a maximum velocity (V_{max}).*

At the heart of Henri's model was the idea that enzyme-catalyzed reactions occurred in two steps: (1) substrates (S) bound to the enzyme (E), and (2) products (P) were released from the enzyme. Each of those steps appeared to have their own characteristic equilibrium constants so that the overall reaction could be written as:

$$E + S \xrightleftharpoons[k_{-1}]{k_1} ES \xrightleftharpoons[k_{-2}]{k_2} P + E.$$

Over the course of the next 10 years, L. Michaelis and M. Menten used carefully designed and controlled laboratory experiments to test that model and presented a slightly modified version of Henri's rate equation that is now commonly known as the **Henri–Michaelis–Menten equation:**

$$v_0 = (V_{max} [S])/(K_m + [S])$$

where V_{max} is the maximum rate at which an enzyme catalyzes a reaction when substrate concentrations are high (as in the right-hand part of the curve in Figure A2.2b); and K_m is the Michaelis–Menten constant $\{K_m = (k_{-1} + k_2)/k_1$; a grouping of the rate constants that have the biggest effect on [ES]$\}$. Simple inspection of the Henri–Michaelis–Menten equation reveals that K_m corresponds to the substrate concentration that allows an enzyme to generate products at half their maximum velocity ($1/2V_{max}$).

V_{max} and K_m

Experimentally determined values for V_{max} and K_m have proven to be fundamentally important descriptors of any given enzyme's kinetic activity as well as the intracellular environment in which natural selection has honed the enzyme to work best. For instance, V_{max} describes what is known as the **turnover number** of an enzyme [the moles of substrate converted to product per mole of enzyme per unit time (usually, 1 minute)]. An enzyme's K_m gives invaluable insights into the normal physiological state inside cells in at least four different ways. First, K_m generally corresponds to the substrate concentration that an enzyme normally encounters within a cell. (Substrate concentrations much below K_m would generate wide variations in reaction velocity and those velocities would be far below V_{max}; substrate concentrations much above K_m would result in only marginally faster reaction rates—a 10,000-fold increase in substrate concentration above K_m results in only a doubling of the reaction rate.) Second, since K_m is a constant for any given enzyme, it is possible to directly compare the efficiency of related (or altered/mutated) enzymes from different tissues or organisms simply by comparing K_m values. Third, for enzymes that utilize a variety of substrates, it is possible to compare the relative efficiency with which they are utilized by comparing the K_m for each substrate. (Lower K_m values correspond to greater enzymatic specificity and imply the substrate is preferred.) Fourth, measurements of the effects of different compounds on an enzyme's K_m provide an objective way of determining their role as activators or inhibitors of the reaction—an issue of particular importance in the field of drug discovery.

Direct Plot

Estimated values for V_{max} and K_m can be determined fairly easily from experimental data. For instance, a direct plot of initial catalytic velocity, v_0, determined at a range of different substrate concentrations, [S], when enzyme concentration is held constant allows a visual estimation of both V_{max} and K_m. Consider the reaction catalyzed by hexokinase, which yields the data provided in Table A2.1. Hexokinases play a central role in metabolism by transferring a phosphate group to six-carbon sugars like glucose, as shown in Figure A2.3. A direct plot of the data ($y = $ [S], $x = v_0$) from Table A2.1 is shown in Figure A2.4 on page 242. A value for V_{max} can be estimated from even a small number of data points by determining the value being asymptotically approached by the curve. One-half the value for V_{max} ($V_{max}/2$) corresponds to the initial velocity observed when the substrate concentration is equal to K_m.

Lineweaver–Burk Reciprocal Plot

Despite the relative simplicity of direct plots such as the one shown in Figure A2.4, the asymptotic nature of the curve prevents precise measurement of values for V_{max}. Algebraic rearrangement of the Henri–Michaelis–Menten equation gives an alternative graphical representation from what is known as the Lineweaver–Burk equation:

$$1/v_0 = (K_m/V_{max})(1/[S]) + 1/V_{max}$$

This equation still conforms to the model originally put forward by Henri, but has the straight-line form of an equation in the format of $y = mx + b$. Here, the two variables (y and x; $1/v_0$ and $1/[S]$, respectively) are described in terms of each

T A B L E A2.1 Biochemical data for human hexokinase.

Glucose (mM)	Initial velocity, v_0, (µmol/min)	1/[S], (mM^{-1})	1/v_0, (min/µmol)	v_0/[S]
0 (blank)	0	—	—	—
0.05	25	20	0.040	500
0.10	40	10	0.025	400
0.15	50	6.7	0.020	333
0.20	57	5.0	0.018	285
0.25	63	4.0	0.016	252
0.30	67	3.3	0.015	223
0.35	70	2.9	0.014	200
0.40	73	2.5	0.014	183

Note: Substrate (glucose) concentrations and corresponding initial velocities of conversion of glucose to glucose-6-phosphate (G6P) are shown. Reciprocal values (for use in a Lineweaver–Burk reciprocal plot) are also shown, as are values for v_0/[S] (for use in an Eadie–Hofstee plot).

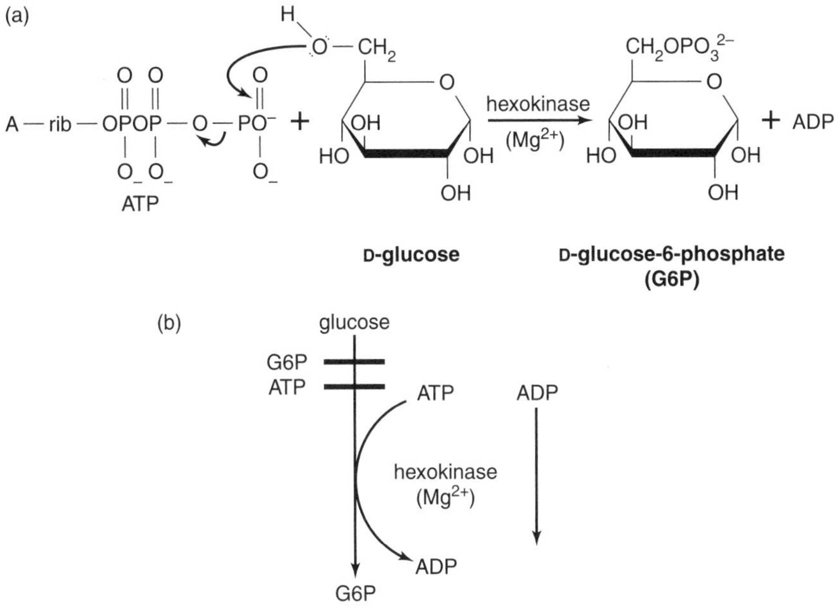

(a)

D-glucose

D-glucose-6-phosphate
(G6P)

(b)

F I G U R E A2.3 *The reaction catalyzed by hexokinase. (a) Hexokinase transfers a phosphate group from ATP to glucose at the very start of glycolysis to produce glucose-6-phosphate (G6P). Magnesium is a required co-factor (as it is for most kinase reactions). (b) Hexokinase is sensitive to two inhibitors (G6P and ATP) and one activator (ADP). Bars across reaction arrows are often used to signify inhibitors, while parallel arrows are used for activators.*

other, a slope ($m = K_m/V_{max}$) and the intercept of the y axis ($b = 1/V_{max}$) (see Figure A2.5 on page 243). A precise value for K_m can be determined by multiplying the slope by the value for V_{max} or by extrapolating the line and determining the negative value of the x intercept.

Eadie-Hofstee Plot

A more recently developed alternative to direct plots, Eadie–Hofstee plots, avoids some potential extrapolation errors introduced by the tendency for data points to be unevenly distributed in Lineweaver–Burk plots. Algebraic manipulations of the Henri–Michaelis–Menten equation also yield the Eadie–Hofstee equation:

$$v_0 = -K_m (v_0/[S]) + V_{max}$$

Here, the two variables (y and x; v_0 and $v_0/[S]$, respectively) are described in terms of each other. Just as before, this equation corresponds to a straight line but now $m = -K_m$ and $b = V_{max}$, as shown in Figure A2.6 on page 243.

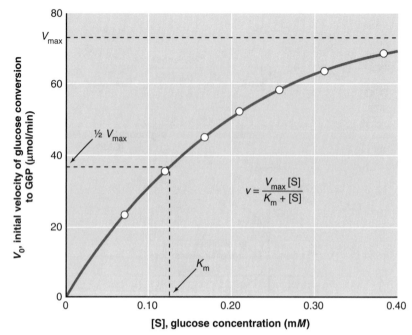

F I G U R E   A2.4 *Direct Henri–Michaelis–Menten plot of experimental enzyme kinetic data for human hexokinase. Data are taken from Table A2.1. V_{max} is determined by estimating the asymptotic value of the curve. Uncertainties in estimating V_{max} lead directly to errors in the estimation of $K_m(V_{max}/2)$ by this approach.*

Simple Inhibition Systems

Any substance that increases the velocity of an enzyme-catalyzed reaction is called an **activator.** By the same token, substances that decrease reaction velocities are called **inhibitors.** Regulation of enzyme activity, particularly by inhibition, is one of the principal ways that cells control the chemical reactions that distinguish them from nonliving materials. In the case of hexokinase, enzyme activity is suppressed by the presence of glucose-6-phosphate and ATP and enhanced by ADP; the regulators are in fact one of the substrates and two of the products of the reaction it catalyzes (Figure A2.3). Practical and economically important applications for these regulatory substances come from their common use as drugs, poisons, antibiotics, and preservatives. It has been argued that the entire history of pharmacology has been built around artificially regulating the activity of approximately 400 enzymes—almost always through the action of inhibitors. The remainder of this appendix describes the way in which studies of enzyme kinetics can distinguish between three different kinds of simple inhibition and other factors that can be used to alter the activity of biological catalysts.

Competitive Inhibition

As their name suggests, competitive inhibitors (I) are molecules that limit access of substrates (S) to an enzyme's (E) active site (i.e., I and S have similar chemical

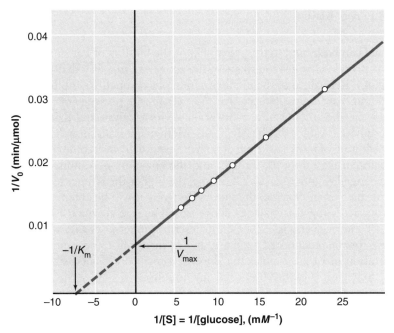

F I G U R E A2.5 *Reciprocal Lineweaver–Burk plot of experimental enzyme kinetic data for carbonic anhydrase. Data are once again taken from Table A2.1, but here the reciprocal of each value is used. Portions of the line determined by extrapolation are dashed.*

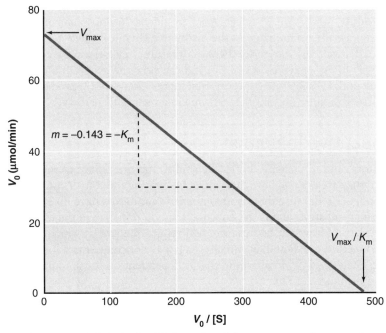

F I G U R E A2.6 *Eadie–Hofstee plot of the experimental enzyme kinetic data for carbonic anhydrase. Data points are once again derived from the values in Table A2.1.*

properties and can both bind to the active site, or the binding of I at some other region of the protein changes the shape of the active site in a way that prevents S from binding). Regardless of the mode of action of a competitive inhibitor, the binding of I and S are mutually exclusive. As a result, the presence of inhibitor effectively lowers the amount of enzyme available for catalysis and that in turn changes the apparent values for the Michaelis–Menten constant (now K'_m) (Figure A2.7a). Addition of more substrate or enzyme eventually overcomes the presence of a competitive inhibitor, though, and the enzyme's maximum velocity remains unchanged (Figure A2.7b). Of course, the higher the affinity a competitive inhibitor has for an enzyme, the more effectively it will be able to prevent substrate from accessing the enzyme's active site. The rate at which EI is converted to E + I and vice versa is conveniently described in terms of a **dissociation constant,** K_I, for the reaction EI $\leftrightarrow$ E + I, and K_I turns out to be equivalent to the concentration of I that doubles the slope of a reciprocal Lineweaver–Burk plot relative to what it is in the absence of any inhibitor.

Competitive inhibition is the basis of action for many widely used drugs and a natural strategy for bioinformaticians interested in rational drug design. For example, benazepril and a variety of other high blood pressure medications are synthetic compounds that competitively inhibit the action of angiotensin-converting enzyme (ACE) in mammals. These drugs are derivatives of the amino acid proline and have very similar chemical features to a proline-rich region near a Phe-His peptide bond in angiotensin I that is cleaved by ACE. Commonly referred to as *ACE inhibitors*, these ACE-competitive inhibitors effectively lower the efficiency of the enzyme while still allowing appropriate physiological responses when high levels of angiotensin I are present.

Competitive inhibition is also commonly used in nature in a phenomenon known as **product inhibition.** Products (such as glucose-6-phosphate and ATP for hexokinase) usually retain many of the distinctive chemical characteristics of the substrates that were used to make them. As a result, they can usually compete quite effectively for an enzyme's active site and can slow the generation of additional product until (1) substrate concentration increases and/or (2) product molecules are further modified by another enzyme in a metabolic pathway.

Noncompetitive Inhibition

Some inhibitors bind to enzymes both when substrates are bound to the active site and when they are not and have their effect by limiting the conversion of substrate to product (P). Because these noncompetitive inhibitors have no effect on the rate at which substrate binds the enzyme, they do not change the enzyme's K_m (Figure A2.7b). However, because they do reduce the rate at which the ES complex is converted to EP and, eventually, to E + P, noncompetitive inhibitors do reduce an enzyme's V_{max} in a fashion that is dependent on the amount of inhibitor present (Figure A2.7b).

Some inhibitors display aspects of both noncompetitive and competitive inhibition and are known as **mixed inhibitors.** Mixed inhibitors usually have a

(a)

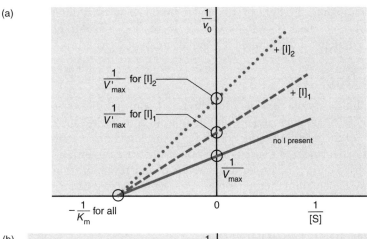

(b)

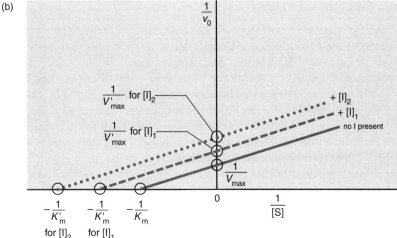

(c)

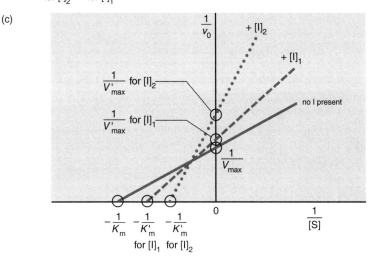

FIGURE A2.7
Enzyme kinetic effects of inhibitors. (a) Lineweaver–Burk plots obtained when different amounts of competitive inhibitor are present. The solid line indicates the plot obtained when no competitive inhibitor is present; the dashed line is obtained with a low concentration of competitive inhibitor; and the dotted line is obtained with higher concentrations of competitive inhibitor. (b) Lineweaver–Burk plots obtained when different amounts of noncompetitive inhibitor are present. The solid line indicates the plot obtained when no noncompetitive inhibitor is present; the dashed line is obtained with a low concentration of noncompetitive inhibitor; and the dotted line is obtained with high concentrations of noncompetitive inhibitor. (c) Lineweaver–Burk plots obtained for mixed inhibition. The solid line indicates the plot obtained when no mixed inhibitor is present; the dashed line is obtained with a low concentration of mixed inhibitor; and the dotted line is obtained with high concentrations of mixed inhibitor.

higher affinity for E than for ES but can still bind to both in a way that diminishes the enzyme's ability to convert S → P. As a result, increasing concentrations of mixed inhibitors simultaneously increase K'_m and decrease V'_{max} (Figure A2.7c).

Irreversible Inhibition

Unlike the reversible inhibitors considered to this point, some inhibitors become permanently attached to enzymes and prevent them from converting substrate to products. Because of the resulting reduction in V_{max}, this kind of irreversible inhibition is sometimes considered a variation of noncompetitive inhibition. Penicillin is a particularly famous and important example of an irreversible inhibitor. The target enzyme of penicillin therapy is converted to an inactive EI form that can no longer participate in the chemical synthesis of bacterial cell walls.

Effects of pH and Temperature

The structure of an enzyme is ultimately what determines its function. Much of what determines an enzyme's precise, highly ordered tertiary structure comes from the linear order in which its amino acids are arranged. For instance, the chemical groups associated with those amino acids dictate the likelihood that a region will fold into a beta sheet or an alpha helix as described in Chapter 7. The stability of those structures, though, can be heavily influenced by changes in temperature or by pH-induced changes of the charges associated with those reactive groups. As a result, it should not be surprising that changes in temperature and pH (the negative log of the hydrogen ion concentration in moles per liter) often result in significant changes in the kinetics of enzyme-catalyzed reactions. All enzymes operate at an optimal temperature that is usually near the organism's body temperature. Similar optimum pHs usually reflect the pH at which the enzyme is typically found within an organism and can differ radically from one enzyme to another (i.e., within humans: the enzyme pepsin has a pH optimum of 2; trypsin has a pH optimum of 8; and alkaline phosphatase has a pH optimum of 9.5).

Readings for Greater Depth

The classic and comprehensive textbook on enzyme kinetics is I. H. Segel, 1975, *Enzyme Kinetics: Behavior and Analysis of Rapid Equilibrium and Steady-State Enzyme Systems*. Wiley-Interscience, New York.

A commonly used general textbook on biochemistry that covers this material in much greater breadth and depth is L. Stryer, 2002, *Biochemistry* (5th ed.), W. H. Freeman, New York.

Questions and Problems

* **A2.1** Assume that the rate at which carbonic acid is converted to carbon dioxide and water by carbonic anhydrase is 1 molecule/second. What would the relative

concentrations of carbonic acid and carbon dioxide be at equilibrium if the enzyme catalyzes the reverse reaction at a rate of 1 molecule per minute?

A2.2 A reaction is found to have a K_{eq} of 1.3×10^{-4} at room temperature (conventionally 25°C or 298.15 K). What is its ΔG?

* **A2.3** What are the advantages of using a Lineweaver–Burk plot relative to a direct plot of enzyme kinetic data? What are the advantages of an Eadie–Hofstee plot relative to a Lineweaver–Burk plot?

A2.4 If the rate at which a forward reaction occurs is 3.5×10^5 reactions per minute and the K_{eq} for substrates and products is 1.0×10^2, then what is the rate at which the reverse reaction occurs?

* **A2.5** Just as inhibitors decrease an enzyme's activity, activators increase it. Most activators are noncompetitive. Would such an activator primarily affect an enzyme's K_m or its V_{max}?

Sample Programs in Perl

Example 1: Conceptual Translation

Example 2: Dot Plot

Example 3: Relative Rate Test

Example 4: UPGMA

Example 5: Common Ancestor

Example 6: Splice Junction Identification

Example 7: Hydrophobicity Calculator—
The 2D-HP Model

Example 8: Atomic Density Calculation

Example 9: Enzyme Kinetics—Linear Regression

The example programs contained herein were selected, one from each chapter plus Appendix 2, to present algorithms that are reasonably straightforward to implement, yet provide a range of challenges for students of varying computational backgrounds. We have endeavored to select programs that can be implemented in two to four pages of code and to provide meaningful comments within the code. Before each program we present a discussion of the overall approach used, along with samples of input and output to make it easier for readers to test their own implementations, and also provide a stepping stone to further experimentation.

Readers with a limited computational background might wish to start with examples 3, 1, 2, and 8. Those with a moderate background might find examples 4, 6, and 9 to be the most interesting, while examples 5 and 7 present the most computational challenge.

Example 1: Conceptual Translation

This program translates from nucleotide strings to amino acids. It prints all three reading frames in the forward direction, skipping nucleotides at the beginning to produce the additional frames, and ignoring nucleotides at the end that do not form a group of 3.

Sample input:

```
UAAUGCAUAGGCUACUCUAG
```

Corresponding output:

```
Nucleotide sequence: UAAUGCAUAGGCUACUCUAG

Reading frame 0: STP Cys Ile Gly Tyr Ser
Reading frame 1: Asn Ala STP Ala Thr Leu
Reading frame 2: Met His Arg Leu Leu STP
```

Code:

```perl
#!/usr/local/bin/perl

# Example program 1. Perform conceptual translation from
# nucleotides to amino acids. Do this for three reading
# frames, skipping the first 0-2 nucleotides to produce the
# reading frames.

# Define some constants that we'll need later.

$minlength      = 3;
$readingframes  = 3;
$unknown        = "UNK";  # If a nucleotide is unknown,
                          # print this.
```

```
# Define a hash to do matching/printing. This allows us to
# say things like $nucleohash{"UUU"} and receive "Phe".

 %nucleohash =
 ( "UUU", "Phe", "UUC", "Phe", "UUA", "Leu", "UUG", "Leu",
   "UCU", "Ser", "UCC", "Ser", "UCA", "Ser", "UCG", "Ser",
   "UAU", "Tyr", "UAC", "Tyr", "UAA", "STP", "UAG", "STP",
   "UGU", "Cys", "UGC", "Cys", "UGA", "STP", "UGG", "Trp",
   "CUU", "Leu", "CUC", "Leu", "CUA", "Leu", "CUG", "Leu",
   "CCU", "Pro", "CCC", "Pro", "CCA", "Pro", "CCG", "Pro",
   "CAU", "His", "CAC", "His", "CAA", "Gln", "CAG", "Gln",
   "CGU", "Arg", "CGC", "Arg", "CGA", "Arg", "CGG", "Arg",
   "AUU", "Ile", "AUC", "Ile", "AUA", "Ile", "AUG", "Met",
   "ACU", "Thr", "ACC", "Thr", "ACA", "Thr", "ACG", "Thr",
   "AAU", "Asn", "AAC", "Asn", "AAA", "Lys", "AAG", "Lys",
   "AGU", "Ser", "AGC", "Ser", "AGA", "Arg", "AGG", "Arg",
   "GUU", "Val", "GUC", "Val", "GUA", "Val", "GUG", "Val",
   "GCU", "Ala", "GCC", "Ala", "GCA", "Ala", "GCG", "Ala",
   "GAU", "Asp", "GAC", "Asp", "GAA", "Glu", "GAG", "Glu",
   "GGU", "Gly", "GGC", "Gly", "GGA", "Gly", "GGG", "Gly"
 );

# Retreive and check the command line parameter.

$input = @ARGV[0];

if ( length( $input) < $minlength )
{
  die( "$0: Place the nucleotide string on the commmand"
     . " line.\n\n" );
} # if

printf( "Nucleotide sequence: $input\n\n" );

# Run through all 3 possible reading frames, skipping the
# first letter or two for frames 1 and 2.

for ( $i = 0; $i < $readingframes; $i++ )
{
  printf( "Reading frame $i:" );

  # Find out how many 3-letter sequences remain, after
  # skipping 0-2 for the reading frame, and loop through
  # all of these sequences.

  $len = int( length( substr( $input, $i ) ) / 3 );

  for ( $j = 0; $j < $len; $j++ )
  {
    # Take the current 3-letter sequence, look up the
    # corresponding amino acid. If it isn't in the hash
```

```
            # table, it is unknown.
            $nuc = substr( $input, $i + $j * 3, 3 );

            if ( defined( $nucleohash{ $nuc } ) )
            {
              $aa = $nucleohash{ $nuc };
            } # if
            else
            {
              $aa = $unknown;
            } # else

            printf( "$aa " );
          } # for j

        printf( "\n" );
      } # for i

    printf( "\n" );
```

Example 2: Dot Plot

Given two nucleotide sequences, the goal is to produce the dot plot of the matching substrings, allowing the user to select the values for the window length and match criteria. The dot plot produced shows the second sequence on the *y* axis and the first sequence on the *x* axis.

Sample input:

```
5 3 ATAAAAATTTT TAATAAA
```

Corresponding output:

```
  Window length: 5
 Match criteria: 3
      Sequence 1: ATAAAAATTTT
      Sequence 2: TAATAAA

  --------
  |****** |
  |*******|
  |***** *|
  --------
```

Code:

```perl
#!/usr/local/bin/perl

# Example program 2. Compute the dot plot for two
# sequences, based only on exact matches. Thus this
```

```
# program is equally useful for both nucleotide and amino
# acid sequences. The input should be of the form
# <window length> <match criteria> <sequence1> <sequence2>.

# Define the output characters for easy modification.

$match_char    = "*";
$mismatch_char = " ";
# Make sure there are 4 inputs, store them for future use,
# and print them out.

if ( @ARGV != 4 )
{
  die( "$0: <window length> <match criteria>"
      . " <sequence 1> <sequence 2>\n\n" );
} # if

$window_length  = $ARGV[0];
$match_criteria = $ARGV[1];
$sequence_1     = $ARGV[2];
$sequence_2     = $ARGV[3];

printf( " Window length: $window_length\n" );
printf( "Match criteria: $match_criteria\n" );
printf( "    Sequence 1: $sequence_1\n" );
printf( "    Sequence 2: $sequence_2\n\n" );

# Set the size of the plot dimensions, based on the
# length of the strings and the window length.

$sizex = length( $sequence_1) - $window_length + 1;
$sizey = length( $sequence_2) - $window_length + 1;

# Do some error checking on the inputs to be sure that they
# make sense.

if ( $match_criteria > $window_length )
{
  die( "$0: Window length ($window_length) must be >="
      . " Match criteria ($match_criteria).\n\n" );
} # if

if (    ( $sizex < 0 )
     || ( $sizey < 0 )
   )
{
  die( "$0: Each input sequence must be of length >="
      . " Window length ($window_length).\n\n" );
} # if
```

```perl
# Draw a line of dashes at the top of the plot.
draw_line( $sizex + 2 );

# Run through all possible plot positions, with sequence 2
# on the y axis, and sequence 1 on the x axis.
for ( $y = 0; $y < $sizey; $y++ )
{
  # Extract the section of sequence 2 to be compared
  # against sequence 1.
  $substr2 = substr( $sequence_2, $y, $window_length );
  printf( "|" );

  for ( $x = 0; $x < $sizex; $x++ )
  {
    # Extract the section of sequence 1 to be compared
    # against $substr2.
    $substr1 = substr( $sequence_1, $x, $window_length );

    # If the number of matches is >= the match criteria, a
    # match has occurred. Mark the appropriate character
    # in the dot plot.
    if (    num_matches( $substr1, $substr2 )
       > = $match_criteria )
    {
      $dotplot[$x][$y] = $match_char;
    } # if
    else
    {
      $dotplot[$x][$y] = $mismatch_char;
    } # else

    printf( "$dotplot[$x][$y]" );
  } # for x

  printf( "|\n" );
} # for y

# Draw a line of dashes at the bottom of the plot.
draw_line( $sizex + 2 );
printf( "\n" );

# Function to compute the number of character positions at
# which two strings of equal length match.

sub num_matches
{
  my( $a, $b) = @_;
  my( $i, $matches );
  for ( $i = 0; $i < length( $a); $i++ )
```

```
  {
    if ( substr( $a, $i, 1 ) eq substr( $b, $i, 1 ) )
    {
      $matches++;
    } # if
  } # for i

  return $matches;
} # num_matches

# Function to draw a line of dashes of a given length.

sub draw_line
{
  my( $len ) = @_;
  my( $i );

  for ( $i = 0; $i < $len; $i++ )
  {
    printf( "-" );
  } # for i

  printf( "\n" );
} # draw_line
```

Example 3: Relative Rate Test

This is the simplest of the algorithms presented, and as such is an excellent starting point for the reader with a limited computational background. Given the similarity measures between three organisms, the program computes the amount of
divergence that has occurred between the two members of the ingroup and their
common ancestor 'A'.

Sample input:

```
95 70 75
```

Corresponding output:

```
d12: 95
d13: 70
d23: 75

dA1: 45
dA2: 50
```

Code:

```
#!/usr/local/bin/perl
```

```
# Example program 3. Perform a relative rate test for
# three related sequences. The program accepts three
# inputs from a dissimilarity matrix. As in Chapter 3,
# elements 1 and 2 represent the ingroup, element 3 the
# outgroup. The inputs to this program are d12, d13, d23.

# Make sure there are 3 inputs, store them for future use,
# and print them out.

if ( @ARGV != 3 )
{
  die( "$0: <d12> <d13> <d23> \n\n" );
} # if

$d12 = $ARGV[0];
$d13 = $ARGV[1];
$d23 = $ARGV[2];

printf( "d12: $d12\n" );
printf( "d13: $d13\n" );
printf( "d23: $d23\n\n" );

# Make sure that the inputs make some sense: that
# element 3 seems to represent the outgroup.

if (     ( ( 2 * $d12 ) >= $d13 )
     && ( ( 2 * $d12 ) >= $d23 )
   )
{
  die( "$0: Element 3 does not appear to represent"
     . " the outgroup.\n\n" );
} # if

# Compute and print dA1 and dA2.

$dA1 = ( $d12 + $d13 - $d23 ) / 2;
$dA2 = ( $d12 + $d23 - $d13 ) / 2;

printf( "dA1: $dA1\n" );
printf( "dA2: $dA2\n\n" );
```

Example 4: UPGMA

Grouping things into a binary tree structure is a common problem in many fields. The general graph produced by this algorithm is called a *dendrogram*. During each iteration, the program finds the two nodes whose values are closest and clusters them. A new label is produced that represents the pairing of the two constituent labels, and also forms the basis for standard Newick format output. For example, the labels "mouse" and "squirrel" would be combined into the label "(mouse,squirrel)". This looping is complete when only one label remains, representing the Newick form of the tree structure. For this program, three different sets of input and output are presented, so that the reader can see how the structure of the output changes as single changes are made to the input.

Sample input:

```
a 12 b 14 c 14.5 d 17 e 18
a 0 b 14 c 14.5 d 17 e 18
a 0 b 14 c 16.5 d 17 e 18
```

Corresponding output:

```
Input sequence: a 12 b 14 c 14.5 d 17 e 18
Final structure: ((a,(b,c )),(d,e))
Input sequence: a 0 b 14 c 14.5 d 17 e 18
Final structure: (a,((b,c),(d,e)))
Input sequence: a 0 b 14 c 16.5 d 17 e 18
Final structure: (a,(b,((c,d),e)))
```

Code:

```perl
#!/usr/local/bin/perl

# Example program 4. Perform a UPGMA (unweighted-pair-group
# method with Arithmetic Mean) analysis of a set of data.
# The input consists of label/value pairs, all inputs
# separated by spaces. Therefore, a label cannot have
# blank spaces inside of it.

# Make sure there are an even number of inputs (matched
# value/label pairs).

if ( ( @ARGV % 2 ) != 0 )
{
  die( "$0: Place the label/value pairs on the commmand"
      . " line.\n\n" );
} # if

printf( "Input sequence: @ARGV\n\n" );

# Store the arguments in a hash, all at once. Recall that
# the first element of ARGV is a key, the second is a
# value, etc.

%labelhash = @ARGV;

@labelkeys = keys( %labelhash );

# Loop through all pairs of nodes, at each cycle finding
# and combining the two nodes which are the closest to each
# other. Halt when there is only one label remaining; that
# label will be the final tree structure.
```

```perl
while ( @labelkeys > 1 )
{
  $smallest = Infinity;

  for ( $i = 0; $i < @labelkeys; $i++ )
  {
    for ( $j = $i+1; $j < @labelkeys; $j++ )
    {
      $a = $labelkeys[$i];
      $b = $labelkeys[$j];
      $distance = abs( $labelhash{$a} - $labelhash{$b} );

      if ( $distance < $smallest )
      {
        $smallest = $distance;
        $smallesta = $a;
        $smallestb = $b;
      } # if
    } # for j
  } # for i

  # Merge $smallesta and $smallestb into one, deleting the
  # old labels, and placing the new label in the following
  # format: ($smallesta,$smallestb).

  # Note that when we compute the new value, we CANNOT
  # simply add the values at $smallesta and $smallestb and
  # divide by two: $smallesta might represent several
  # nodes that have already been merged; weight them by
  # their respective counts. The number of nodes
  # represented by $smallesta or $smallestb is equal to the
  # number of commas in the string, plus one.

  # The regular expression "$smallesta =~ tr/,//" counts
  # the number of commas in the string referred to by
  # $smallesta.

  $counta = ( $smallesta =~ tr/,// ) + 1;
  $countb = ( $smallestb =~ tr/,// ) + 1;
  $newval = (    $labelhash{$smallesta} * $counta
              + $labelhash{$smallestb} * $countb
            ) / ( $counta + $countb );

  delete $labelhash{$smallesta};
  delete $labelhash{$smallestb};
  $labelhash{"($smallesta,$smallestb)"} = $newval;

  # Recompute the list of the keys in the label hash.
  @labelkeys = keys( %labelhash );
} # while

printf( "Final structure: @labelkeys\n\n" );
```

Example 5: Common Ancestor

Given a tree structure in Newick format containing labeled leaf nodes, this program finds the most likely common ancestor. Strangely enough, although this is one of the easiest algorithms to do by hand, the code is the longest, partially due to the fact that Perl does not have an easy way to represent tree structures or perform intersection and union on strings. It is up to the user to ensure that all leaf node labels are of equal length; unpredictable results can occur if this rule is not adhered to. Note that since parentheses have special meaning to UNIX, we must put the input string in quotation marks.

Sample input:

```
"((AAA,TGA),GAG)"
```

Corresponding output:

```
Initial tree: ((AAA,TGA),GAG)

Common ancestor: (ATG)A(AG)
```

Code:

```perl
#!/usr/local/bin/perl

# Example program 5. Perform a common ancestor analysis of
# a tree, given a structure in the standard Newick format.
# Each leaf node specifies a nucleotide, or string of
# nucleotides. All leaves must have the same length.

# Unfortunately, Perl does not have a simple and efficient
# way to represent trees. In this example program, we
# store all of the elements in an array. The root is at
# index 0. For any node X in the tree, its left child
# resides at index 2X + 1, the right child at index 2X + 2.
# Define a way to mark internal nodes in the tree (as
# opposed to leaves) while the input is being read. Thus
# when the tree is evaluated, we know that these nodes must
# be computed. Define the root and current location.

$internal_node = "-";

$root = 0;
$pos = 0;

# Store and echo the input.

$input = @ARGV[0];

printf( "Initial tree: $input\n\n" );

# Parse the input string, one character at a time. The
# characters "(", ",", and ")" have special meaning to the
# parsing. "(" indicates we must move down a level in the
```

```perl
# tree, to the next left child. "," means to switch from
# the left child to the right child. ")" means to move
# upward a level in the tree. Any other character must be
# part of the label for the current node.
for ( $i = 0; $i < length( $input ); $i++ )
{
  $char = substr( $input, $i, 1 );

  if ( $char eq "(" )
  {
    $pos = $pos * 2 + 1;
  } # if
  elsif ( $char eq "," )
  {
    $pos++;
  } #elsif
  elsif ( $char eq ")" )
  {
    $pos = int( $pos / 2 ) - 1;
    $tree[$pos] = $internal_node;
  } # elsif
  else
  {
    $tree[$pos] = $tree[$pos]. $char;
    $leaf_len = length( $tree[$pos] );
  } # else
} # for i

# If the input has at least matching parentheses, we should
# end up back at the root node after parsing the input.
if ( $pos != $root )
{
  die( "$0: invalid input string.\n\n" );
} # if

# Compute the common ancestor, one character at a time.
# Thus we compute and print the common ancestor for the
# first character of all leaf nodes, the second character
# of all leaf nodes, etc. If the result is a single
# letter, simply print it. If it is a longer string, print
# them in parentheses.

printf( "Common ancestor: " );

for ( $i = 0; $i < $leaf_len; $i++ )
{
  $ancestor = evaluate( $root, $i );
```

```
  if ( length( $ancestor ) == 1 )
  {
    printf( "$ancestor" );
  } #if
  else
  {
    printf( "($ancestor )" );
  } # else
} # for i

printf( "\n\n" );

# A recursive function to evaluate a subtree and return
# the common ancestor string. The first input is a pointer
# to the current node being evaluated, the second is which
# input character is currently under consideration.

sub evaluate
{
  my( $ptr, $pos ) = @_;
  my( $left, $right, $eval_str );

  # If this is an internal node, compute it from its
  # children. As stated in Chapter 5, if the intersection
  # of the child nodes is nonempty, it is used. If that
  # intersection is empty, the union of the child nodes is
  # used.

  if ( $tree[$ptr] eq $internal_node )
  {
    $left = evaluate( left_child( $ptr ), $pos );
    $right = evaluate( right_child( $ptr ), $pos );

    $eval_str = intersection( $left, $right );

    if ( length( $eval_str ) == 0 )
    {
      $eval_str = union( $left, $right );
    } # if
  } # if
  else
  {
    # This is a leaf node: it simply evaluates to the
    # correct character position in this string.
    $eval_str = substr( $tree[$ptr], $pos, 1 );
  } # else

  return $eval_str;
} # evaluate
```

```perl
# Function to return the pointer to the left child of a
# given node.
sub left_child
{
  my( $ptr ) = @_;

  return $ptr * 2 + 1;
} # left_child

# Function to return the pointer to the right child of a
# given node.
sub right_child
{
  my( $ptr ) = @_;

  return $ptr * 2 + 2;
} # right_child

# Function to calculate the intersection of two strings.
sub intersection
{
  my( $a, $b ) = @_;
  my( $str, $i, $char );

  for ( $i = 0; $i < length( $a ); $i++ )
  {
    $char = substr( $a, $i, 1 );

    if ( index( $b, $char ) != -1 )
    {
      $str = $str . $char;
    } # if
  } # for i

  return $str;
} # intersection

# Function to calculate the union of two strings.
sub union
{
  my( $a, $b ) = @_;
  my( $str, $i, $char );

  $str = $a;

  for ( $i = 0; $i < length( $b ); $i++ )
  {
    $char = substr( $b, $i, 1 );
```

```
    if ( index( $a, $char ) == -1 )
    {
      $str = $str . $char;
    } # if
  } # for i

  return $str;
} # union
```

Example 6: Splice Junction Identification

This program automates splice junction identification. All locations where "GT" occurs in the string are noted and the probability of a splice junction occurring there is computed from the preceding and succeeding nucleotides. The potential splice junctions are printed in order from most to least likely. Note that although the indices in Perl have the first character being at index 0, the more common method is used for printing, with the first character being index 1. The program makes use of the Perl treatment of strings, in that stepping off the left or right end of a string is allowed; the result is simply the null string.

Sample input:

```
AAGTAACAAGGTAAACAGGTAAGT
```

Corresponding output:

```
Nucleotide sequence: AAGTAACAAGGTAAACAGGTAAGT

Potential splice junctions and associated probabilities:

Index      Probability
-----      -----------
19         0.1070931456
11         0.0119801856
3          0.0039933952
23         0.0011517952
```

Code:

```perl
#!/usr/local/bin/perl

# Example program 6. Find all possible splice junctions in
# a nucleotide sequence, determine the probability of each,
# and print them out in order from most to least likely.
# Define some constants that we'll need later.

$minlength = 2;
```

```perl
@offsets       = ( -2,   -1,    2,    3,    4,    5  );
@nucleotides   = ( "A",  "G",  "A",  "A",  "G",  "T" );
@probabilities = ( 0.64, 0.75, 0.62, 0.68, 0.84, 0.63 );

# Retrieve and check the command line parameter.

$input = @ARGV[0];

if ( length( $input ) < $minlength )
{
  die( "$0: Place the nucleotide string on the commmand"
    . " line.\n\n" );
} # if

printf( "Nucleotide sequence: $input\n\n" );
printf( "Potential splice junctions and associated"
    . " probabilities:\n\n" );
printf( "Index \t Probability\n" );
printf( "----- \t -----------\n" );

# Find all positions where "GT" occurs, and build a list
# of these indices.

$pos = index( $input, "GT" );

while ( $pos != -1 )
{
  push( @indices, $pos );

  # Note that we need to start searching at $pos+1 to make
  # sure that we skip the "GT" we just found; otherwise
  # we'd find the first occurrence over and over again.
  $pos = index( $input, "GT", $pos+1 );
} # while

# For each of the indices where "GT" occurs, compute
# the probability of a splice junction occurring at that
# point.

foreach $index ( @indices )
{
  $prob = 1.0;

  # Run through all of the offsets where important
  # nucleotides occur.

  for ( $i = 0; $i < @offsets; $i++ )
  {
    # Check to see if the nucleotide gives the maximum
    # probability, or the reciprocal thereof. Note: we are
    # counting on Perl's treatment of strings: if we step
```

```
    # off the left or right end of the string, the "eq"
    # test will fail, as the nucleotide at that position is
    # "", the empty string.

    if (  $nucleotides[$i]
        eq substr( $input, $index + $offsets[$i], 1 )
        )
    {
      $prob *= $probabilities[$i];
    } # if
    else
    {
      $prob *= 1.0 - $probabilities[$i];
    } # else

  } # for i

  # Add an entry to a hash table, where the probability is
  # the key and the index where it occurs is the associated
  # value. We do it in this order, since we will later
  # sort on the key values.

  @hash{$prob} = $index;
} # foreach

# Sort the list of probabilities in descending order, then
# print out that sorted list, along with the index into the
# string where the potential splice junction occurs.

@sortedprobs = sort descending_numerical keys( %hash );

foreach $prob ( @sortedprobs )
{
  $printindex = $hash{$prob} + 1;
  printf( "$printindex \t $prob\n" );
}

printf( "\n" );

# Subroutine used for sorting a list in descending
# numerical order.

sub descending_numerical
{
  if ( $a < $b )
  {
    return 1;
  } # if
  elsif ( $a == $b )
  {
    return 0;
```

```
    } # elsif
    else
    {
      return -1;
    } # else
  } # reverse_numerical
```

Example 7: Hydrophobicity Calculator—The 2D-HP Model

One major simplification that can be made to the process of protein folding is to consider only hydrophobic interactions. Taking things a step further, suppose that all amino acids must fall onto the intersections of equally spaced lines in a grid. For a further simplification, consider only a two-dimensional grid, because it is easy to draw examples for such a grid. The program here reads a sequence consisting of classifications of amino acids and directions to get to the location of the next amino acid. It maps these locations into a hash table; counts those amino acids, which **must** be adjacent since they were adjacent in the input sequence; counts those that are adjacent at all; and thus finds the number of adjacent pairs that are not adjacent in the initial ordering. The negative value of this count is a score, representing an energy minimization; more negative scores are thus better.

Sample input:

HRPUHUPLPDHLHUPLHUPLPDHDPRHDHLPDPRHRPUH

Corresponding output:

```
Input sequence: HRPUHUPLPDHLHUPLHUPLPDHDPRHDHLPDPRHRPUH

Score: -9
```

Code:

```perl
#!/usr/local/bin/perl

# Example program 7. Perform a 2DHP (2-dimensional
# hydrophobic/hydrophilic) analysis of a given input
# sequence. The input starts with either H (hydrophobic)
# or P (hydrophilic), and is then followed by pairs of
# either U, D, L, R (up, down, left, right), then H or P.
# For example, a simple input would be: HUPRPDH
# (H up P right P down H).

# Define some constants that we'll need later. Put the
# allowed input characters here, for easy modification.
```

```perl
$minlength    =   3;
$hydrophobic  = 'H';
$hydrophilic  = 'P';
$up           = 'U';
$down         = 'D';
$left         = 'L';
$right        = 'R';

# Start out at coordinates 0,0.

$xpos = 0;
$ypos = 0;

# Retrieve and check the command line parameter.

$input = @ARGV[0];

if (     ( length( $input ) < $minlength )
      || ( ( length( $input ) % 2 ) != 1 )
    )
{
  die( "$0: Place the input string on the commmand"
      . " line.\n\n" );
} # if

printf( "Input sequence: $input\n\n" );

# Run through each input character. If it is invalid,
# print an error and exit. Otherwise process the character
# according to position: even indices are H or P, odd are
# movement directions.

for ( $i = 0; $i < length( $input ); $i++ )
{
  $char = substr( $input, $i, 1 );

  if ( ( $i % 2 ) == 0 )
  {
    # H or P character.

    if (     ( $char ne $hydrophobic )
          && ( $char ne $hydrophilic )
        )
    {
      die( "$0: Input character $i ($char ) must be"
          . " $hydrophobic or $hydrophilic.\n\n" );
    } # if

    # Check to see if the new grid position already exists
    # in the hash. If it does, then the protein has folded
    # back on itself, and is invalid.
```

```perl
      if ( exists( $grid{"$xpos,$ypos"} ) )
      {
        die( "$0: Input sequence has a collision at"
           . " character $i.\n\n" );
      } # if

      # Save this grid position. If we've seen two
      # hydrophobics in a row in the input sequence, count
      # them for later use in the scoring.

      $grid{"$xpos,$ypos"} = $char;

      if (    ( $char eq $hydrophobic )
           && ( $previous eq $hydrophobic )
         )
      {
        $input_adjacencies++;
      } # if

      $previous = $char;

   } # if
   else
   {
   # Movement character. Modify the current position
   # accordingly, exit if the input character is
   # unrecognized.

   if ( $char eq $up )
   {
     $xpos++;
   } # if
   elsif ( $char eq $down )
   {
     $xpos--;
   } # elsif
   elsif ( $char eq $left )
   {
     $ypos--;
   } # elsif
   elsif ( $char = $right )
   {
     $ypos++;
   } # elsif
   else
   {
     die( "$0: Input character $i ($char) must be $up,"
        . " $down, $left, or $right.\n\n" );
   } # else
```

```
  } # else
} # for i

# Run through all PAIRS of keys in the grid (the
# locations), and check whether any locations that are
# adjacent in the grid are both hydrophobic. If they are,
# count them for scoring.

@keys = keys( %grid );

for ( $i = 0; $i < @keys; $i++ )
{
  for ( $j = $i+1; $j < @keys; $j++ )
  {
    $a = $keys[$i];
    $b = $keys[$j];
    if (     ( $grid{$a} eq $hydrophobic )
          && ( $grid{$b} eq $hydrophobic )
          && ( adjacent( $a, $b ) )
        )
    {
      $adjacencies++;
    } # if
  } # for j
} # for i

# Compute the score. Note that when we counted hydrophobic
# positions that were adjacent in the grid, we also counted
# those that MUST be adjacent because they are adjacent in
# the input sequence. Thus we subtract these from the
# score. Also, make the final score a negative value, to
# be consistent with the energy minimization concept.

$score = $adjacencies - $input_adjacencies;
$score = - $score;
printf( "Score: $score\n\n" );

# Function to determine if two locations are adjacent
# in a grid. Note that only adjacencies along the grid
# axes are considered. Returns 1 if they are adjacent,
# 0 otherwise.

sub adjacent
{
  my( $a, $b ) = @_;
  my( $ax, $ay, $bx, $by, $commapos );

  # Find the position of the comma; everything before that
  # is 'x', everything after it is 'y'. Then compute the
  # Euclidean distance. Don't bother with the square root.
```

```
$commapos = index( $a, "," );
$ax = substr( $a, 0, $commapos );
$ay = substr( $a, $commapos+1 );
$commapos = index( $b, "," );
$bx = substr( $b, 0, $commapos );
$by = substr( $b, $commapos+1 );

$distance = ( $ay - $by ) ** 2 + ( $ax - $bx ) ** 2;

# Return the result of the boolean comparison, which
# results in 1 if the comparison is true, 0 if false.

return ( $distance <= 1 );
} # adjacent
```

Example 8: Atomic Density Calculation

This program is fairly straightforward, scanning a PDB file for ATOM lines, saving the *x*, *y*, and *z* coordinates of each one, counting the number of other atoms within a specific distance of each one, sorting this list, and printing it. The 3apr.pdb file was retrieved from the Protein Data Bank (http://www. rcsb.org/pdb) and used as input to this program. Although the program prints the counts for all atoms, only the top 10 atoms are shown here, rather than all 2,464.

Sample input:

```
3apr.pdb
```

Corresponding output:

```
Input file: 3apr.pdb

Atom #      Count
------      -----
  191         16
 1008         16
 1027         16
 1035         16
 1201         16
 1727         16
 2003         16
 2319         16
  476         15
  758         15
     .          .
     .          .
     .          .
```

Code:

```perl
#!/usr/local/bin/perl

# Example program 8. Given the name of a PDB file, read
# the file and locate all ATOM locations. For each atom,
# count the number of neighboring atoms within a threshold
# distance. As PDB files can contain thousands of atoms,
# we want to do this as efficiently as possible.

# Define some constants that will be needed later. Define
# the threshold as the square of the value we want (in
# angstroms). This way, when we compute Euclidean
# distance, we don't have to use the square root function
# on EVERY pair of distances, cutting down on computation
# time.

$threshold      = 3.6 ** 2;
$atom_keyword   = "ATOM";
$atom_start     = 0;
$label_start    = 6;
$label_length   = 5;
$x_start        = 30;
$x_length       = 8;
$y_start        = 38;
$y_length       = 8;
$z_start        = 46;
$z_length       = 8;

# Retreive and check the command line parameter.

$inputfile = @ARGV[0];

if ( @ARGV == 0 )
{
  die( "$0: Place the PDB file name on the commmand"
     . " line.\n\n" );
} # if

printf( "Input file: $inputfile\n\n" );

unless( open( PDB, "$inputfile" ) )
{
  die( "$0: Cannot open PDB file $inputfile.\n\n" );
} # if

while ( <PDB> )
{
  $input = $_;
  chop( $input );
```

```perl
    if ( index( $input, $atom_keyword ) == $atom_start )
    {
      $label[$records] = substr( $input, $label_start,
                                 $label_length );
      $x[$records] = substr( $input, $x_start, $x_length );
      $y[$records] = substr( $input, $y_start, $y_length );
      $z[$records] = substr( $input, $z_start, $z_length );
      $records++;
    } # if
  } # while

  for ( $i = 0; $i < $records; $i++ )
  {
    for ( $j = $i+1; $j < $records; $j++ )
    {
      $distance = ( $x[$i] - $x[$j] ) ** 2
                + ( $y[$i] - $y[$j] ) ** 2
                + ( $z[$i] - $z[$j] ) ** 2;

      if ( $distance < $threshold )
      {
        $count[$i]++;
        $count[$j]++;
      } # if
    } # for j
  } # for i

  # Sort the labels and counts in order by count, from
  # highest to lowest. Note that we cannot simply use 'sort'
  # here, since the information resides in two different
  # arrays. The method presented here is a simple bubble
  # sort: check each pair of counts, swapping them (and the
  # labels) if the later one has a larger value.

  printf( "Atom #   Count\n" );
  printf( "------   -----\n" );

  for ( $i = 0; $i < $records-1; $i++ )
  {
    for ( $j = $i+1; $j < $records; $j++ )
    {
      if ( $count[$i] < $count[$j] )
      {
        ($count[$i], $count[$j]) = ($count[$j], $count[$i]);
        ($label[$i], $label[$j]) = ($label[$j], $label[$i]);
      } # if
    } # for j
```

```
  # Print out each record as it becomes sorted.
  printf( "%6s %5d\n", $label[$i], $count[$i] );
} # for i

# Print out the final record, which was skipped by the
# for i loop going only up to $records-1.
printf( "%6s %5d\n", $label[$i], $count[$i] );
```

Example 9: Enzyme Kinetics— Linear Regression

As a tool for producing Lineweaver–Burk plots, this program calculates a simple least-squares linear regression of the two-dimensional input data. The data are fitted onto the general formula $y_i = mx_i + b$, where x_i and y_i are paired input data. The values of m and b are computed and printed, as well as the x and y intercepts of the fitted line, along with r, the correlation coefficient. Note that the program handles cases where the fitted line is horizontal ($m = 0$), but not a vertical line, because then m would be infinity.

Sample input:

```
1 1.1 2 3.4 3 4.2 4 5.0 6 7.1 7 9.6
```

Corresponding output:

```
Input coordinates: 1 1.1 2 3.4 3 4.2 4 5.0 6 7.1 7 9.6

a = 1.2583850931677, b = 0.242857142857142

X-intercept = -0.192991115498519
Y-intercept = 0.242857142857142

Correlation coefficient: 0.983229656640151
```

Code:

```perl
#!/usr/local/bin/perl

# Example program 9. Perform a linear regression on the
# input data. The input consists of x/y pairs of numerical
# data, all inputs separated by spaces. The output values
# are m and b, such that y = mx + b is the form of the best
# fit, as well as the x- and y-intercepts of this line,
# along with the correlation coefficient.

# Define some constants that we'll need later.

$mininputs = 6;  # With less than 3 input pairs, linear
                 # regression is either unnecessary or
                 # inappropriate.
```

```perl
# Make sure there are a sufficient number of evenly matched
# x/y inputs.

if (     ( @ARGV < $mininputs )
     || ( ( @ARGV % 2 ) != 0 )
   )
{
  die( "$0: Place the x/y pairs on the commmand"
       . " line.\n\n" );
} # if

printf( "Input coordinates: @ARGV\n\n" );

# Store the input values in two arrays.

$numinputs = @ARGV / 2;

for ( $i = 0; $i < $numinputs; $i++ )
{
  $x[$i] = $ARGV[$i*2];
  $y[$i] = $ARGV[$i*2 + 1];
} # for i

# Compute the values that are needed for the linear
# regression.

for ( $i = 0; $i < $numinputs; $i++ )
{
  $sumx   += $x[$i];
  $sumy   += $y[$i];
  $sumxsq += $x[$i] ** 2;
  $sumxy  += $x[$i] * $y[$i];
} # for i

# Compute and print m, b, x-intercept, and y-intercept,
# checking for possible division by 0 if the slope is 0
# (in which case there is no x-intercept).

$m = ( $numinputs * $sumxy - $sumx * $sumy )
   / ( $numinputs * $sumxsq - $sumx ** 2 );

$b = ( $sumxsq * $sumy - $sumxy * $sumx )
   / ( $numinputs * $sumxsq - $sumx ** 2 );

printf( "m = $m, b = $b\n\n" );

if ( $m == 0 )
{
  $xintcp = "DNE";
} # if
else
```

```
{
  $xintcp = - $b / $m;
} # else

$yintcp = $b;

printf( "X-intercept = $xintcp\n" );
printf( "Y-intercept = $yintcp\n\n" );

# Compute the values needed for the correlation
# coefficient.

$avgx = $sumx / $numinputs;
$avgy = $sumy / $numinputs;

for ( $i = 0; $i < $numinputs; $i++ )
{
  $xminusavgx = $x[$i] - $avgx;
  $yminusavgy = $y[$i] - $avgy;

  $sum1 += $xminusavgx * $yminusavgy;
  $sum2 += $xminusavgx ** 2;
  $sum3 += $yminusavgy ** 2;
} # for i

$sum2 = sqrt( $sum2 );
$sum3 = sqrt( $sum3 );

# Compute and print the correlation coefficient.

$r = $sum1 / $sum2 / $sum3;

printf( "Correlation coefficient: $r\n\n" );
```

Glossary

1*s* orbital Spherical orbital closest to the nucleus of an atom, where electrons with the lowest energy are found.

2*p* orbital A set of three dumbell-shaped orbitals in the second sublevel of electron orbitals.

2*s* orbital Lowest energy, spherically shaped orbital in the second sublevel of electron orbitals.

50% majority-rule consensus A consensus tree in which any internal node that is supported by at least half of the trees being summarized is portrayed as a simple bifurcation, and those nodes where less than half of the trees agree are shown as multifurcations.

A Adenine. One of two purines that are used as nitrogenous bases.

absolute direction representation A representation for protein configurations in which the position of each residue is specified according to the direction moved from the previous position. In absolute representation, the previous move's direction is not considered. For example, in a two-dimensional model, the possible values for each position are: up, down, left, and right.

activation energy (E_{act}) The amount of energy required to excite a molecule or molecules into a reactive state that allows new molecules to be made.

activator Any substance that increases the velocity of an enzyme-catalyzed reaction.

active site The region on the three-dimensional surface of a protein where catalysis occurs.

additive Term applied to a scaled tree if the physical length of the branches connecting any two nodes is an accurate representation of their accumulated differences.

alignment A pairing of two homologous nucleotide or protein sequences for the purpose of identifying the location of accumulated changes since they last shared a common ancestor. *See also* global and local alignment.

alleles Different versions of any given gene within a species of organism.

alpha carbon The central carbon atom in an amino acid to which side chains (R-groups) are bound.

alternative splicing The production of two or more mRNA molecules from a single hnRNA by using different splice junctions.

amino terminus (N-terminal) In a polypeptide, the end of the molecule that has an unbound amide group (NH_2) and corresponds to the 5' end of a gene.

anti-parallel Showing opposite orientation; in the case of double-stranded DNA, this means that if one strand is 5' to 3', its complementary strand will be in the opposite, 3' to 5' orientation.

arguments *See* parameters.

aromatic Compounds that have molecular structures based on the six-carbon ring of benzene.

array Variables that can store multiple values. Each value is retrieved using an integer index.

backbone (of an amino acid) Consists of an amide, an alpha carbon, and a carboxylic acid, or carboxylate group.

basal promoter A set of nucleotide sequences such as the "TATA-box" that serves as a minimal promoter within eukaryotes and to which basal transcription factors bind.

basal transcription factor Proteins such as the TATA-binding protein that are needed for RNA polymerase assembly around promoter regions of eukaryotic genes.

base pair (1) The interaction between purines and pyrimidines (specifically between A and T and between G and C) in double-stranded DNA.

(2) The smallest unit of measure of double-stranded DNA length.

beta turns U-turn-like structures within proteins formed when a beta strand reverses direction in an anti-parallel beta sheet.

bifurcating Refers to a point in a phylogenetic tree in which an ancestral taxon splits into two independent lineages.

binding operator In Perl, the =~ operator, which matches a string to a regular expression.

block A set of statements enclosed in curly braces.

blotting and hybridization The transfer of molecules (often nucleic acids) from a gel onto a membrane followed by washing with a labelled probe that binds specifically to a molecule of interest.

blunt end End of a double-stranded DNA molecule that has no single-stranded overhang.

bootstrap test Test that allows for a rough quantification of confidence levels.

branch and bound method A clever and efficient means of streamlining the search for trees of maximum parsimony. Consists of two steps: First, determine an upper bound to the length of the most parsimonious tree for the data set and, second, incrementally grow a tree by adding branches one at a time to a tree that describes the relationship of just a few of the sequences being considered.

branch swapping Pruning and regrafting of branches from phylogenetic trees.

branches In a phylogenetic tree, the graphical representation of an evolutionary relationship between two (bifurcating) or more (multifurcating) lineages arising from a single ancestral node.

bump A steric collision.

C Cytosine. One of two pyrimidines that are used as nitrogenous bases in DNA and RNA molecules.

CAAT box A short segment of many eukaryotic promoters that is typically located approximately 80 nucleotides upstream of the transcriptional start site. A variety of factors bind to this segment that contains the bases C-A-A-T.

capping Refers to a set of chemical alterations, including the addition of a terminal G and methylation, at the 5' end of all hnRNAs.

carboxy terminus In a polypeptide, the end of the molecule that has a carboxylic acid group (—COOH) and corresponds to the 3' end of a gene.

cDNA Complementary DNA. DNA synthesized from an RNA template by a reverse transcriptase enzyme.

cDNA library A collection of DNA sequences generated from mRNA sequences. This type of library contains only protein-coding DNA (genes).

central dogma Process by which information is extracted from the nucleotide sequence of a gene and then used to make a protein (DNA→RNA→protein).

chain-termination method The basis of most DNA sequencing strategies. Dideoxy-nucleotides (missing both the 2' and 3' OH) prevent the addition of any additional nucleotides.

character In a phylogenetic tree, a well-defined feature that can exist in a limited number of different states.

charged amino acid Amino acid that carries a positive or negative charge at biological pH.

chloroplast transit sequence A string of roughly 25 charged amino acids at the N-terminus of a protein destined for delivery to a chloroplast.

Chou-Fasman parameter A set of numeric parameters indicating the empirically observed tendency of an amino acid to be involved in an alpha helix, a beta strand, and in each position of a hairpin turn.

chromatin The roughly equal mixture by mass of DNA and closely associated histones within eukaryotic nuclei.

chromosome In prokaryotes, the DNA molecule containing a cell's genome. In eukaryotes, a linear DNA molecule complexed with proteins that contains a large amount of genetic information.

cladist An evolutionary biologist who is generally more interested in the evolutionary path taken by organisms since they last shared a common ancestor than their relative placement on phylogenetic trees.

cladogram A graphical representation that conveys the evolutionary relationship between organisms.

cloning Insertion of specific DNA fragments into chromosome-like carriers that allow their maintenance and replication within living cells.

codon Group of three nucleotides in an RNA copy of the coding portion of a gene, corresponding to a specific amino acid.

comment In computer programming, nonexecutable notes in a computer program that describe a function; comments make long, complex programs easier to understand.

compiler A computer program that translates a symbolic programming language into machine language so that the instructions can be executed by the computer.

complementary (1) The pairing of specific nucleotides (G and C; A and T; A and U) through hydrogen bonding. (2) The antiparallel pairing of strands of nucleotides.

conceptual translation Using the universal genetic code to convert the nucleotide sequence of the open reading frame of a gene into its corresponding amino acid sequence.

conditional code Code that will only be executed if a test performed on a conditional statement is true.

conditional execution Execution of a program block that may or may not occur, depending on the result of a particular test. For example, the "if" statement allows conditional execution in Perl.

conditional (if) statement Statements that are only executed if certain conditions are met.

conformational parameter Numeric values representing the empirically observed tendency of a particular amino acid to be found in a specific conformation (alpha helix, beta sheet, or turn).

consensus sequence A sequence that represents the most common nucleotide or amino acid at each position in two or more homologous sequences.

consensus tree A single tree that summarizes the graphical representations of a set of trees.

constitutive A gene or operon that is expressed continuously.

contig A set of clones whose sequences can be assembled into an array that is longer than what can be obtained from any single sequencing reaction.

convergent evolution The independent evolution of similar genetic or phenotypic traits. For example, eyes evolved independently in a variety of organisms such as mammals, molluscs, and insects and are not homologous structures.

cot equation An equation that relates the fraction of single-stranded DNA remaining as a function of time (with genomic complexity and concentration as the only variables) in genomic renaturation experiments. The time required for half of a genome to reassociate ($cot_{1/2}$) is a useful measure of genomic complexity.

covalent bonding The sharing of electrons in overlapping orbitals.

CpG island A stretch of 500 to 3,000 bp in which the dinucleotide CpG is found at higher than normal levels relative to the rest of a mammalian genome. Usually associated with the promoters of eukaryotic housekeeping genes.

crystal Solid structure formed by a regular array of molecules.

C value Measure of a cell's total DNA content.

C-value paradox The absence of a perfect correlation between organismal complexity and genome size.

declaring (a variable) Most computer programs require the programmer to list at the start of a program all variables that will be used within the program; this is the process of declaring a variable.

degeneracy The ability of some amino acids to be coded for by more than one triplet codon.

deleterious mutation A mutation that has an adverse effect on the fitness of an organism.

denatured protein A protein that has lost its normal tertiary and quaternary structure usually because of exposure to heat or chemicals such as detergents or urea.

deoxyribonucleic acid (DNA) A usually double-stranded biopolymer of linked nucleotides in which the sugar residue is deoxyribose. The molecular basis of heredity.

dipeptide Two amino acids joined by a peptide bond.

dissociation constant (K_I) A measure of an enzyme's affinity for an inhibitor.

distance In a phylogenetic tree, a measure of the overall, pairwise difference between two data sets.

disulfide bond Cross-linking residues that are far removed from one another in the primary structure of a protein.

DNA *See* deoxyribonucleic acid.

dot plot A graphical method of comparing two sequences. A series of diagonal lines within the graph correspond to regions of sequence similarity.

dynamic programming Program that allows computers to efficiently explore all possible solutions to certain types of complex problems; it breaks a problem apart into reasonably sized subproblems and uses these parts to compute the final answer.

electronegativity Measure of an atom's need to acquire or to donate atoms to fill or empty its outermost shell of orbitals.

element Something that cannot be further reduced by chemical reactions.

endergonic reaction Chemical reaction that requires a net input of energy to convert reactants into products; has a positive Gibbs free energy.

endoplasmic reticulum (ER) A web-like network of membranes that is intimately associated with the Golgi apparatus.

enhanceosomes An assembly of transcription factors bound to the promoter of a eukaryotic gene.

enhancer Any of a number of DNA sequences to which eukaryotic transcription factors can specifically bind. Enhancer sequences function in either orientation and act cumulatively to increase transcription levels.

enzyme A biological catalyst (usually a protein) that causes a specific chemical reaction to proceed more quickly by lowering its activation energy.

equilibrium constant (K_{eq}) The point in a reversible chemical reaction at which reactants are converted to products at the same rate that products are converted to reactants.

escape sequence Multi-character sequence that allows programmers to insert special characters (such as newlines and tabs) into strings. In Perl, escape sequences start with the backslash (\) character.

ESI Electrospray ionization.

EST Expressed sequence tags; short DNA sequences obtained from either the 5' or 3' ends of cDNAs.

euchromatin Open chromatin characterized by high levels of histone methylation and low levels of DNA methylation in eukaryotes.

evaluate In Perl, to replace a variable name with the contents of the variable.

exergonic reaction Chemical reaction that releases energy; has a negative Gibbs free energy.

exhaustive search An evaluation of all possible problem solutions.

exon Parts of an hnRNA molecule spliced together to form mRNA.

exon shuffling The creation of proteins with new functions by the process of recombining exons corresponding to functional domains of existing genes at the level of DNA. Strictly, exon duplication and insertion.

family Consists of proteins that are more than 50% identical in amino acid sequence across their entire length.

file pointer A special type of Perl variable that indicates a file to read from or write to.

fixation A condition in which an allele's frequency within a population reaches 100%.

fold Often used synonymously with the term "structural motif" but typically used to connote large regions of similar secondary structure found in two or more proteins.

fourfold degenerate site Codon position where changing a nucleotide to any of the three alternatives has no effect on the amino acid that ribosomes insert into protein.

four-point condition A situation in which two pairs of taxa are grouped together on a tree with four terminal branches in a way that the distances separating the paired taxa are shorter than both alternatives.

function A subroutine that returns a value.

functional constraint The tendency in particularly important genes to accumulate changes very slowly over the course of evolution.

G Guanine. One of two purines that are used as a nitrogenous base.

gap penalty A reduction in the score for an alignment that is invoked to minimize the introduction of gaps.

gaps A dash or series of dashes introduced to an alignment to reflect the occurrence of an indel in one of two aligned sequences since they last shared a common ancestor.

GC content The measure of the abundance of G and C nucleotides relative to A and T nucleotides within DNA sequences.

gel electrophoresis Process in which an electric field is used to pull charged molecules through a polyacrylamide, starch, or agarose gel to separate them by their size and or charge.

gene A specific sequence of nucleotides in DNA or RNA that is essential for a specific function; the functional unit of inheritance controlling the transmission and expression of one or more traits.

gene expression Process of using the information stored in DNA to make an RNA molecule and then a corresponding protein.

gene tree Phylogenetic tree based on the divergence observed within a single set of homologous genes.

genome The sum total of an organism's genetic material.

genomic equivalent The amount of DNA that corresponds to the size of an organism's complete set of genetic instructions.

genomic library A set of clones containing genomic DNA inserts.

genotype All or part of the genetic constitution of an individual or group.

global alignment A sequence alignment method that provides a score for aligning two sequences in their entirety.

global variable A variable that is active throughout an entire program; contrast with *local variable*.

GU-AG rule Associated with eukaryotic protein-coding genes, this rule states that the first two nucleotides at the 5' end of the RNA sequence of introns are invariably 5'-GU-3' and the last two at the 3' end of the intron are always 5'-AG-3'.

hairpin turn Place in an RNA chain where it reverses to allow intramolecular base pairing.

hash A Perl variable that can store multiple values. Unlike an array where values are retrieved using integer indices, a hash can use any type of value (including strings) as an index.

Henri–Michaelis–Menten equation A mathematical model that uses changes in the initial velocity of an enzyme catalyzed reaction when substrate concentration is varied to determine the enzyme's V_{max} and K_m.

heterochromatin Transcriptionally inactive, densely packed chromatin; associated with high levels of DNA methylation and low levels of histone methylation.

heuristic methods Trial-and-error, self-educating techniques for parsing a tree.

hnRNA Heterogeneous RNA; primary RNA polymerase II transcripts in eukaryotes, converted to mRNAs after capping, splicing, and polyadenylation.

homologs Sequences that share a common ancestor.

homoplasies Character states that have arisen in several taxa independently and not from a common ancestor.

horizontal gene transfer The process of passing genes from one species to another. The mechanism for this movement of genes is unknown, though pathogens and transposons are often suspected as the cause.

housekeeping gene Gene that is expressed at a high level in all tissues and at all times in development.

H-P (hydrophobic-polar) model Simple lattice model that represents each amino acid residue in a protein as a single atom of fixed radius.

hydrogen bonding Interaction between molecules resulting from the slight separation of charges that results from polar covalent bonds.

hydrophilic Easily dissolved in a watery solution; literally, "water friendly."

hydrophobic Having limited interaction with water molecules; literally, "afraid of water."

hydrophobic amino acid Amino acid having an R-group composed mostly or entirely of carbon and hydrogen; it is unlikely to form hydrogen bonds with water molecules.

hydrophobic collapse The process of folding a polypeptide into a compact conformation that isolates hydrophobic residues from solvent.

hydrophobic zipper A theoretical mechanism for the formation of secondary structure in proteins. According to the theory, alpha helix and beta sheet formation is largely driven by the mutual attraction of hydrophobic residues.

if statement *See* conditional (if) statement.

indel event An insertion/deletion event.

index The number of a particular array element.

induced fit docking Changing shape of a receptor's surface as it specifically interacts with a ligand.

inferred ancestor In a phylogenetic tree, an ancestor for which empirical data are no longer available.

inferred tree A depiction of the phylogenetic relationship of three or more homologous sequences that is a close approximation of their true relationship.

informative Diagnostic position for a parsimony analysis; contrast with *uninformative*.

ingroup A species or set of species that is not the most divergent of a set of species; contrast with *outgroup*.

inhibitor Any substance that decreases the velocity of an enzyme-catalyzed reaction.

initiation complex A set of transcription factors interacting with themselves and the promoter region of a gene that facilitates the initiation of transcription.

initiator (Inr) sequence The nucleotides associated with the transcriptional start site of eukaryotic genes that are necessary and essential; the consensus sequence within humans is: 5'-44CARR-3'.

insertion sequence A transposable element containing no information content beyond what is needed for its own transposition; when inserted into a gene, it disrupts the normal structure and function of that gene.

internal node In a phylogenetic tree, a node for which no actual data have been collected; graphical representation of a common ancestor that gave rise to two or more independent lineages at some point in the past.

intractable A problem for which all algorithms require an unacceptable amount of computation time as the problem size grows large.

intrinsic terminator A specific signal for the termination of transcription in prokaryotes; a string of nucleotides in a newly transcribed RNA capable of forming a secondary structure followed by a run of uracils.

intron Internal sequence excised in splicing; present in the primary transcripts (hnRNAs) of eukaryotic genes but not in their mRNAs.

invariant A position within a sequence alignment in which all sequences contain the same character.

isochores Long regions of homogeneous base composition within eukaryotic genomes.

isoelectric focusing The process by which differences in the pI values of proteins are exploited to allow their separation.

isoelectric point (pI) The pH at which a protein has no net charge.

junk DNA Disposable DNA sequences; sequences for which no function is currently known.

kinase Enzymes that catalyze phosphorylation reactions.

labeled feature vector A representation for the examples used to train a pattern recognition algorithm. A labeled feature vector consists of a list of feature values for the example, along with a label indicating the correct classification of the example.

lead compound A molecule that is a viable candidate for use as a drug.

length (of a tree) The total number of substitutions required at both informative and uninformative sites.

length penalty Used by sequence alignment algorithms to penalize the introduction of long gaps.

Levinthal paradox Observation that the number of potential three-dimensional conformations for even a small protein is so large that an exhaustive comparison of them all cannot be accomplished by nature during protein-folding.

ligase Enzyme that catalyzes the formation of a phosphodiester bond between two DNA molecules.

LINE Long interspersed nuclear element.

local alignment A sequence alignment method that searches for subsequences that align well.

local variable A variable that exists only inside a specific subroutine; that is, it is not active throughout the entire program; contrast with *global variable*.

lock and key approach A docking approach in which the conformations of the two docked molecules are rigid and fixed; contrast with *induced fit docking*.

log odds matrix Matrix in which the entries are based on the log of the substitution probability for each amino acid.

loop statement Statement that allows a computer program to repeat a block of code either a certain number of times or until a certain condition is met.

machine language The set of symbolic instruction codes, usually in binary form, that is used to represent operations and data in a computer.

MALDI Matrix assisted laser desorption ionization; a method of mass spectrometric analysis.

match score The amount of credit given by an algorithm to an alignment for each aligned pair of identical residues.

Maxam-Gilbert method An early DNA sequencing strategy that relies on chemical degradation to generate the DNA subfragments.

maximum likelihood approach Phylogenetic approach in which probabilities are considered for every individual nucleotide substitution in a set of sequence alignments; a purely statistically based method of phylogenetic reconstruction.

methylation The attachment of a methyl group ($-CH_3$) to either a nucleotide's nitrogenous base or to a protein.

microarray An ordered grid of DNA probes fixed at known positions on a solid substrate.

microsatellite A region in the genome where relatively short nucleotide sequences such as 5'-CA-3' are tandemly repeated; typically highly variable between individuals.

minisatellite A region in the genome where nucleotide sequences ranging in size from 5 base pairs to a few tens of base pairs long occur multiple times in a tandem array; likely to be highly variable between individuals.

mismatch score The penalty assigned by an algorithm when nonidentical residues are aligned in an alignment.

mitochondrial signal sequence A string of amino acids (specifically an amphipathic helix 12 to 30 amino acids long) that causes a eukaryotic protein to be delivered to a cell's mitochondria.

mixed inhibitor An inhibitor that displays aspects of both noncompetitive and competitive inhibition.

molar A measure of the concentration of solute dissolved in a solvent; i.e., a one molar solution contains one mole of solute in one liter of solvent.

molecular clock A controversial hypothesis that, for a given DNA sequence, mutations accumulate at a constant rate in all evolutionary lineages.

molecular clones Numerous identical copies of a DNA sequence, typically associated with a vector such as a plasmid or virus that allows their maintenance and propagation in bacterial cultures.

Monte Carlo algorithm A method that samples possible solutions to a complex problem such as energy minimization as a means of estimating a general solution.

multifurcating A graphical representation of an unknown branching order involving three or more species in a phylogenetic tree.

multiple sequence alignment An alignment of three or more homologous sequences.

mutation Change in a nucleotide sequence that occurs due to mistakes in DNA replication or repair processes. Strictly, changes prior to passage through the filter of selection.

native structure Unique structure into which a particular protein is usually folded within a living cell.

natural selection (selection) Differential success between individuals in passing on genes to subsequent generations due to differences in fitness; leads to changes in allele frequencies (evolution).

nearest neighbor classifier A statistical method that classifies objects or concepts according to similarity of their features.

nearest neighbor energy rules In computing the energy of an RNA structure, rules that only consider base pairs that can potentially interact. The use of nearest neighbor rules can significantly reduce the computation time required to determine the energy of a particular conformation of an RNA molecule.

negative regulation The binding of a regulatory protein that prevents transcription from occurring.

neighbor-joining method Phylogenetic approach that starts with a star-like tree in which all species come off of a single central node regardless of their number. Neighbors are then sequentially found that minimize the total length of the branches on the tree.

neighborliness approach Phylogenetic approach that considers all possible pairwise arrangements of four species and determines which arrangement satisfies the four-point condition.

neighbors In a phylogenetic tree, the pairs of species that are separated from each other by just one internal node; sister taxa.

nested block A block of code embedded within another block. For example, nested "if" blocks can be used to enforce multiple conditions.

neural network A computer program that learns by emulating the function of a small set of neurons;

can be used to predict specific properties of data sets based on statistical similarity.

neutral mutation A mutation that has no effect on the fitness of an organism.

Newick format In a computer program, the format in which basic information about the structure of a phylogenetic tree is conveyed in a series of nested parentheses. For example, (A, (B,C)) means that taxa B and C are more like each other than either are to taxa A.

N-linked glycosylation The addition of an oligosaccharide to asparagine residues during post-translational modification of proteins within the Golgi apparatus.

NMR Nuclear magnetic resonance; technique for resolving protein structures.

nodes In a phylogenetic tree, a distinct taxonomic unit.

nondegenerate site Codon position where mutations always result in substitutions within the amino acid sequence of a protein.

nonsynonymous substitution Any nucleotide substitution that alters a codon to one for a different amino acid.

nuclear localization sequence A string of amino acids (specifically 7 to 41 basic residues) that cause a eukaryotic protein to be delivered to a cell's nucleus.

oligosaccharide A short chain of sugars.

O-linked glycosylation A post-translational process in which the enzyme *N*-acetylglucosaminyl-transferase attaches an oligosaccharide to the oxygen atom of a serine or threonine residue of a protein.

open reading frame (ORF) Any nucleotide sequence that contains a string of codons that is uninterrupted by the presence of a stop codon in the same reading frame.

operator sequence Nucleotide sequence, associated with the promoter of a gene, to which prokaryotic regulatory proteins bind.

operon A group of closely linked genes that produces a single mRNA molecule in transcription and that consists of structural genes and regulating elements.

origination penalty Penalty assessed as a result of starting a new series of gaps; part of the gap penalty.

orthologs Sequences that share similarity because of a speciation event that allowed them to evolve independently from an ancestral sequence.

outgroup A species or set of species that is least related to a group of organisms.

PAM unit A unit of evolution; specifically, the amount of evolutionary time required for an average of one substitution per 100 residues to be observed.

paralogs Sequences that share similarity because they are descendants of a duplicated ancestral gene.

parameters In computer programming, the values on which a subroutine will operate; also referred to as arguments.

parsimony The process of attaching preference to one evolutionary pathway over another on the basis of which pathway requires the invocation of the smallest number of mutational events.

pathogen A disease-causing agent.

peptide A chain of several amino acids.

peptide bond The covalent chemical bond between carbon and nitrogen in a peptide linkage.

peptide mass fingerprint A representation of the sizes of peptide fragments obtained when a specific protein is digested to completion by a protease.

Perl interpreter The program that reads and executes Perl code.

Perl script A text file that contains a list of Perl commands.

peroxisomal targeting signal A string of amino acids (specifically Ser-Lys-Leu at the carboxy-terminus) that causes a eukaryotic protein to be delivered to a peroxisome.

pH Unit of measure used to indicate concentration of hydrogen ions in a solution; specifically, the negative log of the molar concentration of H^+.

pharmacogenomics Field that uses information about an individual's genetic makeup to maximize the efficacy of treatments, while at the same time minimizing the unwanted side effects.

pheneticist Someone who studies the relationships among a group of organisms or sequences on the basis of the degree of similarity between them.

phenotype The visible properties of an organism that are produced by the interaction of its genotype and environment.

phosphatase Enzyme responsible for removing phosphate groups from phosphorylated residues.

phosphodiester bond The covalent chemical bond that connects the phosphate group of one nucleotide to the deoxyribose sugar of another.

phylogenetic tree A graphical representation of the evolutionary relationship among three or more genes or organisms.

pKa Unit of measure of the relative ease with which an amino acid releases its dissociable protons.

point accepted mutation (PAM) A mutation that has been "accepted" by natural selection in the sense that organisms bearing the mutation have survived.

polar amino acid Amino acid that often contains oxygen and/or nitrogen in its side chain and readily forms hydrogen bonds with water.

polar bond Interaction between a molecule with a full positive charge and another with a full negative charge.

polyadenylation The process of replacing the 3' end of a eukaryotic hnRNA with a stretch of approximately 250 A's that are not spelled out in the nucleotide sequence of a gene.

polycistronic Containing the genetic information of a number of genes (cistrons).

polymerase chain reaction An *in vitro* technique for rapidly synthesizing large quantities of a given DNA segment that involves separating the DNA into its two complementary strands, using DNA polymerase to synthesize double-stranded DNA from each single strand, and repeating the process.

polynucleotide A polymeric chain of nucleotides; DNA or RNA molecules.

polypeptide A polymeric chain of amino acids; protein.

position-specific scoring matrix A matrix of values that represent the frequency with which a particular amino acid type occupies a certain position in a set of aligned homologous sequences.

positive regulation When the binding of a regulatory protein makes it easier for an RNA polymerase to initiate transcription.

primary structure Sequence in which the various amino acids are assembled into a protein.

probe A piece of labeled DNA or RNA or an antibody that can specifically interact with a molecule of interest.

program control The ability to tell a computer to execute one set of instructions if a certain condition is true and another set of instructions otherwise.

promoter sequence Sequences that are recognized by RNA polymerases as being associated with a gene.

proteasome A multiprotein structure involved in protein degradation and immune response.

protein backbone The non-side-chain atoms in a polypeptide chain.

protein electrophoresis Method of using an electric field to separate and compare related proteins on the basis of superficial features such as size and charge.

protein sequencing Determining the order in which amino acids are linked together to make a given protein; often obtained by the Edman procedure in which amino acids are removed one at a time from a polypeptide's carboxy-terminus.

protein threading A process by which the conformation of a polypeptide is assumed, and then the energy of the resulting structure is calculated. By calculating the energy for a variety of known structures, the conformation that best "fits" a particular protein sequence can be determined. Because the structure is assumed rather than calculated, threading is sometimes referred to as "reverse protein folding."

proteome The sum total of an organism's proteins.

pseudogene A gene that acquires mutations that make it nonfunctional and transcriptionally inactive.

pseudoknot Created when bases involved in a loop pair with other bases outside of the loop; the most difficult type of RNA structure to predict.

purine Nucleotides whose nitrogenous bases have a two-ring structure; usually guanine and adenine.

pyrimidine Nucleotides whose nitrogenous bases have a one-ring structure; usually cytosine, thymine, and uracil.

quantifier In regular expressions, a special character that specifies the count for a specific character or character class. For example, in the regular expression /A*/, which matches zero or more A characters, the * character is a quantifier for A.

quaternary structure The intermolecular interactions that occur when multiple polypeptides associate; overall structure formed by interacting proteins.

$R_0/t_{1/2}$ value A measure of the time required for half of an organism's RNA polymerase II transcripts to hybridize to complementary sequences; a measure of transcriptome complexity.

reading frame Linear sequence of codons in a protein-coding gene starting with the start codon and ending with a stop codon.

regulatory Allowing or preventing the expression of genes under particular circumstances; contrast with *constitutive*.

relative direction representation A representation for a protein conformation in which the position of each successive residue is encoded relative to the position and direction of the previous two residues. In a two-dimensional square lattice, the possible directions for such a representation are forward (F), left (L) and right (R).

relative mutability A measure of the number of times an amino acid was substituted by any other amino acid within an alignment of homologous protein sequences.

relative rate test A check for the constancy of the rate of nucleotide substitutions in different lineages; see also *molecular clock*.

residue The portion of an amino acid that remains as a part of a polypeptide chain. In the context of a peptide or protein, amino acids are generally referred to as residues.

restriction enzymes Proteins that introduce double-stranded breaks in DNA molecules whenever they encounter a specific string of nucleotides.

restriction mapping Using simultaneous digestions with two or more restriction enzymes to determine the relative positions of restriction enzyme recognition sequences within a DNA molecule.

restriction site String of nucleotides recognized by a restriction enzyme; restriction enzyme recognition site.

retroposon A transposable element that is propagated by an RNA-intermediate but not as part of a virus and does not have terminally redundant sequences.

retrotransposition Transposition that involves an RNA-intermediate.

reverse transcriptase A special enzyme used to convert RNA to DNA.

reversible reaction Chemical reaction in which the products can be converted back into the reactants.

ribosome Complex of proteins and rRNA that are responsible for catalyzing translation.

ribozyme RNA molecules that are capable of catalyzing specific chemical reactions such as self-cleavage.

RNA polymerase Enzyme responsible for transcription; converts the information in DNA molecules into RNA molecules.

rooted tree Phylogenetic tree in which a single node is designated as a common ancestor and a unique path leads from it through evolutionary time to any other node.

rotamer A commonly observed conformation of an amino acid side chain.

satellite DNA Eukaryotic DNA fragments with unusual densities and little information storage capacity relative to other genomic data.

saturation mutagenesis The process of making all possible changes to the nucleotide sequence of a gene to determine which alter the gene's function.

scalar variable A variable that can hold only one value.

scaled tree Phylogenetic tree in which branch lengths are proportional to the differences between pairs of neighboring nodes.

scoring matrix Matrix used to score each nongap position in the alignment.

secondary structure Structural features such as alpha helices and beta sheets of a protein that arise from primary structure.

selectively neutral See *neutral mutation*.

semiglobal alignment A sequence alignment in which gaps at the start or end of the sequences do not contribute to the alignment score.

sequence (1) The linear order of nucleotides in a DNA or RNA molecule or the order of amino acids in a protein. (2) The act of determining the linear order of nucleotides or amino acids in a molecule.

serial analysis of gene expression (SAGE) An experimental technique used to assess gene expression levels.

Shine–Delgarno sequence A ribosome loading site on prokaryotic mRNAs; specifically, a string of nucleotides whose consensus sequence is 5'-AGGAGGU-3' that is complementary to a short sequence at the 3' end of the 16S rRNA found in the 30S ribosomal subunit.

side chain A short chain or group of atoms attached to the central carbon of an amino acid that confers a distinctive chemistry.

signal cascade A signal amplification strategy used by many biological systems in which an event causes one protein to interact with and activate the next in the cascade and so on until a large number of the final proteins in the cascade have been activated.

signal peptidase An enzyme that specifically removes the signal polypeptide (sequence) of a eukaryotic protein.

signal sequence (polypeptide) A string of 15 to 30 amino acids at the amino-terminus of a eukaryotic protein that causes it to be translated by a ribosome associated with the endoplasmic reticulum.

SINE Short interspersed nuclear element.

species tree Phylogenetic tree based on the divergence observed in multiple genes.

spliceosomes Enzyme complexes responsible for splicing in eukaryotes.

splicing Process of excising internal sequences of eukaryotic hnRNAs, introns, and rejoining the exons that flank them.

start codon Triplet codon (specifically, AUG) at which both prokaryotic and eukaryotic ribosomes begin to translate an mRNA.

statement Basic unit of execution in Perl; represents one instruction and is generally terminated with a semicolon.

stem A region of intramolecular base pairing in an RNA molecule.

steric collision (bump) The physical impossibility of two or more atoms occupying the same space at the same time.

sticky ends Single-stranded DNA at the cleaved end of a double-stranded fragment.

stop codon One of three codons (specifically, UGA, UAG and UAA) that does not instruct ribosome to insert a specific amino acid and, thereby, causes translation of an mRNA to stop.

strict consensus tree A consensus tree in which all disagreements are treated equally even if only one alternative tree is not consistent with hundreds of others that are in agreement regarding a particular branching point.

structural protein A term used to describe proteins generally involved with maintaining a cell or tissue's shape such as those that provide rigidity and support in bones and connective tissues.

structured programming A method of computer programming in which consistent indentation, liberal comments, and the use of subroutines are employed to create readable code.

subroutine A re-usable portion of a computer program. Subroutines are usually supplied with one or more values ("arguments", or "parameters") from the calling routine. Subroutines that return a value to the calling routine are often called functions.

substitution Mutation that has passed through the filter of selection on at least some level.

superfamily Groups of protein families that are related by detectable levels of sequence similarity that are reflective of an ancient evolutionary relationship.

synapomorphies Informative sites that support the internal branches in an inferred tree; a derived state that is shared by several taxa.

synonymous substitution Change at the nucleotide level of coding sequences that does not change the amino acid sequence of the protein.

T Thymine. One of two pyrimidines that are used as a nitrogenous base in DNA molecules.

target identification The process of identifying biological molecules essential for the survival or proliferation of a particular pathogen.

taxonomist One who studies the general principles of scientific classification including the naming and placement of taxonomic groups.

terminal node In a phylogenetic tree, a node at the tip of a branch for which data have been collected.

tertiary structure The overall three-dimensional shape of a folded polypeptide chain.

thermodynamically favorable A chemical reaction that has a large negative Gibbs free energy value is said to be thermodynamically favorable and can therefore occur without an input of energy.

topology The topographical features of a molecule; its configuration.

transcription The first step in the process of gene expression; making an RNA copy of a gene.

transcriptome The complete set of an organism's RNA sequences.

transformed distance method A distance-based method of phylogenetic reconstruction that takes the different rates of evolution within different lineages into account.

transition Mutation in which a purine (A or G) is replaced with another purine or in which a pyrimidine (C or T) is replaced by another pyrimidine.

transition state theory Theory that states that products are formed only after reactants have (1) collided in an appropriate spacial orientation and (2) acquired enough activation energy to reach a transition state.

translation Process of converting the information from the nucleotide sequences in RNA to the amino acid sequences that make a protein.

transliteration Replacement of one or more of a set of characters with corresponding characters from another set as performed by the tr operator in Perl.

transversion Mutation in which a purine (G or A) is replaced with a pyrimidine (C or T) or vice versa.

triplet code A set of three nucleotides that can be used to specify a particular amino acid during translation by ribosomes.

turnover number The number of substrate molecules converted to product by a single enzyme in a unit of time (usually seconds or minutes).

twofold degenerate site Codon position where two different nucleotides result in the translation of the same amino acid, but the two other nucleotides code for a different amino acid.

uninformative In a parsimony analysis, a position within a sequence alignment that does not allow alternative trees to be differentiated on the basis of the number of mutations they invoke; contrast with *informative*.

unrooted tree Phylogenetic tree that specifies the relationship among nodes, but does not make any representation about the direction in which evolution occurred.

unscaled tree Phylogenetic tree that conveys information about the relative kinship of terminal nodes, but does not make any representation regarding the relative number of changes that separate them.

unweighted-pair-group method with arithmetic mean (UPGMA) The simplest method of tree reconstruction, it employs a sequential clustering algorithm to build trees in a stepwise manner.

UPGMA *See* unweighted-pair-group method with arithmetic mean.

upstream promoter element Nucleotide sequences associated with the promoters of eukaryotic genes to which proteins other than RNA polymerase bind.

valence The number of unpaired electrons in an atom's outermost orbital.

vector An agent, such as a virus or a plasmid, that carries a modified or foreign gene. When used in gene therapy, a vector delivers the desired gene to a target cell.

word In sequence searching, a subsequence of fixed length. Some database search algorithms divide a query sequence into fixed-sized words, and then search for instances of these words in a sequence database.

Solutions to Odd-Numbered Questions and Problems

Chapter 1

1.1 The structure of deoxyribose is shown in Figure 1.1 while the structure of ribose shown in Figure 1.2.

1.3 See Figure 1.4.

1.5 The hydrophilic (or polar) amino acids all have either oxygen, nitrogen, or sulfur in their R groups, while the hydrophobic (non-polar) amino acids generally do not (methionine with its internal sulfur and tryptophan with its internal nitrogen are slight exceptions).

1.7 The answer to this question is the smallest value for n that satisfies this equation: $3,000,000,000 < 4^n$. That value is 16.

1.9 Using the genetic code provided in Table 1.1, the nucleotide sequence would be translated into the following string of amino acids: Met-Gly-Cys-Arg-Arg-Asn. Changing the sequence to 5'-UGG GAU GUC GCC GAA ACA-3' would cause it to code for the following string of amino acids: Trp-Asp-Val-Ala-Glu-Thr.

1.11 cDNA libraries contain clones that each contain a DNA copy of an mRNA from a cell. Since intergenic sequences and most promoter sequences are usually not transcribed by RNA polymerase (and since introns are removed from eukaryotic RNA polymerase II transcripts) sequences that correspond to those regions are not usually found in cDNA libraries. Genomic libraries are a group of clones that contain portions of an organism's genomic DNA.

Chapter 2

2.1 A pairwise sequence alignment might be useful in determining whether genetic sequences from two species are evolutionarily related. Pairwise alignments are also a useful step in database searching, since the alignment scores provide a measure of similarity between sequences. Likewise, pairwise alignment scores can be used as a distance metric for constructing phylogenetic trees (see Chapters 4 and 5). Multiple sequence alignments are useful for identifying regions of conserved sequence between more than two nucleotide or amino acid sequences. They are useful in constructing phylogenies, protein modeling, understanding substitution rates and tendencies, etc. Sequence database searches are useful for finding sequences similar to a particular target sequence. Database searches can be invaluable in identifying the functional role of a new genetic sequence, or inferring the structure of a new protein sequence.

2.3 A region of strong identity is revealed starting at position 3 of each sequence, and continuing until nearly the end of the two sequences. The region of similarity is much more clearly identified than in the previous plot.

	G	C	T	A	G	T	C	A	G	A	T	C	T	G	A	C	G	C	T	A
G								•					•							
A																				
T			•																	
G					•				•											
G						•														
T						•								•						
C							•													
A								•												
C							•													
A										•										
T						•							•							
C												•								
T													•							
G														•						
C																•				
C																		•		
G																				
C																				

2.5

	A	C	A	G	T	C	G	A	A	C	G
	0	−1	−2	−3	−4	−5	−6	−7	−8	−9	−10	−11
A	−1	1	0	−1	−2	−3	−4	−5	−6	−7	−8	−9
C	−2	0	2	1	0	−1	−2	−3	−4	−5	−6	−7
C	−3	−1	1	2	1	0	0	−1	−2	−3	−4	−5
G	−4	−2	0	1	3	2	1	1	0	−1	−2	−3
T	−5	−3	−1	0	2	4	3	2	1	0	−1	−2
C	−6	−4	−2	−1	1	3	5	4	3	2	1	0
C	−7	−5	−3	−2	0	2	4	5	4	3	3	2
G	−8	−6	−4	−3	−1	1	3	5	5	4	3	4

One of the optimal alignments is:

```
ACAGTCGAACG
ACCGTC---CG
```

As there are multiple paths from the lower right to the upper left corners of the partial scores table, other optimal alignments are also possible.

2.7 Assuming the same match, mismatch, and gap scores as in problem 2.5, the partial alignment scores table would be:

		A	C	G	T	A	T	C	G	C	G	T	A	T	A
	0	-1	-2	-3	-4	-5	-6	-7	-8	-9	-10	-11	-12	-13	-14
G	-1	0	0	0	0	0	0	0	0	0	0	0	0	0	0
A	-2	0	0	0	0	1	0	0	0	0	0	0	1	0	1
T	-3	0	0	0	1	0	2	1	0	0	0	1	0	2	1
G	-4	0	0	1	0	1	1	2	2	1	1	0	1	1	2
C	-5	0	1	0	1	0	1	2	2	3	2	1	0	1	1
T	-6	0	0	1	1	1	1	1	2	2	3	3	2	1	1
C	-7	0	1	0	1	1	1	2	1	3	2	3	3	2	1
T	-8	0	0	1	1	1	2	1	2	2	3	3	3	4	3
C	-9	0	1	0	1	1	1	3	2	3	2	3	3	3	4
G	-10	0	0	2	1	1	1	2	4	3	4	3	3	3	3
G	-11	0	0	1	2	1	1	1	3	4	4	4	3	3	3
A	-12	0	0	0	1	3	2	1	2	3	4	4	5	4	4
A	-13	0	0	0	0	2	3	2	1	2	3	4	5	5	5
A	-14	0	0	0	0	1	2	3	2	1	2	3	5	5	6

The highest value in this table is 6, in the lower right. Following this value back towards the upper left until we reach a 0 value, we can obtain the following local alignment:

```
TCGCGTATA
TCTCGGAAA
```

Chapter 3

3.1 The mean time for fixation for a new neutral mutation is equal to $4N$ generations. For this question, $N = 6{,}000{,}000{,}000$ and the generation time is 30 years, so the fixation time for a neutral mutation would be $(4)(6{,}000{,}000{,}000)(30 \text{ years})$ = 72,000,000,000 years (more than 20 times longer than the current age of our solar system and over 2,000 times longer than the age of our species).

3.3 93.3% of all possible substitutions (126/135) at the first position will be nonsynonymous (so about 7% will be synonymous), 100% of all possible substitutions at the second position will be nonsynonymous, and 25.2% of all possible substitutions at the third position will be nonsynonymous (75% will be synonymous). Based on these calculations, the second position is likely to be the most highly conserved position, as any change at this position will result in a nonsynonymous substitution.

3.5 The substitution rate is calculated from the simple formula $r = K/2T$ where K is the estimated frequency of substitutions and T is the amount of time the two sequences have been diverging independently (in this case 100 million years). Here, $r = (0.13 \text{ substitutions/site})/[2(100 \text{ million years})]$ or 0.065 substitutions per site per 100 million years.

3.7 The rate at which a sequence accumulates mutations is always greater than the rate at which it acquires substitutions. Substitutions are a subset of mutations—those that have passed through the filter of selection.

Chapter 4

4.1 Molecular data is less likely to suffer from problems associated with convergent evolution. It is also generally easier to find molecular characters for the purpose of comparison in distantly related or morphologically simple organisms. Randomly chosen nucleotide sequences are less likely to be subject to natural selection than morphological characters.

4.3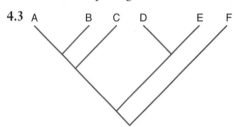

4.5 A total of 135,135 different rooted trees describe the possible relationships between eight organisms, so the chances of choosing the correct one randomly are 1 in 135,135. A total of 10,395 unrooted trees are possible for the same set of species so the chances of randomly choosing the correct unrooted tree are 13 times better than randomly choosing the correct rooted tree.

4.7 Three numbers are shown in each cell below. The first corresponds to the pairwise number of transitions, the second to the number of transversions, and the third to a weighted number of substitutions.

Species	A	B	C	D
B	9, 0, 9	—	—	—
C	6, 2, 10	8, 2, 12	—	—
D	12, 0, 12	15, 0, 15	9, 2, 13	—
E	14, 1, 16	17, 1, 19	10, 3, 16	4, 1, 6

Note that the distance between C and D is now further than the distance between A and C when this weighting scheme is applied.

4.9 A and B are closest so (A,B) and:

Species	A	B	C
B	9	—	—
C	8	11	—
DE	13.5	16.5	11.5

Now (A,B) is closest to C so ((A,B),C) and:

Species	B	AC
AC	10	—
DE	16.5	12.5

Here ((A,B),C) and D are closest so (((A,B),C),D) and then ((((A,B),C),D),E).

4.11 $x = (d_{AB} + d_{AC} - d_{BC})/2$
      $y = (d_{AC} + d_{BC} - d_{AB})/2$
      $z = (d_{AB} + d_{BC} - d_{AC})/2$

Chapter 5

5.1 Informative sites have at least two different nucleotides, and each of these nucleotides has to be present at least twice. They are underlined in the following alignment:

```
1    GAATGCTGAT ATTCCATAAG TCACGAGTCA AAAGTACTCG
2    GGATGGTGAT ACTTCGTAAG TCCCGAGTCG AAAGTACTCG
3    GGATGATGAT ACTTCATAAG TCTCAAATCA AAGGTACTTG
4    GGATGCTGAC ACTTCATAAG TCGCGAGTCA AAAGTACTTG
5    GGATGCTGAC ACTCCGTAAG TCCCGAGTCA AATGTACTCG
```

5.3 Only one tree invokes just one substitution. The remaining two trees both invoke a minimum of two substitutions.

5.5 Strict consensus tree for six taxa:

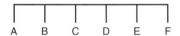

A   B   C   D   E   F

Chapter 6

6.1 The –35 and –10 sequences of the lactose operon's promoter are 5'-TTTACA-3' and 5'-TATGTT-3', respectively. The consensus sequence for promoters recognized by prokaryotic RNA polymerases containing the σ^{70} σ-factor at –35 is 5'-TTgACA-3' and at –10 is 5'-TATaaT-3'. The three differences are shown in lower case letters. Changing the nucleotides in the lactose operon so that they more closely match those consensus sequences would increase the expression levels of this operon.

6.3 Primers could be designed based on the sequences flanking the gap and then used with PCR to amplify and then clone the intervening sequence. Probing a library with sequences based on the ends of either of the two flanking clones could yield new clones that bridge the gap. A third, much less efficient alternative would simply involve the random sequencing of additional clones in the hopes of eventually finding one that yields the required sequence information.

6.5 The three substitutions that would stabilize the formation of a secondary structure would be to replace the mismatching nucleotides within the inverted repeats and to extend the region capable of base pairing.

6.7 The beta (β) subunit of prokaryotic RNA polymerase is responsible for binding to nucleotides and linking them together. As a result, the beta subunit would need to be mutated in order to be able to distinguish between nucleotides and their analogs (probably at the cost of making the enzyme significantly slower).

6.9 The C's of 5'-CG-3' dinucleotides (on both strands) are methylated in transcriptionally inactive regions of eukaryotic genomes but not in transcriptionally active regions. Therefore, 10 nucleotides would be methylated in a transcriptionally inactive region and none would be methylated in a transcriptionally active region.

6.11 Only 11,057 of roughly 2,400,000 nucleotides (<0.5%) in the primary transcript of the human dystrophin gene correspond to coding information. 85 to 88% of the nucleotides of prokaryotic genomes are associated with the coding regions of genes.

6.13 From the consensus sequences shown in Figure 6.6, it can be seen that most of the nucleotides scrutinized by spliceosomes during splicing are within the introns. The only nucleotides within exons that are scrutinized to some extent by spliceosomes during splicing are the last two nucleotides (AG) at the 3' end of an exon. The only triplet codons that contain the dinucleotide 5'-AG-3' are: the two codons for serine (AGU and AGC); two of the six codons for arginine (AGA and AGG); one of the three stop codons (UAG); one of the two codons for glutamine (CAG); one of the two codons for lysine (AAG); and one of the two codons for glutamic acid (GAG). Taken all together, the only amino acid that is not likely to be found at the end of a eukaryotic exon is serine—and, that is only if the 5' splice junction is a very good match to the consensus for that feature.

6.15 Open reading frames do not have to begin with a start codon. By definition, they are simply long runs of triplet codons that are not interrupted by a stop codon (UAG, UAA or UGA). The longest ORF in the sequence provided is 13 codons long and has two occurrences of the GUU codon within it. It is underlined in the sequence below:

5'-GAGCGGAAGUGUUCGAUGUACUGUUCCAGUCAUGUGUUCACC-3'

Chapter 7

7.1 At a low pH, such as 3.5, the side chains of the polypeptide are likely to be protonated, resulting in a net positive charge. At pH 8, more of the side chains will be deprotonated, resulting in a more negative overall charge. This change can result in a reduced binding affinity between the polypeptide and the column, allowing the protein to be eluted.

7.3 Since the calculations for this problem are extensive, it is easiest to write a short Perl script or use a spreadsheet to determine the values of P(t), etc. for each residue in the sequence. The following table shows the value of P(t) at each position, as well as the average P(turn), P(a), and P(b) values for the four consecutive residues starting at each position. The final column shows the predicted turn positions, where P(t) > 0.000075, and the average P(turn) value is greater than the average P(a) and average P(b) values:

Res	P(t)	Avg P(turn)	Avg P(a)	Avg P(b)	Turn
C	7.9E-05	103.75	107.5	82	
A	6.5E-05	99.25	118.5	70.75	
E	2.3E-05	97.5	113.25	82.5	
N	5.4E-05	115.5	100.75	86.75	
K	1.3E-05	100.25	109	86.25	
L	3.3E-05	87.5	107	110.25	
D	1.1E-05	89.25	112.25	98.5	
H	1.9E-05	89.25	112.25	98.5	
V	1.1E-04	95.25	104.75	106.5	
A	9.9E-05	112.5	95.75	93.75	T
D	4.8E-05	107.75	87.25	113	
C	6.8E-06	86	92.25	132	
C	1.2E-05	71.25	103	136.75	
I	3.8E-06	56.5	121.75	133.25	
L	2.8E-06	68.75	115.5	123	
F	5.3E-05	78	112.25	124.75	
M	5.9E-05	91.5	101.25	127	
T	1.2E-05	115.5	81.75	123	
W	7.7E-05	128	86.25	106.75	T
Y	1.9E-04	143	73.5	91.25	T
N	2.3E-04	152.5	70.5	68.25	T
D	5.4E-05	143.25	71.25	75.75	
G	2.0E-05	118.5	73	102.25	T
P	4.3E-06	94.5	87	118	
C	1.8E-05	68.25	99.75	144.25	
I	2.9E-06	67	99.5	151.25	
F	1.9E-05	91.75	97.75	124.75	
I	4.6E-05	115.75	86.25	112.5	
Y	2.6E-04	143	73.5	91.25	T
D	1.6E-04	152.5	70.5	68.25	T
N	#N/A	#N/A	#N/A	#N/A	#N/A
G	#N/A	#N/A	#N/A	#N/A	#N/A
P	#N/A	#N/A	#N/A	#N/A	#N/A

7.5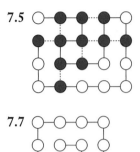

7.7

Chapter 8

8.1 cAMP activates protein kinase A. Protein kinase A (PKA) then phosphory-lates and activates phosphorylase kinase, which, in turn, phosphorylates and ac-tivates phosphorylase—the enzyme responsible for glycogen breakdown. PKA simultaneously phosphorylates and *deactivates* glycogen synthase, the enzyme re-sponsible for glycogen synthesis. Since each PKA molecule can activate multiple phosphorylase kinase molecules, the rate at which phosphorylase kinase is acti-vated is faster than the rate at which PKA is activated. Likewise, each phospho-rylase kinase can activate multiple phosphorylase molecules, so phosphorylase is activated at an even higher rate. This increase in activation velocity at each step in the cascade allows a rapid response to increased cAMP levels.

8.3 The following solution includes the entire program from Example 8, Ap-pendix 3. Boldfaced regions have been modified from the example program:

```perl
#!/usr/local/bin/perl

# Example program 8. Given the name of a PDB file, read
# the file and locate all ATOM locations. For each atom,
# count the number of neighboring atoms within a threshold
# distance. As PDB files can contain thousands of atoms,
# we want to do this as efficiently as possible.

# Define some constants that will be needed later. Define
# the threshold as the square of the value we want (in
# angstroms). This way, when we compute Euclidean
# distance, we don't have to use the square root function
# on EVERY pair of distances, cutting down on computation
# time.

$threshold    = 3.6 ** 2;
$atom_keyword = "ATOM";
$atom_start   = 0;
$label_start  = 6;
$label_length = 5;
```

```perl
$x_start       = 30;
$x_length      = 8;
$y_start       = 38;
$y_length      = 8;
$z_start       = 46;
$z_length      = 8;
$atom_count    = 0;
$sum_x         = 0;
$sum_y         = 0;
$sum_z         = 0;

# Retrieve and check the command line parameter.
$inputfile = @ARGV[0];

if ( @ARGV == 0)
{
  die( "$0: Place the PDB file name on the commmand"
     . " line.\n\n");
} # if

printf( "Input file: $inputfile\n\n");

unless( open( PDB, "$inputfile"))
{
  die( "$0: Cannot open PDB file $inputfile.\n\n");
} # if

while ( <PDB>)
{
  $input = $_;
  chop( $input);
  if ( index( $input, $atom_keyword) == $atom_start)
  {
    $label[$records] = substr( $input, $label_start,
                                $label_length);
    $x[$records] = substr( $input, $x_start, $x_length);
    $y[$records] = substr( $input, $y_start, $y_length);
    $z[$records] = substr( $input, $z_start, $z_length);
    $records++;
    $atom_count++;
    $sum_x += $x[$records];
    $sum_y += $y[$records];
    $sum_z += $z[$records];
  } # if
} # while

for ( $i = 0; $i < $records; $i++)
{
  for ( $j = $i+1; $j < $records; $j++)
  {
```

```
      $distance = ( $x[$i]-$x[$j]) ** 2
                + ( $y[$i]-$y[$j]) ** 2
                + ( $z[$i]-$z[$j]) ** 2;
      if ( $distance < $threshold)
      {
        $count[$i]++;
        $count[$j]++;
      } # if
    } # for j
  } # for i

# Sort the labels and counts in order by count, from
# highest to lowest. Note that we cannot simply use 'sort'
# here, since the information resides in two different
# arrays. The method presented here is a simple bubble
# sort: check each pair of counts, swapping them (and the
# labels) if the later one has a larger value.
printf( "Atom # Count\n");
printf( "------ -----\n");
for ( $i = 0; $i < $records-1; $i++)
{
  for ( $j = $i+1; $j < $records; $j++)
  {
    if ( $count[$i] < $count[$j])
    {
      ($count[$i], $count[$j]) = ($count[$j], $count[$i]);
      ($label[$i], $label[$j]) = ($label[$j], $label[$i]);
    } # if
  } # for j
  # Print out each record as it becomes sorted.
  printf( "%6s %5d\n", $label[$i], $count[$i]);
} # for i

# Print out the final record, which was skipped by the
# for i loop going only up to $records-1.
printf( "%6s %5d\n", $label[$i], $count[$i]);
# Compute the centroid position
$centroid_x = $sum_x / $atom_count;
$centroid_y = $sum_y / $atom_count;
$centroid_z = $sum_z / $atom_count;

# Keep track of the closest and furthest atoms
# from the centroid
$closest_dist = Infinity;
$furthest_dist = -1;
```

```
# Loop through the list of atoms again, finding the atoms
# closest to and furthest from the centroid
for ( $i = 0; $i < $records; $i++)
{
    # Compute the distance from the current atom to the
    # centroid:
    $distance = ( $x[$i] - $centroid_x ) ** 2
          + ( $y[$i] - $centroid_y ) ** 2
          + ( $z[$i] - $centroid_z ) ** 2;

    # Keep track of the closest and furthest
    if ($distance < $closest_dist) {
        $closest_dist = $distance;
        $closest_atom = $i;
    }
    if ($distance > $furthest_dist) {
        $furthest_dist = $distance;
        $furthest_atom = $i;
    }
}

# Print the centroid position, and the closest and
# furthest atoms from the centroid:

printf ("Centroid position: (%f, %f, %f)\n", $centroid_x,
    $centroid_y, $centroid_z);

printf("Closest atom to centroid is atom %d",
    $label[$closest_atom]);

printf("at position (%f, %f, %f)\n", $x[$closest_atom],
    $y[$closest_atom], $z[$closest_atom]);

printf("Furthest atom from centroid is atom %d",
    $label[$furthest_atom]);

printf("at position (%f, %f, %f)\n", $x[$furthest_atom],
    $y[$furthest_atom], $z[$furthest_atom]);
```

8.5 First, one would need a database of cysteine residues to serve as a training and testing example for the empirical algorithm. To obtain this database, one might select high-resolution structures from the PDB, and identify both a set of cysteine residues involved in disulfide bridges and another set of cysteine residues not involved in disulfide bridges. Next, one would identify and measure features of each cysteine residue in each set. Potential features might include sequence features (neighboring residues, overall hydrophobicity over a window, and so on), and structural features (number of neighboring atoms, number of neighboring water molecules, surface exposure, local hydrophobicity, local charge, and so on). Finally, one would select a classifier algorithm, and train it using a subset of the examples from each class (disulfide and non-disulfide cysteines). Possible classifiers include neural networks, nearest neighbor methods, Bayesian methods, decision trees, and many others. Once the classifier is trained, the accuracy can be measured using the cysteine residues from the database that were not used to train the classifier.

8.7 A signal peptide of length 5 would have $4^5 = 1024$ possible variations, insuring that there is a unique sequence for each possible destination within the cell.

Appendix 1

A1.1
```
# printnums - print the integers from 1 to 100
for ($i = 1; $i <= 100; $i++)
{
    print("$i\n");
}
```

A1.3
```
# average - print the average of the numbers in
#           values.txt to the screen
# Open the file:
open(VALUES, "<values.txt");

# Keep track of the number of values we have read
$count = 0;

# Read each value into an array
while(<VALUES>)

{
    # Remove the \n from the end of the line and save
    # it to the array @varray:
    chomp;
    $varray[$count] = $_;
    $count++;
}

# Now that all the numbers are stored in @varray,
# compute the average:
$sum = 0;
foreach $value (@varray)   # We could use an ordinary
{                          # for loop instead here,
    $sum += $value;        # but this is shorter.
}
$average = $sum/$count;
print ("The average value is: $average\n");
```

A1.5 The following solution allows you to place the filename containing the data on the command line. For example, if we name the program `findclose` and the coordinates above are the file `coords.txt`, then we can type `findclose coords.txt` to run the program.

```
# Findclose — count the number of atoms within 20
#              angstroms of the point (45.0, 45.0,
#              100.0).

# Retreive and check the command line parameter:
if ( @ARGV == 0)
{
  die( "$0: Place the coordinates filename on the"
     . " command line.\n\n");
}

$inputfile = @ARGV[0];
open (INFILE, "$inputfile")
  or die ("Cannot open $inputfile");

# Count the number of atoms within the distance cutoff
$count = 0;
while ( <INFILE>)
{
  $input = $_;
  chop( $input);
  ($x, $y, $z) = split(", $input);

  # $distance is actually the squared distance, no
  # need to take the square root
  $distance = ( $x — 45.0) ** 2
            + ( $y — 45.0) ** 2
            + ( $z — 100.0) ** 2;

  # again, we are checking the squared distance
  if ($distance < (20.0 ** 2))
  {
    $count++;
  }
}

# Print the results:
print("The number of atoms < 20 angstroms from\n");
print("the point (45.0, 45.0, 100.0) is: $count\n");
```

For the input given above, the program would print out the following:

```
The number of atoms < 20 angstroms from
the point (45.0, 45.0, 100.0) is: 4
```

Appendix 2

A2.1 $K_{eq} = k_1/k_{-1} = 60$

A2.3 Lineweaver-Burk plots have the straight-line form of an equation in the format of $y = mx + b$. The two variables (y and x; $1/v_0$ and $1/[S]$, respectively) are described in terms of each other, a slope ($m = K_m/V_{max}$) and the intercept of the y-axis ($b = 1/V_{max}$). With a direct plot, V_{max} must be estimated from an asymptote. Eadie-Hofstee plots also yield a straight line, but now both $m = -K_m$ and $b = V_{max}$.

A2.5 Noncompetitive activators have no effect upon the rate at which substrate binds the enzyme so they do not change the enzyme's K_m. However, since they do increase the rate at which the ES complex is converted to EP and, eventually to E + P, noncompetitive activators do increase an enzyme's V_{max} in a fashion that is dependent upon the amount of inhibitor present.

Index

Absolute direction
    representation, 169
ACE inhibitors, 244
Acidic solutions, 158
Activation energy (E_{act}), 236, 237
Activator, 241
Active site, 188
Additive trees
    description, 81
    neighbor-joining methods, 93
    neighbor's relation method, 92
Adenine (A)
    base pairing, 5, 6
    description, 2, 3
    as purine, 67
    transcriptional termination,
      125–26
Advantageous mutations, 58
Africa and human origins, 114
Agricultural implications, 78, 112
AIDS. *See* HIV virus
Algorithms
    alignments, 41–48, 107
    assigning ancestral positions,
      103
    database screening, 191
    docking, 189–91
    dynamic programming,
      129–30
    Folding@Home, 172
    gene recognition, 134, 136,
      142, 143
    glycosylation sites, 202–03
    promoter recognition, 123–24,
      129
    protein folding, 166, 167–72
    PSI-BLAST, 50
    Smith-Waterman, 46–48, 51
    structure prediction, 161–62,
      197–98, 199

    validation, 174
Alignments
    algorithms, 41–48, 107
    database searches, 48–51
    depth, 108
    dot plots, 34–35, 36
    evaluation, 34–53
    gaps, 35, 36–37, 45, 46, 47
    multiple sequences, 40, 52–53,
      93–94
    overview, 34, 53
    scoring matrices, 38–41
    scoring system, 36, 37–38
    semiglobal alignment, 45–46
    simple alignments, 35–36
    statistical significance, 51
    substitution numbers, 65
Alleles, 63
Alpha (α) proteins, 121–22
Alpha helix
    description, 14–15
    evaluation for, 125
    secondary structure prediction,
      160–61, 162–63, 164
Alternative splicing, 12, 135–37
Altschul, S., 48
Alu repeats, 69, 150
Amersham Pharmacia Biotech's
    ImageMaster, 185
Amino acids
    abbreviations, 157
    backbone, 13, 14, 156, 160,
      161
    categories, 9
    chemical structures, 10, 157
    Chou-Fasman parameters, 163
    codons for, 11, 61
    conceptual translation, 125
    function overview, 9
    generic structure, 10, 156

    hydrophobic/nonpolar, 9, 156,
      157
    pKa, 158
    polar, 9, 156, 157
    side chains, 13, 156
    structure, 9, 10, 13–14,
      156–57, 159
Amino terminus, 13, 159
Anfinsen, C., 156, 166
Angiotensin-converting enzyme
    (ACE), 244
Anthrax genomes, 120
Anthropologists, 105
Antibodies, 78, 187
Antiparallel beta sheets, 14, 16,
    160, 169
Antiparallel DNA strands, 5
Apolipoproteins, 70
Arabidopsis thaliana, 128, 129
Archaea, 113–14
Arguments, subroutines, 225,
    226, 227, 229
Aromatic residues, 202
Arrays, Perl, 210, 220–21, 227
Atomic density, 270–73
Atoms, 17
AUG codon, 11, 124
AutoDock algorithm, 189, 190
Autosomes, 128

Bacillus subtilis, 121
Back mutations, 66, 67, 68, 69
Bacteria
    as evolutionary group, 113–14
    GC content, 126–27
Basal promoter, 130
Basal transcription factors, 131
Base pairing, 5–6
Basic solutions, 158
Benazepril, 244

Beta (β) protein, 121
Beta-like globin gene, 59–60,
    61–62, 64, 138–139
Beta-prime (β') protein, 121
Beta sheets
    description, 14–15, 160
    evaluation for, 125
    secondary structure, 160–61,
        163–64
Beta strands, 160
Beta turns, 160–61, 164
Bifurcating nodes/trees
    consensus trees, 108–09
    description, 81
Binding operator, Perl, 231
Bioinformatics, description, 2
Bioterrorism mailings, 120
BLAST algorithms, 48–50, 53,
    162, 173
BLAST matrix, 38, 39
Block, Perl, 212
Blood pressure medications, 244
BLOSUM matrix
    description, 41
    use, 48, 52
Blotting and hybridization,
    21–23, 24, 30
Blunt ends, DNA, 20
Bootstrap tests, 109–11
Branch and bound method,
    105–07, 169
Branches
    description, 80–81
    length estimation, 88–90
    swapping, 107–08
Britten, R., 28–29
Bump/steric collision, 160, 162,
    169–70
Buoyant density gradients, 141,
    149

CAAT box, 132
CAAT transcription factors,
    131–32
C$_\alpha$RMSD, 170, 172
Cantor, C., 65–66
Capping, hnRNAs, 133–34
Carbonic anhydrase, 236, 243
Carboxylate group, 156
Carboxylic acid, 156
Carboxy terminus, 13, 159
Catalysts

enzyme nomenclature, 182
enzymes as, 6, 156, 236–46
function, 236–37
CATH database, 174, 183
C/C++ computer languages, 208,
    232–33
cDNA library
    description, 24, 143–44
    example method, 144
Cell maintenance. See
    Housekeeping genes
Centers for Disease Control and
    Prevention, 120
Central dogma, molecular
    biology, 6–7
Chain-termination method, 25,
    27, 28
Chaperonins, 165
Character-based methods
    consensus trees, 108–09, 110
    faster searches, 105–08
    inferred ancestral sequences,
        102, 103, 104–05
    overview, 114–15
    parsimony, 90, 98–105, 112,
        114–15
    tree confidence, 109–12
Character class, Perl, 231–32
Character data, 84–85
Charged amino acids, 9, 156, 157
Chemical bonds, 15, 17–19
Chloroplast DNA (cpDNA), 74
Chloroplast proteins, 200–201
Chloroplast transit sequence,
    200–201
Chou-Fasman method, 162–64
Chou-Fasman parameters, 163
Chromatin, 140–41
Chromosomes, 3
Cladists, 85, 98
Cladograms, 88
Cloning, 23–24, 30
CLUSTAL algorithms, 52, 162,
    173
Cluster analysis, 41, 78, 86
Codon AUG, 11, 124
Codons, definition, 9
Codon usage bias, 126–27, 130,
    142–43
Comments, Perl, 218–19
Common ancestors. See also
    Phylogenetic trees

homologs, 35
inferred ancestors, 81, 102,
    103, 104–05, 115
Perl sample program, 259–63
Comparative modeling, 173–74
Competitive inhibition, 242, 244
Compiler, computer
    programming, 208–09
Complementary information,
    DNA, 5–6
Compugen's Z3, 185
Computer programming. See also
    Perl codes/commands;
    Perl computer
    programming; Perl
    sample programs
C/C++, 208, 232–33
Java, 208, 232–33
Python, 208, 232–33
source codes, 208
Computer use. See also
    Algorithms
crystal diffraction patterns,
    193
inferred trees, 83, 93
maximum likelihood
    approaches, 93
Concentration, solutions, 158
Conceptual translation
    amino acids, 125
    Perl sample program, 250–52
    prokaryotes, 126
Conditional execution, Perl
    conditional code, 213
    else block, 213–14
    else/if statement, 213–14
    if statement, 212–15
Conformational parameters, 162,
    163
Consensus sequence, 122
Consensus trees, 108–09, 110
Conservation implications, 112,
    147
Constitutive vs. regulatory
    proteins, 131
Contig assembly
    description, 119
    eukaryotes, 128, 143
Convergent evolution, 80, 105
Cot equation/analyses, 29–30,
    144
Covalent bonding, 18

CpG islands, 137–41
Creationists, 105
Crick, F. H. C., 5, 20
Crystal (protein) growing, 191, 197. *See also* X-ray crystal structures
C-value paradox, 27, 29, 30
C values, 27, 29, 30
Cyclic AMP cascade, 203
Cyclic AMP receptor protein, 123, 124
Cystic fibrosis, 12, 136, 181
Cytoplasm, 199, 200
Cytosine (C). *See also* GC content
  base pairing, 5, 6
  description, 2, 3
  as pyrimidine, 67

Databases
  alignments, 48–51
  GenBank, 48
  heuristics, 48, 53
  introns, 136
  ligand screening, 188, 190–91, 192
  protein grouping, 174, 183
  proteomics, 195
  screening algorithms, 191
  word searches, 49, 50
Declaring variables, 210–11
Degeneracy, genetic code, 9
Deleterious mutations, 58
Deletions
  description, 35
  frequency, 62, 104
  sequence alignments, 36
Denatured proteins, 156
Dendrograms. *See* Phylogenetic trees
Deoxyribonucleic acid. *See* DNA
Deoxyribose sugar
  in nucleotides, 2, 3
  orientation, 4
Deprotonated amino acids, 158–59
Dill, K., 168
DINO visualization tool, 195
Dipeptide, 159, 160
Directionality
  DNA, 5, 24
  polypeptides, 13, 159

Direct plot, V_{max}/K_m, 240, 242
Dissociation constant, 244
Distance data, 84–85
Distance matrix methods
  branch lengths, 88–90
  comparing results, 112
  neighbor-joining, 92–93
  neighbor's relation, 91–92
  overview, 85–86
  transformed distance, 90–91
  "tree of life," 113
  UPGMA, 85, 86–90
Disulfide bonds, 166, 167, 171
Divergence time
  beta-like globin genes, 59–61, 62
  estimating, 71–73, 80
  phylogenetic scaled trees, 89
DNA
  cDNA library, 24, 143–44
  complementary information, 5–6
  directionality, 5, 24
  junk DNA, 30, 118, 128, 150
  mitochondrial DNA, 74, 114
  overview, 2–3, 5–6, 30
  satellite DNA, 148–49
DNA chip microarrays, 22–23, 145–47, 187
DNA polymerases, 24–25, 27, 126
DNA sequencing machines, 120
DNA sequencing overview, 25, 27, 28
DOCK algorithm, 190
Docking algorithms, 189–91
Dorit, R. L., 182–83
Dot plots
  alignments, 34–35, 36
  Perl sample program, 252–55
"Downstream" features, 5
Drosophila melanogaster
  alternative splicing, 137
  codon usage bias, 142
  genome, 128, 129
Drugs
  design, 181, 187–91, 244
  discovery, 187–88, 239
  inhibition, 188, 242
  pharmacogenomics, 147
  testing, 187–88
Dynamic programming
  eukaryotic genomes, 129

Needleman/Wunsch algorithm, 42–45

Eadie-Hofstee plot, 241, 243
*Eco*RI, 20
Electronegativity, 18–19, 158
Electrons
  electronegativity, 18–19
  energy/orbits, 17–18
  traits, 17
Electrophoresis
  gel, 21, 22, 30, 184–85
  protein, 78–79
Electrospray ionization, 186
Electrostatic forces, 165, 171
Elements, 17
Else block, Perl, 213–14
Else/if statement, Perl, 213–14
Empirical algorithms, structure, 197–98
"Empirical" energy, 171–72
Endergonic chemical reactions, 237
Endoplasmic reticulum (ER), 200, 201
Energy functions and modeling, 171–72
Enhanceosomes, 133
Enhancers, 132–33
Environmental monitoring, 147
Enzyme kinetics
  catalysts, 6, 156, 236–46
  Eadie-Hofstee plot, 241, 243
  Henri-Michaelis-Menten equation, 238–41, 242, 243, 244
  inhibition systems, 241–42, 244–46
  K_m, 239–41, 242, 243, 244, 245, 246
  Lineweaver-Burk reciprocal plot, 240–41, 243
  Perl sample program, 273–75
  pH effects on, 246
  temperature effects on, 246
  V_{max}, 239–41, 242, 243, 244, 245, 246
  V_{max}/K_m direct plot, 240, 242
Enzymes
  nomenclature, 181–82
  structure/function, 6–7, 13

Epinephrine, 203
Equilibrium constant (K_{eq}), 237–38
Escape sequences, Perl, 223
Escherichia coli
   codons, 124
   gene density, 127
   genome, 21, 119, 120
   insertion sequences (ISs), 148
   lac operon promoter sequence, 123
   restriction enzymes, 20
   sigma (σ) factors, 121, 122
E score, 51
ESI, 186
Ester bonds, 3
ESTs
   description, 119
   eukaryotes, 128, 143
Eucarya, 113–14
Euchromatin, 141
Eukaryotes
   description, 7
   gene expression, 8, 9, 12, 143–47
   genome, 127–29, 150, 151
   in life divisions, 113, 114
   sequenced species list (partial), 129
   transcription, 12, 130–31, 133–35
   translation, 12, 133–34
Eukaryotic gene structure
   GC content, 137–43
   gene density, 150–51
   gene expression, 8, 9, 12, 143–47
   open reading frames, 12, 129, 133–37
   overview, 129–30
   promoter elements, 129, 130–31
   regulatory protein binding sites, 131–33
   repetitive elements, 148–50
   transposition, 148
Evolution
   alignment representations, 34, 35, 37–38, 39, 51, 53
   allelic changes, 63
   bacteria, 126–27
   chloroplast DNA, 74

creationists, 105
exons/introns, 135
gene variations, 70–71
human origins, 114
"missing links," 105
organelles, 74
populations, 84
proteins, 182–83
rate variations, 73
substitution patterns, 58–59
"tree of life," 112–14
Evolutionary computation, 161, 169
Exergonic chemical reactions, 237
Exhaustive searches, 105, 107, 168
Exons
   description, 12–13
   humans, 136
   lengths, 134
   protein evolution, 182–83
   structure, 134, 135
   yeast example, 135
Exon shuffling, 184
ExPASy server, 195
Expressed sequence tags. *See* ESTs

"Fallacy of multiple tests," 111
Families/superfamilies classification, 182–83
Family, definition, 183
FASTA algorithms, 50–51, 162, 173
FASTX algorithms, 50, 53
50% majority rule-consensus, 108–09
File extension names, 209
File pointer, 229, 230
5' carbon, 4, 5
Fixation, alleles, 63, 65
FLEXX algorithm, 190
Folding@Home, 172
Folds. *See also* Protein structure
   definition, 184
   native structure, 13–14, 156, 164
   protein classification, 174, 183–84
Foreach loop statement, 217, 226–27

For loop statement, 216–17, 220, 221
Fossil record, 71, 105, 114
Fourfold degenerate sites, 61–62
Four-point condition, 92, 93
Fruit flies. *See Drosophila melanogaster*
FSSP database, 174, 183
FTDock algorithm, 190
Functional constraint, 38, 59–61, 65
Functions, Perl, 227–29

Gap penalty
   description, 37, 38
   dynamic programming, 42, 43
Gaps
   description, 35, 36
   penalties, 37, 46, 47
   terminal gaps, 45
GC content
   eukaryotes, 137–43
   identifying bacteria, 126, 127
   isochores, 141–42
   LINEs/SINEs, 142, 149–50
   prokaryotes, 126–27
Gel electrophoresis
   description, 21, 22, 30
   two-dimensional (2D), 184–85
GenBank database, 48
Gene chip microarrays, 22–23, 145–47, 187
Gene density
   eukaryotes, 150–51
   prokaryotes, 127
Gene expression. *See also* Tissue-specific genes
   environmental stimuli for, 8, 122, 131, 143
   eukaryotes, 8, 9, 12, 143–47
   gene recognition test, 143
   isochore association, 141
   process, 121
   prokaryotes, 8, 12
   regulation, 7–8, 141
Gene expression profiling, 147
Generation times, 73
Genes
   distance between, 150, 151
   genetic material overview, 2–7
   length, 141–42
   multiple copies, 150–51

regulatory/structural, 8
structure overview, 7–13
Genetic code, 9, 10, 11, 134
Genetic library, 23, 24, 143–44
Genetic maps, 128
Gene trees, 83–84
Genome
    description, 2–3
    information content, 27–30
Genomic equivalent, 23, 119
Genomics
    eukaryotes
        GC content, 137–43
        gene density, 150–51
        gene expression, 8, 9, 12,
            143–47
        gene structure, 129–33
        genomes, 127–29, 150, 151
        open reading frames, 12,
            129, 133–37
        promoter elements, 129,
            130–31
        regulatory protein binding
            sites, 131–33
        repetitive elements, 148–50
    genome projects, 129, 150,
        180
    overview, 118, 151
    prokaryotes
        conceptual translation, 126
        GC content, 126–27
        gene density, 127
        gene expression, 8, 12
        gene structure, 120–26
        genomes, 118–20, 126–27
        open reading frames, 12,
            124, 127
        promoter elements, 121–24,
            127
        termination sequences,
            125–26, 127
    proteomics vs., 180–81
    repetitive elements, 148–50
    transposition, 148
Genotypes, 79–80
GenScan, 129
Gibbs free energy, 237
Gilbert, W., 25, 27, 182–83
Global alignment, 45
Global variables, 226
Glycosylation, 202–03
GOLD algorithm, 190

Golgi apparatus, 200, 201
GOR statistical approach, 164
Grail EXP, 129
"Grand challenge" problem, 156
GT-AG rule, 12
GU-AG rule, 134
Guanine (G). See also GC
        content
    base pairing, 5, 6
    description, 2, 3
    as purine, 67

Haemophilus influenzae, 118
Hairpin turns, 175
Hammerhead algorithm, 190
Hasegawa, M., 111
Hashes, Perl, 210, 221–22, 266
HDAs, 146–47
Hemoglobin, 166
Henri, V., 238, 240
Henri-Michaelis-Menten
        equation, 238–41, 242,
        243, 244
Heterochromatin, 141
Heuristic methods
    database searches, 48, 53
    ligand docking, 189
    sequence information, 107–08
HEX algorithm, 190
Hexokinase, 240, 241, 242
Hidden Markov models, 161,
        176, 177
Hierarchical (protein) databases,
        174, 183
Higgins, D. G., 52
High-density oligonucleotide
        arrays, 146–47
High-throughput screening
        methods, 188
H isochores, 141, 142, 150
Histones
    DNA affinity, 140–41
    evolutionary rates, 70
    post-translation sorting, 199
HIV protease, 188
HIV protease inhibitor, 188
HIV virus, 149, 176, 188
hnRNAs, 133–34, 135, 136, 176
Hodgkin, D., 191
Homologs, 35
Homology, 35
Homology modeling, 173–74

Homoplasies, 105
Horizontal gene transfer, 126
Housekeeping genes
    description, 139
    genomic information, 118
    H3 isochore, 141
    numbers, 145
H-P (hydrophobic-polar) model,
        168
HTS methods, 188
Human genome
    CpG paucity, 138, 139
    introns, 135
    isochores, 141, 142
    substitutions, 69
Human genome project
    gene density, 150
    sequence data, 129
Human α-globin, 138–39
Human hexokinase, 240, 241,
        242
Human leukocyte antigen (HLA)
    evolutionary change, 70–71
    phylogenetic trees, 84
Humans
    chromosomes, 128
    differences/relatedness, 114
    genome, 128, 129
    introns/exons, 136
    origins, 114
Hydrogen bonds
    anti-parallel beta sheets, 16
    description, 19
    in nucleotides, 6
    protein folding, 165, 171
Hydrophilicity, 17, 19
Hydrophobic collapse, 165–66,
        168
Hydrophobicity
    description, 19
    enzyme function, 17
    Perl sample program, 266–70
    protein structure effects,
        165–66
Hydrophobic zipper mechanism,
        168, 169

Identity matrix, 39
IF-SDS procedure, 184–85
If statement, Perl, 212–15
Immobilized pH gradient strips,
        184

Immune system, 70–71
Indel events
   alignment evaluation, 37
   bias against, 62
   frequency variations, 104
Indexes
   arrays, 220
   database searches, 48, 53
   hashes, 221
Induced fit docking, 189
Inferred ancestors
   description, 81
   parsimony determination, 102,
      103, 104–05, 115
Inferred protein sequences, 125
Inferred trees. *See also* Distance
      matrix methods
   description, 83
Information
   eukaryotes vs. prokaryotes, 19
   gene structure, 7–13
   genome content, 2, 5, 27–30
   trait of life, 2
Information theory, 164
Informative sites, 98–99, 102,
      103, 105
Ingroup, 90, 91
Inhibition
   competitive, 242, 244
   irreversible, 246
   mixed, 244, 246
   noncompetitive, 244–46
Inhibitors
   description, 241–42, 244–46
   drug design, 188
Initiation complex, 130
Initiator (Inr) sequence, 131, 132
Insertions
   description, 35
   frequency, 62, 104
   sequence alignments, 36
Insertion sequences (ISs), 148
The Institute of Genetic
      Research, 119–20
Interfacial residues, 198
Internal nodes
   consensus trees, 108–09
   description/function, 81, 100
International Enzyme
      Commission, 181–82
International Union of Crystal-
      lographers (IUCr), 195

Internet, 172. *See also* Web sites
Intractable searches, 40–41
Intrinsic terminators, 125, 126
Introns
   description, 12–13, 134–35
   human, 136
   lengths, 134, 141–42
   structure, 135
   web site, 136
   yeast example, 135
Invariant position, 99
IPG strips, 184
Irreversible inhibition, 246
Isochores, 141–42
Isoelectric focusing (IF), 184
Isoelectric point (pI), 159, 184

Jacob, F., 8
Java computer language, 208,
      232–33
Jukes, T., 65–66
Jukes-Cantor model, 65–66, 67
Junk DNA
   in eukaryotes, 118, 128, 150
   indications of, 30
   LINEs/SINEs, 150

Keppler, K., 92
Kimura, M., 67
Kimura's two-parameter model,
      67–68
Kinases, 203
Kishino, H., 111
"Knockout" organisms, 150

Labeled feature vector, 198, 199
Lactose operon, 122–23
Lactose repressor protein, 122–23
Lattice models, 168–70, 172
Laue, M. von, 191
Lead compounds identification,
      172, 188–89. *See also*
      Ligand screening
Length of tree, 103
Length penalties, 37–38
Levinthal, C., 167
Levinthal paradox, 167
Life divisions, 113–14
Ligand screening
   accuracy for, 172, 174
   database screening, 188,
      190–91, 192

   ligand docking, 188, 189–90
   overview, 188–89
Ligase, 20
Linear regression, 273–75
LINEs, 142, 149–50
Lineweaver-Burk reciprocal plot,
      240–41, 243, 273
L isochores, 141, 142, 149–50
Local alignment, 47–48
Local variables, 226
Lock and key approaches, 189
Log odds matrix, 39
Loops, Perl, 216–17, 220, 221,
      227, 230
Lymphomas, 147

Machine language, 208
Mac systems, 209
MALDI, 186
Mariner transposon, 148
Mass spectrometry, 185–86
Match score
   description, 36, 42, 43
   dynamic programming, 42, 43
   semiglobal alignment, 47
Matrix assisted laser desorption
      ionization, 186
Maxam, A. M., 25
Maxim-Gilbert method, 25
Maximum likelihood approach,
      93, 112
Mechanoenzymes, 156
Medical applications. *See also*
      Drugs
   diagnosis, 147
   proteomics, 181
   treatments, 78, 112, 147
Membrane-bound compartments
   functions, 127–28
   post-translation sorting,
      199–201
   transcription/translation
      separation, 12, 133–34
Menten, M., 239
Messenger RNA
   alternative splicing, 12–13
   in cloning, 24
   formation, 133–34, 136
   location, 199
   ORFs, 19
   protein correspondence, 180
Methionine codon, 11, 202

Methylation, 140–41
Michaelis, L., 239
Microarrays
    gene chips, 22–23, 145–47,
        187
    protein, 187
Mini/microsatellites, 148, 149
Mismatches and substitutions, 66
Mismatch penalty/score
    description, 36, 37
    dynamic programming, 42, 43
    semiglobal alignment, 47
"Missing links," 105
Mitochondrial DNA (mtDNA),
    74, 114
"Mitochondrial Eve," 114
Mitochondrial proteins, 200
Mitochondrial signal sequence,
    200, 201
Mixed inhibition, 244, 246
mmCIF format, 195
Molecular biology
    central dogma, 6–7
    first sequence data, 66, 67, 79
    gene/protein relationship, 156
    overview, 30
    tools, 19–27, 30
Molecular clocks, 71–73, 80
Molecular clones, 23
Molecular docking algorithms,
    189–91
Molecular mechanics, 171
Molecular phylogenies. See also
        Phylogenetics
    advantages, 79–80
    applications, 112–14
Molecular weight, 158
Mole/molar, 158
Monod, J., 8
Monte Carlo algorithm, 189–90
Monte Carlo methods, 169
Morphological character
        analysis, 86, 90
Mullis, K., 24
MultiDock, 190
Multifurcating nodes/trees
    in consensus trees, 108–09
    description, 81
Multiple sequence alignment, 40,
    52–53, 93–94
Mutational analyses, 150
Mutations

description, 35
    mutagens in mitochondria, 74
    point mutations, 124
    rates, 58–59, 60–61, 104
    substitutions vs., 62–63, 74
    types, 58
Mycoplasma genitalium, 120, 150
Myosin, 156

National Center for Biological
        Information (NCBI), 48
Native structure, proteins,
    13–14, 156, 164
Natural selection
    data-sampling effects from,
        62–63
    fixation, 63, 65
    function, 59, 74
    function level, 59, 61–62
    gene level, 64, 70–71
    phenotypic differences, 80
    substitutions, 61–62, 64
Nearest neighbor classifier, 201
Nearest neighbor energy rules,
    176
"Needle in a haystack"
        comparison, 129
Needleman, S., 42, 53
Needleman and Wunsch
        algorithm
    example, 42–45
    modifications, 45–46, 52
    significance, 42
Negatively charged amino acids,
    9, 156
Negative regulation, 8
Negative regulator, 122–23
Nei, M., 92
Neighbor-joining method, 92–93
Neighborliness approaches,
    92–93, 161
Neighbors, definition, 91
Neighbor's relation method,
    91–92
Nested block of code, Perl, 218
NetPhos, 203
Neural networking
    description, 129
    glycosylation site prediction,
        202
    phosphorylation target
        prediction, 203

secondary structure prediction,
    161, 176, 177
Neutral mutations, 58
Neutrons, 17
Newick format, 81, 88, 90, 100
Nitrogenous bases
    base pairing, 5–6
    in nucleotides, 2, 3
N-linked glycosylation, 202
NMR, 193, 197
Nodes, 80–81
Noncoding sequences, 59–60,
    104
Noncompetitive inhibition,
    244–46
Nondegenerate sites, 61–62
Nonsynonymous substitutions
    HLA locus, 70–71
    in mitochondrial DNA, 74
    synonymous vs., 61–62, 63, 64
Nuclear localization sequence,
    200, 201
Nuclear magnetic resonance,
    193, 197
Nuclear membrane, 12, 133–34
Nuclear proteins, 200
Nucleotides. See also Alignments;
        specific nucleotides
    description, 2–3
    making RNA, 7
    orientation, 3–5
Nuttall, G. H. F., 78

Off-lattice models, 170–71
Oligosaccharides, 202
O-linked glycosylation, 202–03
Open reading frames
    description, 9, 12
    E. coli lac operon, 123
    eukaryotes, 12, 129, 133–37
    eukaryotes vs. prokaryotes, 19
    prokaryotes, 12, 124, 127
Operator sequence, 122–23
Operons, 122, 123–24, 130
Orbitals, 17–18
ORFs. See Open reading frames
Organelles, 74
Orientation of nucleotides, 3–5
Origination penalties, 37–38
Outgroup
    description, 72, 81–82
    function, 90, 91

"Out-of-Africa theory," 114
Oxygen free radicals, 74

Paleontological information, 79
Palindromic sequences, 126
PAM matrix
    construction, 40
    substitution rates, 39, 40, 41, 70
    use, 48, 52, 70
PAM unit, 41
Pande, V., 172
Parallel beta sheets, 14–15, 16, 160
Parallelism, evolution, 105
Parameters, subroutine, 225, 226, 227, 229
Parametric tests, 111–12
Parsimony
    comparing results, 112
    description, 98
    examples, 99, 100–101, 102
    inferred ancestral sequences, 102, 103, 104–05, 115
    informative sites, 98–99, 102, 103, 105
    multiple sequences, 102–03, 115
    premises, 98, 99, 114–15
    "tree of life," 113
    uninformative sites, 90, 98–99, 103
    unweighted, 99, 102–03
    weighted, 104
Partial scores table, 43–44, 46, 47
Pathogen, 188
Pauling, L., 17, 71
PCR method
    description, 24–25, 26, 30
    significance, 79
PCR primers, 25
PDB, 193, 195, 196, 270
Penicillin, 246
Pepsin, 13, 159, 246
Peptide, 159
Peptide bond, 159, 161
Peptide mass fingerprinting, 186, 195
Perl codes/commands
    condition opposite, 215
    ending statements, 210, 212

marking blocks, 212
move to next line, 210–11
numerical equality, 214, 215
operators, 211, 214–15, 231
printing, 210–11, 219
quotes, 223
remainder computation, 209–10
running a program, 209
tab moves, 219, 223
text files, 229–30
variable evaluation, 223–24
variable naming, 209–10, 219
wildcards, 232
Perl computer programming
    advantages, 233
    arrays, 210, 220–21, 227
    comments, 218–19
    conditional execution, 212–15
    data structures, 219–23
    data typing, 210–11
    functions, 227–29
    hashes, 210, 221–22, 266
    input/output, 229–31
    interpreter, 209
    loops, 216–17, 220, 221, 227, 230
    operations/operators, 211, 214–15, 231
    overview, 208–09
    PDB files, 193
    printing, 210–11, 219
    program control, 211–17
    readability, 217–19, 230–31
    regular expressions, 231–32
    script, 209
    statements/blocks, 212
    strings, 222–23
    structured programming, 217–18
    subroutines, 224–29
    variable naming, 219
    variables/values, 209–11, 219–23, 227
Perl sample programs
    atomic density, 270–73
    common ancestor, 259–63
    conceptual translation, 250–52
    dot plot, 252–55
    enzyme kinetics, 273–75
    hydrophobicity calculator, 266–70

linear regression, 273–75
relative rate test, 255–56
splice junctions, 263–66
UPGMA, 256–58
Peroxisomal targeting signals, 201
Peroxisomes, 199, 201
pH
    description, 158
    enzyme effects, 246
Pharmacogenomics, 147
Pharmacology. See Drugs
PHD algorithms, 162
Pheneticists, 85, 98
Phenotypes, 79–80
Phi angles, 14, 160, 162, 170
Phosphatases, 203
Phosphate groups
    in nucleotides, 2, 3
    orientation, 4
Phosphodiester bonds, 3–4
Phosphorylation, 203
Photons, 17
Phylogenetics
    applications, 112–14
    comparison of methods, 84–85, 112
    history, 66, 67, 78–79, 125
    molecular method advantages, 79–80
Phylogenetic trees
    biological subtleties, 85
    character-based methods, 98–112
    character data, 84–85
    description, 80
    distance data, 84–85
    distance matrix methods, 85–93, 112
    gene vs. species, 83–84
    maximum likelihood approaches, 93, 112
    multiple sequence alignments, 40, 52–53, 93–94
    PAM matrix, 40
    possibilities, 82–83, 93, 102, 105, 108
    relative rate tests, 72
    rooted/unrooted, 81–83, 88
    scaled trees, 81, 88–90
    terminology, 80–81
    topology, 88

tree confidence, 109–12
pKa, 158
pLacI protein, 122–23
Point accepted mutation matrix. *See* PAM matrix
Point mutations, 124
Polar amino acids, 9, 156, 157
Polar bonds, 18–19
Polyadenylation, 133, 134
Polycistronic RNA molecules, 122, 124
Polymerase chain reaction method. *See* PCR method
Polynucleotides, 3
Polypeptide composition, 159–60
Populations and evolution, 84
Position-specific scoring matrices, 50
Positively charged amino acids, 9, 156
Positive regulation, 8
Positive regulator, 123, 131
"Post-genome era," 180
Post-translational modification, 180, 198–203
Predator algorithm, 162
Preference-ordered representations, 170
Preinitiation complex, 132
Primary structure, proteins, 13–14, 160
Probabilities, genome sequencing, 119
Probes, 22, 187
PROCHECK software, 174
Product inhibition, 244
ProFound software, 186
Prokaryotes
  description, 7
  gene expression, 8, 12
  genomes, 118–20, 126–27
  in life divisions, 113, 114
  sequenced species list (partial), 120
  transcription, 12, 121, 122, 125–26
  translation, 12, 120–21, 124, 125
Prokaryotic gene structure
  conceptual translation, 125
  GC content, 126–27

gene density, 127
open reading frames, 12, 124, 127
overview, 120–21
promoter elements, 121–24, 127
termination sequences, 125–26, 127
transposition, 148
Promoter elements
  description, 7–9
  eukaryotes, 129, 130–31
  prokaryotes, 121–24, 127
Promoter recognition algorithms, 123–24, 129
Prosite database, 195
Proteases, 199
Proteasomes, 202
Protein crystals, 191, 193. *See also* X-ray crystal structures
Protein Data Bank (PDB), 193, 195, 196, 270
Protein electrophoresis, 78–79
Protein explorer visualization tool, 195
Protein Information Resource (PIR), 195
Protein kinase A (PKA), 203
Protein localization signals, 200–201
Protein microarrays, 187
Proteins. *See also* Protein structure; Proteomics
  activation factors, 180
  backbone, 13, 14, 156, 160, 161
  classification, 174, 181–84
  formation overview, 13
  function overview, 9, 13
  identification, 181
  mRNA correlation, 180
  multiple functions, 150
  post-translational sorting, 199–201
  sequencing history, 79
  structural proteins, 13, 156
Protein structure
  amino acids, 156–57, 159
  disulfide bonds, 166, 167, 171
  example representations, 196
  folding modeling, 167–72

hydrophobic effects on, 165–66
native structure, 13–14, 156, 164
overview, 13–15, 156, 176–77
polypeptide composition, 159–60
prediction, 172–74
primary structure, 13–14, 160
quaternary structure, 15, 164–67
secondary structure, 14, 160–64
stability, 167
tertiary structure, 15, 164–67
Protein threading, 174
Protein visualization tools, 195
Proteolytic cleavage, 202
Proteome, 180
Proteomics. *See also* Proteins
  applications, 181
  database websites, 195
  difficulties, 180–81, 184, 185, 187
  drug design, 187–91
  empirical methods, 197–98, 199
  experimental techniques, 184–87
  genomics comparison, 180–81
  ligand screening, 188–91, 192
  NMR, 193, 197
  overview, 180, 203–04
  post-translational modification, 180, 198–203
  protein classification, 174, 181–84
  structural classification, 174, 182, 183–84
  tools websites, 195
  X-ray crystal structures, 191–96, 197
Protons, 17
P score, 51
Pseudogenes, 62
Pseudoknots, 175
Psi angles, 14, 160, 162, 170
PSI-BLAST algorithm, 50
PSORT, protein localization, 201
Purines, 38, 67
Pyrimidines, 38, 67

Pyrrolysine, 11
Python computer language, 208, 232–33

Quantifiers, Perl, 232
Quantum, 17
Quaternary structure, proteins, 15, 164–67

$R_0t_{1/2}$ values, 144–45
Ramachandran plot, 160, 162, 170
RasMol/RasWin, molecular graphics, 195
Reading frame, 11–12
Reassociation kinetics, 28–30, 144–45
Regular expressions, Perl, 231–32
Regulatory protein binding sites, 131–33
Regulatory vs. constitutive proteins, 131
Relative direction representation, 169
Relative mutability, 39, 40
Relative rate tests
    description, 71–73, 74
    Perl sample program, 255–56
Remainder computation, 209–10
Repetitive elements, 148–50
Residues, 159, 164
Restriction enzymes
    digestion description, 20, 21, 30
    use history, 20, 79
Restriction mapping, 20, 79
Restriction site, 20
Retrotransposition, 149
Retrotransposons/retroposons, 148, 149
Retroviruses, 149
Reversals, evolution, 105
Reverse Fourier transformations, 193, 197
Reverse protein folding, 174
Reverse transcriptase
    cDNA, 24, 144
    retrotransposition, 149
Reversible chemical reactions, 237
Ribonucleic acid. *See* RNA
Ribosome loading sites, 123, 124

Ribosomes
    description, 7
    free-floating, 199, 200, 201
    function, 13, 24
Ribozymes, 176
RNA. *See also* Messenger RNA
    catalytic properties, 176
    hnRNAs, 133–34, 135, 136, 176
    overview, 7
    polycistronic RNA, 122, 124
    population abundances, 144–45
    ribosomal RNA/tree of life, 113–14
    secondary structure, 125–26, 175–76, 177
    small nuclear RNAs, 136
    stem, 175
    tRNA, 143
RNA polymerases
    eukaryotes, 130–31
    function, 7, 8, 9
    I, II, III, 130–31, 132, 133
    prokaryotes, 121–23
    retrotransposition, 149
Roentgen, W. C., 191
Rooted trees, 81–83, 88
Rotamer, 170–71
R position, amino acids, 13

SAGE, 145
Saitou, N., 92
Sanger, F., 25, 27, 28
Sanger dideoxy method, 25, 27, 28
Sarich, V. M., 71–72
Satellite DNA, 148–49
Sattah, S., 92
Saturation mutagenesis, 65
Scalar variables, 209–10
Scaled trees, 81, 88–90
Schoenback, L., 182–83
SCOP database, 174, 183
Scoring matrices, 38–41
Secondary structure
    proteins, 14, 160–64
    RNA, 125–26, 175–76, 177
Selectively neutral variation, 65
Selenocysteine, 11
Semiglobal alignment, 45–46
Sequenced species lists, 120, 129

Sequences -35 and -10, 8, 121–22, 123, 124, 127
Sequence tagged sites. *See* STS
Serial analysis of gene expression, 145
Sex chromosomes, 128
Sharp, P. M., 52
Shine-Delgarno sequence, 123, 124
Sickle-cell anemia, 166
Side chains, 13, 156
Sigma (σ) protein
    E. coli, 122
    RNA polymerase, 121, 122
Signal cascades, 203
SignalP, protein localization, 201
Signal peptide/peptidase, 201
Signal sequence, 201
Similarity based matrices, 38–39
Simulated annealing, 169, 189–90
Simulation studies, 112
SINEs, 142, 149–50
SLIDE algorithm, 191, 192
Sliding windows, description, 34, 35
Small nuclear RNAs, 136
Smith, F., 47, 53
Smith, H., 20
Smith-Waterman algorithm, 46–48, 51
Source codes, algorithms, 208
Sp1, 132, 133, 139
Species distinction, 112
Species tree, 83–84
Splice junctions
    description, 134, 135–36
    Perl sample program, 263–66
Spliceosomes, 12, 135
Splicing, 12–13, 133–34
Spock visualization tool, 195
Start codons, 11, 202
Statements, Perl, 212
Stem, RNA, 175
Steric collision/bump, 160, 162, 169–70
Sticky ends, DNA, 20
Stop codons, 9, 11, 12, 124
Strict consensus trees, 108–09
Strings, Perl, 222–23
Structural motif. *See* Folds
Structural proteins, 13, 156
Structure and function, 5

Structured programming, 217–18
Structure prediction algorithms, 162, 197–98, 199
STS
  description, 119
  eukaryotes, 128
Studier, J., 92
Subclones, 119
Subroutines, Perl, 224–29
Substitution patterns
  fixation, 63, 65
  functional constraint, 38, 59–61, 65
  gene variations, 64, 70–71
  indels, 62
  mutation rates, 58–59, 60–61, 104
  mutation vs., 62–63, 74
  organelles, 74
  overview, 38, 58, 74
  pseudogenes, 62
  synonymous/nonsynonymous, 61–62, 64
  time frame, 61
Substitution rates
  beta-like globin gene, 59–60, 61–62
  BLOSUM matrix, 41
  estimating numbers, 65–70
  Jukes-Cantor model, 65–66, 67
  Kimura's two-parameter model, 67–68
  molecular clocks, 71–73, 80
  multiple parameters, 68–69, 74
  PAM matrix, 39, 40, 41, 70
  protein sequences, 69–70
  species relative rates, 72–73
Superfamily, 183
Swiss PDB viewer, 195
SwissProt database, 195
Synapomorphies, 105
Synonymous substitutions
  HLA locus, 70–71
  in mitochondrial DNA, 74
  nonsynonymous vs., 61–62, 63, 64

Target identification, drug discovery, 188
TATA-binding protein (TBP), 131, 132

Taxonomy, 78, 79
TBP-associated factors (TAFs), 131, 132
Temperature and enzyme kinetics, 246
Template structures, modeling, 173
Terminal gaps, 45
Terminal nodes, 81, 100
Termination sequences, 125–26, 127
Tertiary structure, proteins, 15, 164–67
Thermodynamically favorable reactions, 237
3' carbon, 4, 5, 24
Thymine (T)
  base pairing, 5, 6
  description, 2, 3
  as pyrimidine, 67
  uracil replacement for, 12
TIGR, 119–20
Tissue-specific genes
  CpG islands, 139
  gene expression, 128, 130, 131, 133, 134
  L isochores, 141
Topology, phylogenetic trees
  determination, 92, 93
  information from, 88
Training, algorithms, 198, 199
Transcription. *See also* Promoter elements; RNA polymerases
  chromatin wrapping effects, 140–41
  description, 7
  eukaryotes, 12, 130–31, 133–35
  eukaryotes vs. prokaryotes, 12
  prokaryotes, 12, 121, 122, 125–26
  termination, 125–26
  translation separation, 12, 133–34
Transcriptional profiling, 147
Transcription factors
  eukaryotes, 131–32, 133
  examples, 133
Transcriptomes, 143
Transformed distance method, 90–91

Transitions
  description, 38, 67
  matrix, 39
  rate, 67–68, 93, 104
Transition state theory, 236, 237
Transition/transversion matrix, 39
Translation. *See also* Conceptual translation
  description, 7, 9, 11
  eukaryotes, 12, 133–34
  function, 9
  prokaryotes, 12, 120–21, 124, 125
  separation from transcription, 12, 133–34
Transliteration statements, Perl, 231, 232
Transposition, 148
Transversions
  description, 38, 67
  matrix, 39
  rate of, 67–68, 93, 104
"Tree of life," 112–14
Triplet code, 9
Troponin T, 136, 137
Turnover number, 239
Tversky, A., 92
2D gel electrophoresis, 184–85
Twofold degenerate sites, 61–62

Uninformative sites, 90, 98–99, 103
Unix systems, 209, 259
Unrooted trees, 81–83
Unscaled trees, 81
Unweighted-pair-group method with arithmetic mean. *See* UPGMA
UPGMA
  description/examples, 85, 86–90
  multiple sequence alignments, 94
  parsimonious trees, 105, 107
  Perl sample program, 256–58
  variation, 91, 92
  weakness, 90, 91
"Upstream" features, 5
Upstream promoter elements, 130–31

Uracil
function, 7, 12
as pyrimidine, 67
transcriptional termination,
125, 126

Valence, 17–18
Validation algorithms, 174
van der Waals forces, 165, 171,
189
Variables
arrays, 210, 220–21, 227
declaring, 210–11
evaluation, 222–23
global variables, 226
hashes, 210, 221–22, 266
local variables, 226
naming, 209–10, 219
scalar variables, 209–10
strings, 222–23
Vectors, cloning, 23, 24
Verify-3D software, 174
Viruses
evolution pressure on, 71
HIV virus, 149, 176, 188
retroviruses, 149
Visualization tools, protein, 195
VMD visualization tool, 195

Water, polar bonding, 19, 158.
See also Hydrogen bonds;
Hydrophilicity;
Hydrophobicity
Waterman, M., 47, 53
Watson, J. D., 1, 5, 20
Web sites
analyzed 2D gels, 185
AutoDock, 189
CATH, 183
codon usage bias, 142
ExPASy server, 195
FLEXX, 190
Folding@Home, 172
FSSP, 183
FTDock, 190
International Enzyme
Commission, 182
intron database, 136
ligand docking, 189, 190
localization signals, 201
medical diagnosis, 147
ProFound software, 186
protein classification, 183
Protein Data Bank (PDB),
193, 195
protein visualization tools, 195
proteolytic cleavage, 202

proteomics tools, 195
SCOP, 183
sequenced species
(eukaryotes), 129
sequenced species
(prokaryotes), 120
TIGR, 120
WHAT CHECK software, 174
While loop statement, 216, 217,
230
Wilson, A. C., 71–72
Windows systems, 208–09
Woese, C., 113–14
Words, database searches, 49, 50
Wunsch, C., 42, 53

X-ray crystal structures, 191–96,
197
X-ray discovery, 191

"Y chromosome Adam," 114
Yeast
codon usage bias, 142–43
genome, 128, 129, 151
intron/exon structure, 135

Zuckerkandl, E., 71
Zuker's Mfold program, 176